SONGS & HYMNS OF FELLOWSHIP

SONGS & HYMNS OF FELLOWSHIP

SONGS OF FELLOWSHIP BOOKS 1, 2 & 3
and
HYMNS OF FELLOWSHIP

Integrated Music Edition

THANKYOU MUSIC
NASHVILLE

KINGSWAY MUSIC
EASTBOURNE

Most of the songs in this publication
are covered by the Church Copyright Licence Scheme.
Details of the scheme are obtainable from:
The Christian Music Association, Glyndley Manor,
Stone Cross, Eastbourne, E. Sussex BN24 5BS.

ISBN 0 86065 528 8
Gift Edition (slipcased)   ISBN 0 86065 575 X
Leather Edition (slipcased)   ISBN 0 86065 701 9

Scripture quotations adjacent to some of the songs
in this volume are from the Holy Bible: New International Version,
copyright © International Bible Society 1973, 1978, 1984.
Published by Hodder & Stoughton and
used by permission.

All enquiries regarding the reproduction of
Thankyou Music songs in North America should be directed to
Maranatha! Music, P.O. Box 31050,
Laguna Hills, CA 92654-1050.

North American distributors:
Thankyou Music Inc., c/o Alexandria House Inc.,
468 McNally Drive, Nashville, TN 37211.

Printed in Great Britain for
KINGSWAY MUSIC LTD
1 St. Anne's Road, Eastbourne, E. Sussex BN21 3UN by
Richard Clay Ltd, Bungay, Suffolk.

Contents

*   These indexes refer to pieces from *Hymns of Fellowship*.

Important note on the order of songs

The songs appear in alphabetical order by first line, not necessarily by author's title, for easy use in praise and worship meetings. An index of titles and first lines is included at the back, along with other useful indexes and chord charts (see Contents page).

To further facilitate the use of this book, all two-page songs and hymns appear on facing pages to avoid turning over, while maintaining the strict alphabetical order.

1.

Abba Father

Capo 3 (G)

Dave Bilbrough

Thoughtfully

Ab - ba Fa - ther, let me be Yours and Yours a -
lone. May my will for - e - ver be
Ev - er more Your own. Ne - ver let my heart grow
cold, Ne - ver let me go, Ab - ba
Fa - ther, let me be Yours and Yours a - lone.

2.
Abide with me

Capo 3 (C)
EVENTIDE

William Henry Monk (1823-89)

Peacefully

1. A - bide with me, fast falls the e - ven -
tide; the dark - ness deep - ens,
Lord, with me a - bide; when o - ther
help - ers fail and com - forts flee,
Help of the help-less, O a - bide with me.

2. Swift to its close ebbs out life's little day;
   Earth's joys grow dim, its glories pass away;
   Change and decay in all around I see;
   O Thou who changest not, abide with me.

3. I need Thy presence every passing hour;
   What but Thy grace can foil the tempter's power?
   Who like Thyself my guide and stay can be?
   Through cloud and sunshine, O abide with me.

4. I fear no foe, with Thee at hand to bless;
   Ills have no weight, and tears no bitterness.
   Where is death's sting? Where, grave, thy victory?
   I triumph still, if Thou abide with me.

5. Reveal Thyself before my closing eyes;
   Shine through the gloom, and point me to the skies,
   Heaven's morning breaks, and earth's vain shadows flee;
   In life, in death, O Lord, abide with me.

Henry Francis Lyte (1793-1847)

Mt 28: 20; Lk 24: 28; Jn 15: 5-8; Rom 8: 37-39; 1 Cor 15: 54-57; Heb 12: 28-29

3.
Ah Lord God

Capo 2 (C)

Kay Chance
Jer 32: 17-19

Ah Lord God, Thou ___ hast made the hea-vens and the earth by Thy great po-wer. ___ Ah Lord God, Thou ___ hast made the hea-vens and the earth by Thine out-stretched arm. No-thing is too dif-fi-cult for

4.

Ain't Jesus good

Mark Waner

Capo 3 (C)

With strength and rhythm

1. Ain't Je-sus good, — don't you know. —

Ain't Je-sus good, — ain't it so. —

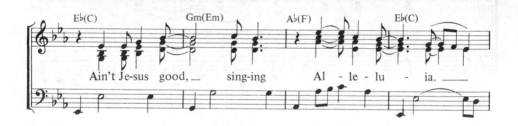

Ain't Je-sus good, — sing-ing Al - le - lu - ia. —

I just wan-na praise — Him — for ev-er — a-gain. —

2.   He filled me up when I was empty,
He set me free when I was a slave.
He loves me so, and He always will.
I just wanna praise Him for ever again.

5. Alleluia, Alleluia, give thanks to the risen Lord

Donald Fishel
Gal 2:20

Capo 5 (C)

Triumphantly

Chorus

Al - le - lu - ia, Al - le - lu - ia, give thanks to the ri - sen Lord, Al - le - lu - ia, Al - le - lu - ia, give _ praise to His _ name. name.

Verse

1. Je - sus is Lord of all the _ earth, He is the King of cre - a - tion.

2. Spread the good news o'er all the earth,
   Jesus has died and has risen.

3. We have been crucified with Christ,
   Now we shall live for ever.

4. God has proclaimed the just reward,
   Life for all men, Alleluia!

5. Come let us praise the living God,
   Joyfully sing to our Saviour.

6. All hail King Jesus!

Dave Moody

Rev 17:14

Worshipfully with strength

All hail King Je - sus! All hail Em - man - u - el! __

__ King of kings, Lord of lords, bright morning star. __

__ And through-out e - ter - ni - ty I'll sing Your prai - ses, __

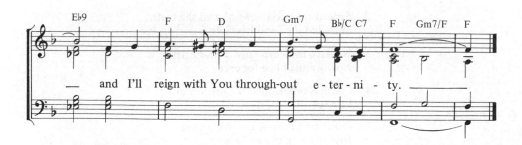

__ and I'll reign with You through-out e - ter - ni - ty.

7. All hail the power of Jesus' name!
(First tune)

MILES LANE

With vigour

William Shrubsole (1760-1806)

1. All hail the pow'r of Je - sus' name! Let an - gels prostrate fall; bring forth the roy - al di - a - dem, and crown Him, crown Him, crown Him, crown Him Lord of all.

2. Crown Him, ye martyrs of your God,
Who from His altar call;
Extol Him in whose path ye trod,
And crown Him Lord of all.

3. Ye seed of Israel's chosen race,
Ye ransomed of the fall,
Hail Him who saves you by His grace,
And crown Him Lord of all.

4. Sinners, whose love can ne'er forget
The wormwood and the gall,
Go, spread your trophies at His feet,
And crown Him Lord of all.

5. Let every kindred, every tribe
On this terrestrial ball,
To Him all majesty ascribe,
And crown Him Lord of all.

6. O that, with yonder sacred throng,
We at His feet may fall,
Join in the everlasting song,
And crown Him Lord of all!

Edward Perronet (1726-92)
Revised by John Rippon (1751-1836)
Acts 10: 36; Heb 2: 9; Rev 4: 9-11

All hail the power of Jesus' name!
(Second tune)

James Ellor (1819-99)

Capo 1 (G)
DIADEM

With strength

1. All hail the pow - er of Je - sus' name! Let _ an - gels pros-trate fall, _ let an - gels pros - trate fall; bring _ forth the roy - al di - a - dem and crown Him and crown Him crown Him and crown Him crown Him Him, crown Him crown Him, Him crown Him, crown Him, crown Him crown

crown Him, and crown___ Him Lord of all.

_____ Him.

2. Crown Him, ye martyrs of your God,
   Who from His altar call;
   Extol Him in whose path ye trod,
   And crown Him Lord of all.

3. Ye seed of Israel's chosen race,
   Ye ransomed of the fall,
   Hail Him who saves you by His grace,
   And crown Him Lord of all.

4. Sinners, whose love can ne'er forget
   The wormwood and the gall,
   Go, spread your trophies at His feet,
   And crown Him Lord of all.

5. Let every kindred, every tribe
   On this terrestrial ball,
   To Him all majesty ascribe,
   And crown Him Lord of all.

6. O that, with yonder sacred throng,
   We at His feet may fall,
   Join in the everlasting song,
   And crown Him Lord of all!

Edward Perronet (1726-92)
Revised by John Rippon (1751-1836)

Acts 10: 36; Heb 2: 9; Rev 4: 9-11

8. All people that on earth do dwell

OLD 100th

French Psalter (1551)

1. All peo-ple that on earth do dwell, sing to the Lord with cheer - ful voice; Him serve with mirth, His praise forth tell, come ye be - fore Him and re - joice.

2. Know that the Lord is God indeed,
Without our aid He did us make:
We are His flock, He doth us feed,
And for His sheep He doth us take.

3. O enter then His gates with praise,
Approach with joy His courts unto:
Praise, laud, and bless His name always,
For it is seemly so to do.

4. For why, the Lord our God is good;
His mercy is for ever sure;
His truth at all times firmly stood,
And shall from age to age endure.

5. Praise God from whom all blessings flow,
Praise Him all creatures here below,
Praise Him above, ye heavenly hosts;
Praise Father, Son and Holy Ghost.

William Kethe (d. 1594)

Ps 100

9. Almighty God

Worshipfully

Austin Martin
2 Pet 1:19

Al-might-y God, _____ we bring You praise _____ for Your Son, _____ the Word of God, _____ by whose power _____ the world was made, _____ by whose blood _____ we are re-deemed. Mor-ning star, _____ the Fath-er's glo - ry, _____ we now wor - ship _____ and a - dore You. _____ In our hearts _____ Your light has ri - sen; _____ Je-sus, Lord, _____ we worship You.

10. Amazing grace!

AMAZING GRACE

With feeling

Early American melody

1. A - maz - ing __ grace! how sweet the sound that saved a __ wretch like me; I once __ was __ lost, but now __ am __ found, was blind, but __ now I see.

2. 'Twas grace that taught my heart to fear,
And grace my fears relieved;
How precious did that grace appear,
The hour I first believed!

3. Through many dangers, toils and snares
I have already come:
'Tis grace that brought me safe thus far,
And grace will lead me home.

4. The Lord has promised good to me,
His word my hope secures;
He will my shield and portion be
As long as life endures.

5. Yes, when this heart and flesh shall fail,
And mortal life shall cease,
I shall possess within the veil
A life of joy and peace.

6. When we've been there a thousand years,
Bright shining as the sun,
We've no less days to sing God's praise
Then when we first begun.

John Newton (1725-1807)

Jn 1: 16-17; Rom 5: 1-2; 8: 28-35; Rev 14: 1-5

———— □ ▢ □ ————

*I will proclaim the name of the
    Lord.
Oh, praise the greatness of our
    God!
He is the Rock, his works are
    perfect,
and all his ways are just.
A faithful God who does no wrong,
    upright and just is he.*

DEUTERONOMY 32:3–4

———— □ ▢ □ ————

11. An army of ordinary people

Dave Bilbrough
Rom 9:8

With feeling

1. An ar-my of or-di-na-ry people, _____ a kingdom where love is the key, _____ a ci-ty, a light to the na-tions, ___ heirs to the pro-mise __ are we. _____ A people __ whose life is in Je - sus, _____ a na-tion to-geth-er we stand. On-ly through grace are we worth-y, __ in-he-ri-tors of the land. __ A new day is dawn-ing, __

a new age to come, when the child-ren of promise ___ shall flow to-geth-er as one: ___ a truth long ne-glect-ed, ___ but the time has now come, when the child-ren of promise ___ shall flow to-geth-er as one. _____

2. A people without recognition,
   But with Him a destiny sealed,
   Called to a heavenly vision:
   His purpose shall be fulfilled.
   Come let us stand strong together,
   Abandon ourselves to the King.
   His love shall be ours for ever,
   This victory song we shall sing.

12.   And can it be?

Thomas Campbell (1825-76)

SAGINA

With strength

1. And can it be that I should gain an in - t'rest in the Sav - iour's blood? Died He for me, who caused His pain? For me, who Him to death pur - sued? A - maz - ing love! how can it be that

Thou, _____ my God, _____ shouldst die _____ for me? A-

maz - ing love! How can it be that

A - maz - ing love! How can it be

Thou, my God, shouldst _ die for me?

that Thou, my God, shouldst die for me?

2. 'Tis mystery all! The Immortal dies:
   Who can explore His strange design?
   In vain the first-born seraph tries
   To sound the depths of love divine!
   'Tis mercy all! let earth adore,
   Let angel minds inquire no more.

3. He left His Father's throne above,
   So free, so infinite His grace;
   Emptied Himself of all but love,
   And bled for Adam's helpless race;
   'Tis mercy all, immense and free;
   For, O my God, it found out me.

4. Long my imprisoned spirit lay
   Fast bound in sin and nature's night;
   Thine eye diffused a quickening ray,
   I woke, the dungeon flamed with light;
   My chains fell off, my heart was free;
   I rose, went forth, and followed Thee.

5. No condemnation now I dread;
   Jesus, and all in Him, is mine!
   Alive in Him, my living Head,
   And clothed in righteousness divine,
   Bold I approach the eternal throne,
   And claim the crown, through Christ my own.

Charles Wesley (1707-88)

Jn 3: 16; Rom 8: 1-2; Phil 2: 6-11

13.

And the warriors
(The warriors)

Jane Norton

Joel 3: 9-11

And the war-ri-ors, and the war-ri-ors, — and the war-ri-ors shall come

(2nd part -- 3rd and 4th times)

Vic-to-ry, —

down. _____ And the war-ri-ors, and the

vic-to-ry, — vic-to-ry — is the

war - ri-ors, and the war-ri - ors shall come

1st time Lord's. *2nd time* Lord's. *Fine*

down. And the down. 1. A-wake you sleep-ing

men! A - rise, pre - pare for war! Take up your shields and ar - mour, for the bat - tle plans are drawn. _____ And the

2. Now feeble men be strong,
   And fighting men draw near;
   And beat your ploughshares into swords,
   And turn your hooks to spears.

3. The nations shall assemble,
   From every side they come.
   Bring down your warriors, O Lord,
   The battle has begun.

14. A new commandment

Author unknown
Arr. Margaret Evans
Jn 13: 34-35·

Capo 2(C)

Smoothly

A new com - mand-ment I give un - to

you, that you love one an - oth - er as

I have lov'd you, that you love one an -

oth - er as I have lov'd you. By

15. Angel voices ever singing

ANGEL VOICES

(First tune)

Edwin George Monk (1819-1900)

Worshipfully

1. An-gel voi-ces ev-er sing-ing round Thy throne of light, an-gel harps for ev-er ring-ing, rest not day nor night; thou-sands on-ly live to bless Thee, and con-fess Thee Lord of might.

2. Thou who art beyond the farthest
   Mortal eye can scan,
   Can it be that Thou regardest
   Songs of sinful man?
   Can we know that Thou art near us
   And wilt hear us?
   Yes, we can.

3. Yes, we know that Thou rejoicest
   O'er each work of Thine;
   Thou didst ears and hands and voices
   For Thy praise design;
   Craftsman's art and music's measure
   For Thy pleasure
   All combine.

4. In Thy house, great God, we offer
   Of Thine own to Thee,
   And for Thine acceptance proffer,
   All unworthily,
   Hearts and minds and hands and voices
   In our choicest
   Psalmody.

5. Honour, glory, might, and merit
   Thine shall ever be,
   Father, Son, and Holy Spirit,
   Blessèd Trinity.
   Of the best that Thou hast given
   Earth and heaven
   Render Thee.

Francis Pott (1832-1909)

Ps 8: 3-5; 134; Rev 4: 8-11; 5: 11-14

Angel voices ever singing
(Second tune)

Capo 5(A)
MAIQUEZ

Geoffrey Beaumont (1903-70)

16.

Arise, my soul, arise

ADORATION (ST JOHN)

William Henry Havergal (1793-1870)

With strength

1. A - rise, my soul, a - rise, shake off thy guil - ty fears; the per - fect sac - ri - fice in my be - half ap - pears; be - fore the throne my sure - ty stands; my name is writ - ten on His hands.

Alternative tune: DARWALL'S 148th (627)

2. He ever lives above,
For me to intercede,
His all-redeeming love,
His precious blood, to plead;
His blood atoned for all our race,
And sprinkles now the throne of grace.

3. The Father hears Him pray,
His dear Anointed One;
He cannot turn away
The presence of His Son:
His Spirit answers to the blood,
And tells me I am born of God.

4. My God is reconciled,
His pardoning voice I hear;
He owns me for His child,
I can no longer fear;
With confidence I now draw nigh,
And 'Father, Abba, Father!' cry.

Charles Wesley (1707-88)

Is 60: 1-3; Rom 8: 15-17; Heb 7: 25; 9: 14; 10: 10

———— □ ▢ □ ————

The eternal God is your refuge,
and underneath are the
everlasting arms.
He will drive out your enemy
before you,
saying, 'Destroy him!'

DEUTERONOMY 33:27

———— □ ▢ □ ————

17. A safe stronghold our God is still

EIN' FESTE BURG
With strength

Martin Luther (1483-1546)

1. A safe strong - hold_ our God_ is still, a trust- y shield and_
   help us clear_ from all _ the ill that hath us now o'er_
   wea - pon; He'll tak - en. The an - cient prince of
   hell hath ris'n with pur - pose fell; strong
   mail of craft and pow'r he wear - eth in ___ this
   hour; on earth is not his ___ fel - low.

2. With force of arms we nothing can,
   Full soon were we down-ridden;
   But for us fights the proper Man,
   Whom God Himself hath bidden.
   Ask ye: Who is this same?
   Christ Jesus is His name,
   The Lord Sabaoth's Son;
   He, and no other one,
   Shall conquer in the battle.

3. And were this world all devils o'er,
   And watching to devour us,
   We lay it not to heart so sore;
   Not they can overpower us.
   And let the prince of ill
   Look grim as e'er he will,
   He harms us not a whit:
   For why? his doom is writ;
   A word shall quickly slay him.

4. God's word, for all their craft and force,
   One moment will not linger;
   But, spite of hell, shall have its course;
   'Tis written by His finger.
   And though they take our life,
   Goods, honour, children, wife,
   Yet is their profit small:
   These things shall vanish all;
   The city of God remaineth.

Martin Luther (1483-1546)
Tr. Thomas Carlyle (1795-1881)

Nahum 1:7; Jn 14:30; Eph 6:10-18; Jas 4:7; 1 Jn 3:8; Rev 20:7-10

18.
Ascribe greatness

Capo 2 (G)

Mary Lou Locke
& Mary Kirkbride

Deut 32: 3-4

Thoughtfully with strength

As-cribe greatness to our God, the Rock, His work is per-fect and all His ways are just. ___ As-cribe greatness to our God, the Rock, ___ His work is per-fect and all His ways are just. ___ A God of faithfulness and without in-just-ice, ___ good and up-right is He; ___ a God of faithful-ness and with-out in-just-ice, ___ good and up-right is He. ___

19.

Ascribe to the Lord

Carolyn Govier
Ps 29:1-4, 9-10

1. A-scribe to the Lord O hea-ven-ly be-ings, A-scribe glo-ry and strength. Wor-ship the Lord in ho-ly ar-ray, And a-scribe the glo-ry of His Name.

Chorus

Glo-ry to the Lord who sits en-throned, Glo-ry to the Lord who lives for e-ver-more.

2.   The voice of the Lord is upon the waters,
Full of majesty.
His voice thunders through the clouds,
His temple cries, 'Glory!'

3.   The Lord is enthroned as King for ever,
Triumph is given to Him.
Victory He shares with His anointed,
Earth belongs to Him.

20. Ask and it shall be given

Alan Woodroffe/Chris Head
Mt 7:7

Ask and it shall be gi - ven un - to you, Ask and it shall be done. As we pray in the name of our Lord Je - sus Christ; As we

pray   in   the   name   of   God's   Son._____

____   God   has   placed   with-

in   our____ hearts_____ A know - ledge__ of

His____ per - fect   will,_____   And

God _____ will draw all these things _____ from our

hearts _____ As we learn _____ to be qui - et and

still. _____ hearts As we

learn to be qui - et and still. _____

21.

As the deer

Capo 2 (C)

Martin Nystrom

Ps 42: 1-2

Flowing

Verse

1. As the deer pants _ for the wa-ter, so my soul longs af - ter You.

You a -lone are my heart's de-sire _ and I long to wor - ship You.

Chorus

You a - lone are my strength, my shield, to You a-lone may my spi - rit yield.

You a-lone are my heart's de-sire _ and I long to wor - ship You.

2. I want You more than gold or silver,
   Only You can satisfy.
   You alone are the real joy-giver
   And the apple of my eye.

3. You're my Friend and You are my Brother,
   Even though You are a King.
   I love You more than any other,
   So much more than anything.

22.

As the deer pants

Robert Newey

Ps 42:1-2,11

Medium paced

As the deer pants af-ter the wa-ter brooks,_so my soul seeks for You,_ O

Lord.   My _ soul thirsts for God,_for the liv-ing God,_ that His

song   might live with-in me.   Why be down-cast, my soul, or dis-

turb'd with in me?   Put your hope in God,   for I_will yet praise _ Him,

my   Sav-iour_and my God, Lord my soul thirsts for_You, the liv-ing God._

23.

As the sun is high

Phil Lawson Johnston
Gen 9:13

As the sun is high _____ so is my love up-
on _____ you, _____ As the rain _____ falls _____ so will my
love _____ flow. _____ As the rain - bow _____ my pro-mise for
ev - er _____ is true love a - mong _____ you, _____ So let my
love _____ flow _____ from your heart. _____

24.

As we are gathered

John Daniels
Mt 18:20

Slowly

As we are gath-ered Je - sus is here; one with each oth-er, Je - sus is here; joined by the Spi - rit, washed in the blood, part of the bo - dy, __ the church of God. As we are gath-ered Je - sus is here; one with each oth - er, Je - sus is here.

———————— □ ▢ □ ————————

*The Lord does not look at the things
man looks at. Man looks at the outward
appearance, but the Lord looks at the
heart.*

1 SAMUEL 16:7

———————— □ ▢ □ ————————

25.

As we come with praise

(Come with praise)

Dale Garratt

Ps 149: 6-9

Capo 3 (Am)

With a strong beat

As we come with praise be-fore His maj - es - ty, we will

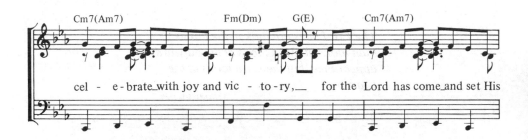

cel - e-brate with joy and vic - to-ry, for the Lord has come and set His

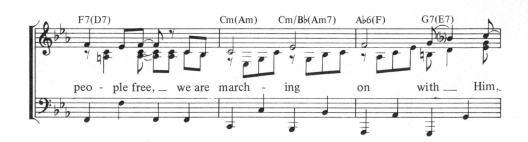

peo - ple free, we are march - ing on with Him,

He's our de-liv - er-er. (He's)

26.
At the name of Jesus
(First tune)

CAMBERWELL

John Michael Brierley (1932 -)

With strength

1. At the name of Je - sus ev - 'ry knee shall bow,

ev - 'ry tongue con - fess Him King of glo - ry — now;

'tis the Fa - ther's pleasure we should call Him Lord,

who from the be - gin - ning was the migh - ty

Word. now.

2. Humbled for a season,
   To receive a name
   From the lips of sinners
   Unto whom He came;
   Faithfully He bore it
   Spotless to the last,
   Brought it back victorious,
   When from death He passed.

3. Bore it up triumphant
   With its human light,
   Through all ranks of creatures
   To the central height,
   To the throne of Godhead,
   To the Father's breast,
   Filled it with the glory
   Of that perfect rest.

4. In your hearts enthrone Him;
   There let Him subdue
   All that is not holy,
   All that is not true:
   Crown Him as your captain
   In temptation's hour,
   Let His will enfold you
   In its light and power.

5. Brothers, this Lord Jesus
   Shall return again,
   With His Father's glory,
   With His angel-train;
   For all wreaths of empire
   Meet upon His brow,
   And our hearts confess Him
   King of glory now.

Caroline Maria Noel (1817-77)
Phil 2: 6-11; 2 Pet 3: 3-13; Rev 22: 20

At the name of Jesus
(Second tune)

Capo 2(C)
EVELYNS
Moderate

William Henry Monk (1823-89)

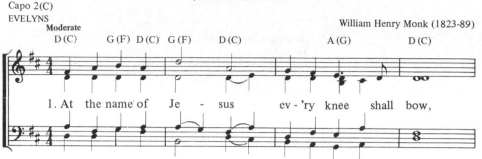

1. At the name of Je - sus ev - 'ry knee shall bow,

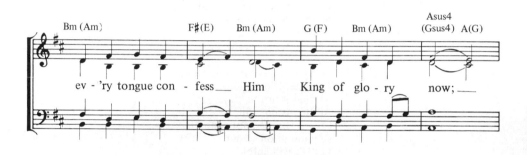

ev - 'ry tongue con - fess___ Him King of glo - ry now; ___

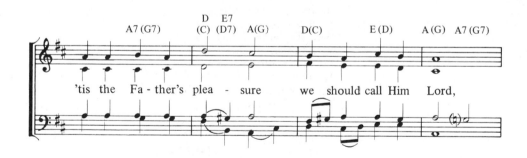

'tis the Fa - ther's plea - sure we should call Him Lord,

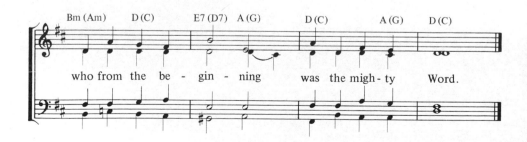

who from the be - gin - ning was the migh - ty Word.

2. Humbled for a season,
   To receive a name
   From the lips of sinners
   Unto whom He came;
   Faithfully He bore it
   Spotless to the last,
   Brought it back victorious,
   When from death He passed.

3. Bore it up triumphant
   With its human light,
   Through all ranks of creatures
   To the central height,
   To the throne of Godhead,
   To the Father's breast,
   Filled it with the glory
   Of that perfect rest.

4. In your hearts enthrone Him;
   There let Him subdue
   All that is not holy,
   All that is not true:
   Crown Him as your captain
   In temptation's hour,
   Let His will enfold you
   In its light and power.

5. Brothers, this Lord Jesus
   Shall return again,
   With His Father's glory,
   With His angel-train;
   For all wreaths of empire
   Meet upon His brow,
   And our hearts confess Him
   King of glory now.

Caroline Maria Noel (1817-77)
Phil 2: 6-11; 2 Pet 3: 3-13; Rev 22: 20

27.

At Your feet O Lord

Janis Miller

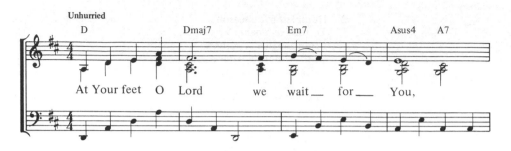

At Your feet O Lord we wait for You,

yearn-ing Lord, hun-gry Lord, for more of You.

Bow'd be-fore You, Lord, we de-sire on-ly You:

fill us Lord, re-vive us Lord, with more of You.

———————— □ ▢ □ ————————

O Lord, our Lord,
how majestic is your name in all
the earth!
You have set your glory
above the heavens.

PSALM 8:1

———————— □ ▢ □ ————————

28.

At Your feet we fall

Capo 2 (G)

Dave Fellingham
Rev 1:14-18

With steady strength

Verse

1. At Your feet we fall, _____ might-y ris - en Lord, _____

_____ as we come be-fore Your throne to wor-ship You. _____

_____ By Your Spi - rit's power _____ You now draw our hearts, _____

_____ and we hear Your voice in tri-umph ring-ing clear. _____

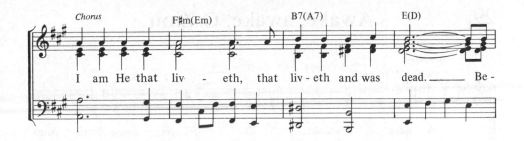

I am He that liv - eth, that liv - eth and was dead. ____ Be -

- hold, I am a - live for ev - er - more. ____

2. There we see You stand, mighty risen Lord,
   Clothed in garments pure and holy, shining bright.
   Eyes of flashing fire, feet like burnished bronze,
   And the sound of many waters is Your voice.

3. Like the shining sun in its noonday strength,
   We now see the glory of Your wondrous face.
   Once that face was marred, but now You're glorified,
   And Your words like a two-edged sword have mighty power.

29.

Awake, awake, O Zion

David J. Hadden

Is 52:1,7,9

Triumphantly

Chorus

A-wake, a-wake, O Zi - on, come clothe your-self with strength. A-

Verse

1. Put on your gar - ments of splen - dour, O Je-ru - sa - lem. Come sing your songs of joy and tri - umph, see that your God reigns. A-

2. Burst into songs of joy together,
   O Jerusalem.
   The Lord has comforted His people,
   The redeemed Jerusalem.

30. Because Your love

Phil Potter
Ps 63:3-4

Slowly with feeling

1. Be-cause Your love ＿ is better than life, with my lips I will glor-i-fy ＿ You, I will praise You ＿ as long as I live; in Your name ＿ I lift my hands. Hal - le-lu - jah, Hal - le - lu - jah, Hal - le-lu - jah, the Lord is here. ＿

2. Because Your Son has given me life,
With my lips I will glorify You,
I will praise You as long as I live;
In Your name I lift my hands.

3. Because Your Spirit is filling my life,
With my lips I will glorify You,
I will praise You as long as I live;
In Your name I lift my hands.

———————— □ ☐ □ ————————

I have set the Lord always before
me.
Because he is at my right hand,
I shall not be shaken.
Therefore my heart is glad and my
tongue rejoices.

PSALM 16:8–9

———————— □ ☐ □ ————————

31. Before the throne of God above

(First tune)

FESTUS

Adapted from a melody in
Freylinghausen's *Gesangbuch* (1704)

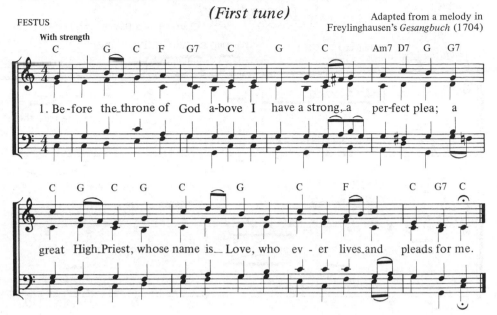

With strength

1. Be-fore the throne of God a-bove I have a strong, a per-fect plea; a great High Priest, whose name is Love, who ev - er lives and pleads for me.

2. My name is graven on His hands,
   My name is written on His heart;
   I know that while in heaven He stands
   No tongue can bid me thence depart.

3. When Satan tempts me to despair,
   And tells me of the guilt within,
   Upward I look, and see Him there
   Who made an end of all my sin.

4. Because the sinless Saviour died,
   My sinful soul is counted free;
   For God, the Just, is satisfied
   To look on Him and pardon me.

5. Behold Him there! the risen Lamb!
   My perfect, spotless, Righteousness,
   The great unchangeable I AM,
   The King of glory and of grace!

6. One with Himself, I cannot die;
   My soul is purchased by His blood;
   My life is hid with Christ on high,
   With Christ, my Saviour and my God.

Charitie Lees Bancroft (1841-1923)

Jn 1: 29; 1 Cor 6: 17; Col 3: 3; Heb 7: 23-25

Before the throne of God above
(*Second tune*)

Capo 2 (C)
JERUSALEM

Charles Hubert Hastings Parry (1848-1918)

1. Be-fore the throne of God a - bove I have a strong, a per - fect plea; a great High Priest, whose name is Love, who ev - er lives and pleads for me. My name is gra - ven on His hands, my name is writ - ten on His heart; I know that

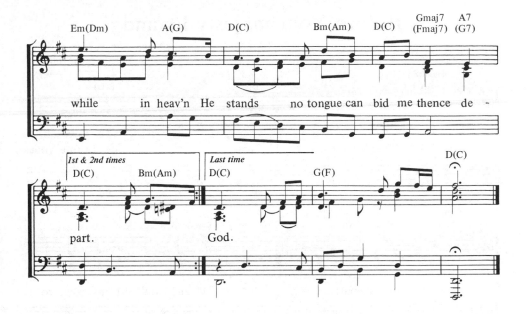

while in heav'n He stands no tongue can bid me thence de -

part.

God.

2. When Satan tempts me to despair,
   And tells me of the guilt within,
   Upward I look, and see Him there
   Who made an end of all my sin.
   Because the sinless Saviour died,
   My sinful soul is counted free;
   For God, the Just, is satisfied
   To look on Him and pardon me.

3. Behold Him there! the risen Lamb!
   My perfect, spotless, Righteousness,
   The great unchangeable I AM,
   The King of glory and of grace!
   One with Himself, I cannot die;
   My soul is purchased by His blood;
   My life is hid with Christ on high,
   With Christ, my Saviour and my God.

Charitie Lees Bancroft (1841-1923)
Jn 1: 29; 1 Cor 6: 17; Col 3: 3; Heb 7: 23-25

32.

Before Your majesty I stand

Capo 2(G)

Majestically

Ian Townend

Ps 93:1-2

1. Be-fore Your maj-es-ty I stand,_____ be-fore Your throne I lift my hands,_____ and I will lift my voice to You,_____

1st and 2nd time
Lord, I'll give wor-ship un-to You._____

3rd time
____ Lord, I'll give wor-ship un - to You._____

2. For You are clothed in righteousness
   And all Your people You will bless;
   I will declare Your majesty
   For in Your presence I can be.

— □ ▢ □ —

Who may ascend the hill of the
Lord?
Who may stand in his holy place?
He who has clean hands and a pure
heart.

PSALM 24:3–4

— □ ▢ □ —

33. Behold I tell you a mystery

Capo 3 (C)

Phil Rogers

1 Cor 15:51-57

1. Be-hold I tell you a mys-te-ry, _____ be-hold I tell you a mys-te-ry: we shall not all sleep, but we shall all be changed, in a mo-ment, in a twink-ling of an eye, in a mo-ment, in a twink-ling of an eye.

For the last trumpet shall sound, and the dead shall be raised in-cor-

34.

Behold the darkness
(Arise, shine)

Eric Glass
Is 60:1-5

1. Be - hold the dark - ness shall co - ver the earth, __ and gross dark-ness the people, but the Lord shall a-rise up-on thee and His glory shall be seen up - on thee. So a - rise, shine, for thy light is come, __ and the glory of the Lord is ri - sen; __ so a - rise, shine, for thy light is come, __ and the glory of the Lord is up - on thee. __

2. The Gentiles shall come to thy light,
   And Kings to the brightness of thy rising;
   And they shall call thee the city of the Lord,
   The Zion of the Holy One of Israel.

3. Lift up thine eyes round about and see,
   They gather themselves together;
   And they shall come, thy sons from afar,
   And thy daughters shall be nursed at thy side.

4. Then shalt thou see and flow together,
   And thy heart shall be enlarged;
   The abundance of the sea is converted unto thee,
   And the nations shall come unto thee.

5. The sun shall no more go down,
   Neither shall the moon withdraw itself;
   But the Lord shall be thine everlasting light,
   And the days of thy mourning shall be ended.

35. Being myself in the Lord

Gerald Coates/Mick Ray
2 Cor 6:2

Be-ing my-self in the Lord seems the great-est thing on earth, Lov-ing Him, prais - ing His name's not a dif-fi-cult thing,— He's my ev-'ry-thing.— Choos-ing His will day by day I'm find-ing grace— He's giv-ing, no time for look-ing back, I'm look-ing for-ward to liv-ing.— For now is the day of sal -

36. Beneath the cross of Jesus

ST CHRISTOPHER
With feeling

Frederick Charles Maker (1844-1927)

1. Be-neath the cross of Je - sus I fain would take my
stand, the sha - dow of a migh - ty rock with -
in a wear - y land; a home with - in the
wild - er - ness, a rest up - on the way, from the
burn - ing of the noon-tide heat, and the bur - den of the day.

2. O safe and happy shelter!
   O refuge tried and sweet!
   O trysting place where heaven's love
   And heaven's justice meet!
   As to the holy patriarch
   That wondrous dream was given,
   So seems my Saviour's cross to me
   A ladder up to heaven.

3. There lies, beneath its shadow,
   But on the farther side,
   The darkness of an awful grave
   That gapes both deep and wide;
   And there between us stands the cross,
   Two arms outstretched to save;
   Like a watchman set to guard the way
   From that eternal grave.

4. Upon that cross of Jesus
   Mine eye at times can see
   The very dying form of One
   Who suffered there for me;
   And from my smitten heart, with tears,
   Two wonders I confess —
   The wonders of His glorious love,
   And my own worthlessness.

5. I take, O cross, thy shadow,
   For my abiding place;
   I ask no other sunshine than
   The sunshine of His face;
   Content to let the world go by,
   To know no gain nor loss —
   My sinful self my only shame,
   My glory all the cross.

Elizabeth Cecilia Clephane (1830-69)
Gen 28:12-15; Mt 16:24; Mk 15:21-39; Heb 12:2

37.

Be still and know

Author unknown
Arr. Margaret Evans
Ex 15: 26; Ps 31: 1; 46: 10

2. I am the Lord that healeth thee. . . (*etc*).

3. In Thee, O Lord, do I put my trust. . . (*etc*).

—— □ ▢ □ ——

Clap your hands, all you nations;
shout to God with cries of joy.
How awesome is the Lord Most High,
the great King over all the earth!

PSALM 47:1–2

—— □ ▢ □ ——

38.

Be Thou my vision

Capo 3 (C)

SLANE

Joyfully

Ancient Irish melody

1. Be Thou my__ vi - O__ Lord of my heart, be__ all else but naught to me, save that Thou art; be Thou my__ best__ thought in the day and the night, both wak - ing and sleep - ing, Thy__ pre - sence my light.

2. Be Thou my wisdom, be Thou my true word,
   Be Thou ever with me, and I with Thee, Lord;
   Be Thou my great Father, and I Thy true son;
   Be Thou in me dwelling, and I with Thee one.

3. Be Thou my breastplate, my sword for the fight;
   Be Thou my whole armour, be Thou my true might;
   Be Thou my soul's shelter, be Thou my strong tower:
   O raise Thou me heavenward, great Power of my power.

4. Riches I need not, nor man's empty praise:
   Be Thou mine inheritance now and always;
   Be Thou and Thou only the first in my heart:
   O Sovereign of heaven, my treasure Thou art.

5. High King of heaven, Thou heaven's bright Sun,
   O grant me its joys after victory is won;
   Great Heart of my own heart, whatever befall,
   Still be Thou my vision, O Ruler of all.

Ancient Irish
Tr. Mary Elizabeth Byrne (1880-1931) & Eleanor Henrietta Hull (1860-1935)
Josh 13: 33; Prov 29: 18; 1 Cor 1: 30-31; Eph 6: 10-18

39.

Bind us together

Bob Gillman
Col 3:14

Bind us to - ge -ther, Lord, Bind us to - ge -ther with

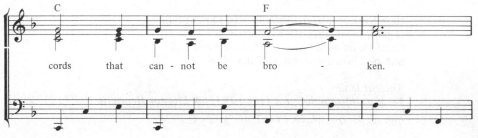

cords that can - not be bro - ken.

Bind us to - ge - ther, Lord, Bind us to - ge - ther, —

Bind us to - ge - ther with love.

Verse

1. There is on-ly one God. ___

There is on-ly one King. ___

There is on-ly one Bo-dy. ___

D.C. al Fine

That is why we sing. ___

2. Made for the glory of God,
   Purchased by His precious Son.
   Born with the right to be clean,
   For Jesus the victory has won. . . .

3. You are the family of God.
   You are the promise divine.
   You are God's chosen desire.
   You are the glorious new wine. . . .

40. Blessed are the pure in heart

2. To see God, the everlasting Father.
   To see God, whose love endures for ever.
   To see God, how wonderful to think that this could be.

3. To see God, the God who talked with Moses.
   To see God, whose mercies are so endless.
   To see God, what better incentive for purity.

4. To see God, the One I've loved and longed for.
   To see God, the Father of my Saviour.
   To see God, a dream come true, at last His face I'll see.

41.

Blessèd assurance

BLESSÈD ASSURANCE

Worshipfully
Verse

Phoebe Palmer Knapp (1839-1908)

1. Bless-èd as - sur - ance, Je - sus is mine: ___ O what a

fore - taste of glo - ry di - vine! ___ Heir of sal - va - tion, pur-chase of

God; ___ born of His Spi - rit, wash'd in His blood. ___ This is my

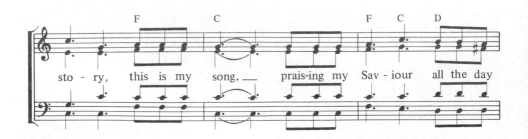

sto - ry, this is my song, ___ prais-ing my Sav - iour all the day

long. _____ This is my sto - ry, this is my
song, _____ prais-ing my Sav - iour all the day long. _____

2. Perfect submission, perfect delight,
   Visions of rapture burst on my sight;
   Angels descending bring from above
   Echoes of mercy, whispers of love.

3. Perfect submission, all is at rest,
   I in my Saviour am happy and blessed;
   Watching and waiting, looking above,
   Filled with His goodness, lost in His love.

Fanny J. Crosby (1820-1915)

Acts 2: 36, 46-47; Col 2: 2-3; Heb 10: 19-22; 13: 15

42.

Blessed be

Capo 1 (G)

Dave Fellingham
Eph 1:3-5

43. Bless the Lord, O my soul
(King of kings)

Author unknown
Arr. Margaret Evans
Ps 103:1

* The 2nd Part singers can divide into altos, tenors and basses if prefered.

Arr. Copyright © 1985 Thankyou Music, P.O. Box 75, Eastbourne BN23 6NW.

———— □ ▢ □ ————

*God has ascended amid shouts of
joy,
 the Lord amid the sounding of
 trumpets.
Sing praises to God, sing praises;
 sing praises to our King, sing
 praises.
For God is the King of all the earth;
 sing to him a psalm of praise.*

PSALM 47:5–7

———— □ ▢ □ ————

44. Break forth and sing for joy

Paul Armstrong
Ps 98:4; 100:1-3

Joyfully

45. Break forth into joy, O my soul

Nancy Roberts
Ps 16:11

Break forth in-to joy, O my soul, _____ Break forth in-to joy, O my soul. In the pres-ence of the Lord there is joy for ev-er-more, Break forth, break forth in-to joy. _____

46. Break Thou the Bread of Life

Capo 3(C)
LATHBURY

William F. Sherwin (1826-88)

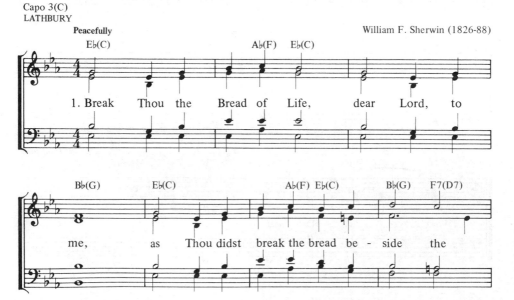

1. Break Thou the Bread of Life, dear Lord, to me, as Thou didst break the bread be - side the

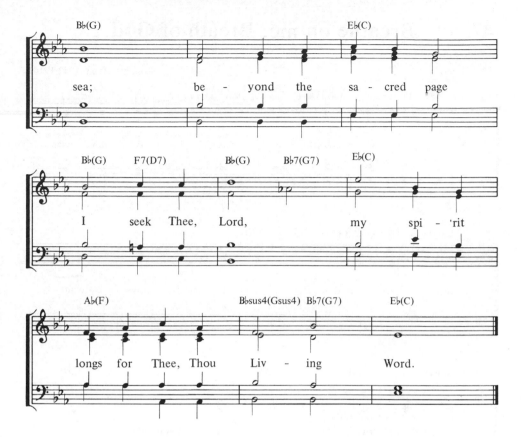

sea; be - yond the sa - cred page I seek Thee, Lord, my spi - 'rit longs for Thee, Thou Liv - ing Word.

2. Thou art the Bread of Life,
   O Lord, to me,
   Thy holy Word the truth
   That saveth me;
   Give me to eat and live
   With Thee above,
   Teach me to love Thy truth,
   For Thou art love.

3. O send Thy Spirit, Lord,
   Now unto me,
   That He may touch my eyes
   And make me see;
   Show me the truth concealed
   Within Thy Word,
   And in Thy Book revealed,
   I see Thee, Lord.

4. Bless Thou the Bread of Life
   To me, to me,
   As Thou didst bless the loaves
   By Galilee;
   Then shall all bondage cease,
   All fetters fall,
   And I shall find my peace,
   My all in all.

   Mary A. Lathbury (1841-1913)
   vv. 2 & 3 Alexander Groves (1843-1909)
   Mt 6:11; Mk 14:22; Jn 6:11, 35

47. Breathe on me, Breath of God

Capo 3(D)
TRENTHAM

Robert Jackson (1842-1914)

Prayerfully

1. Breathe on me, Breath of God, fill me with

life a - new; that I may love what

Thou dost love and do ___ what Thou wouldst do.

2. Breathe on me, Breath of God,
   Until my heart is pure;
   Until my will is one with Thine
   To do and to endure.

3. Breathe on me, Breath of God,
   Till I am wholly Thine;
   Until this earthly part of me
   Glows with Thy fire divine.

4. Breathe on me, Breath of God,
   So shall I never die,
   But live with Thee the perfect life
   Of Thine eternity.

Edwin Hatch (1835-89)

Ez 37:6; Jn 3:8; 2 Cor 3:17-18

― □ ◻ □ ―

Within your temple, O God,
* we meditate on your unfailing love.*
Like your name, O God,
* your praise reaches to the ends of*
*   the earth;*
* your right hand is filled with*
* righteousness.*

PSALM 48:9–10

― □ ◻ □ ―

48.

Bring a psalm

Capo 1 (Em)

Brently
Brent Chambers

Bring a psalm to the Lord, from the Spirit and from His word. Lift your voice and re-joice, for our God is a migh - ty King, so come and clap your hands, raise a shout, as we stand before the Lord, for the

49.

Burn, Holy Fire

Sally Karselis

Mal 3: 2-3; Jn 4: 23-24; Rev 5: 13

Boldly

1. Burn, Ho-ly Fire, let the Fa-ther's will be done until we con-form to the im-age of His Son, and
then we shall rise, and stand be-fore His throne, sing-ing:
'Glo-ry to the Lamb that was slain.'

2. Burn, Holy Fire, till our spirits pure and free
   Can worship our God in truth and liberty;
   And then we shall sing as Jesus we see,
   And we bow before His Royal Majesty.

50.

But ye are washed

Paul Simmons

1 Cor 6:11

51.

By the working
(He is alive)

Dave Fellingham
Eph 1:18-20

1. By the work-ing of the strength of His might, in acc-
or-dance with His great sur-pass-ing pow'r, _____ He has
rais'd Je-sus Christ from the dead _____ and _____
seat-ed Him at God's right ____ hand. _____

Chorus

He is a-live, He is a-live,

Je - sus has con-quer'd death, ___ now He's a - scend - ed in glo - ry. __

___ We bring _ our praise, bring _ our love, our ad - or - a - tion.

Je - sus _ is King, Lord o - ver all. _____

2. Far above all authority and rule,
   Greater than all dominion and power,
   Jesus Christ is the Head of the church
   And His throne stands for evermore.

3. With all things crushed beneath His feet,
   Jesus reigns in total victory.
   We bow to Him as the Head of the church,
   The fulness of Him who fills all in all.

4. We are now raised up with Him
   And His power is now working in us,
   We are now growing up into Him,
   To the fulness of the stature of Christ.

52. Cause me to come

R. Edward Miller
Ps 143:8; Jer 31:9

Capo 2 (C)

Thoughtfully

1. Cause me to come to Thy ri - ver, ___ O Lord,

Cause me to come to Thy ri - ver, ___ O Lord,

Cause me to come to Thy ri - ver, ___ O Lord, Cause me to

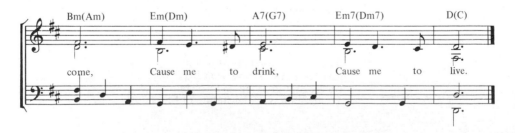

come, Cause me to drink, Cause me to live.

2. Cause me to drink from Thy river, O Lord, *(three times)*
   Cause me to come, cause me to drink, cause me to live.

3. Cause me to live by Thy river, O Lord, *(three times)*
   Cause me to come, cause me to drink, cause me to live.

53.   Change my heart, O God

Eddie Espinosa
Ps 51: 10; Jer 18: 6; Rom 9: 21

54. Christh is made the sure foundation

WESTMINSTER ABBEY
Joyfully

Henry Purcell (c. 1659-95)

1. Christ is made the sure foun - da - tion, Christ the head ___ and cor - ner - stone, chos - en of the Lord, and pre - cious, bind - ing all ___ the church _ in one, Ho - ly Zi - on's help for ev - er, and her con - fi - dence a - lone.

2. All that dedicated city
   Dearly loved of God on high,
   In exultant jubilation
   Pours perpetual melody,
   God the One in Three adoring
   In glad hymns eternally.

3. To this temple, where we call Thee,
   Come, O Lord of hosts, today;
   With Thy wonted loving-kindness
   Hear Thy servants as they pray;
   And Thy fullest benediction
   Shed within its walls always.

4. Here vouchsafe to all Thy servants
   What they ask of Thee to gain,
   What they gain from Thee for ever
   With the blessèd to retain,
   And hereafter in Thy glory
   Evermore with Thee to reign.

5. Praise and honour to the Father,
   Praise and honour to the Son,
   Praise and honour to the Spirit,
   Ever Three and ever One;
   One in might, and One in glory,
   While unending ages run.

7th or 8th century
Tr. John Mason Neale (1818-66)

2 Cor 6:16; 1 Pet 2:4-10; Rev 21:2-3

55.

City, O City

Capo 3(C)

Leonard E. Smith Jnr.

Ps 17:5-7

Brightly with pace

1. Ci-ty, O Ci-ty, O Ci-ty of God, glo-ri-ous things are spo-ken of you. Ci-ty, O Ci-ty, O Ci-ty of God, glo-ri-ous things are spo-ken of you. Such glor - ious things are spo - ken of you, are spo - ken of you, Ci-ty, O Ci-ty, O Ci-ty of God,

glor- i - ous things are spo-ken — of you. _____

Popular Version

2. This one and that one were born in her,
   All my springs of joy are in You. *(repeat)*
      Yes all my springs of joy are in You:
   This one and that one were born in her,
   All my springs of joy are in You.

3. Singers and dancers together say,
   'All our springs of joy are in You.' *(repeat)*
      Yes, all our springs of joy are in You:
   Singers and dancers together say,
   'All our springs of joy are in You.'

Original Version

2. More than every other dwelling place
   The Lord loves Zion's gates. *(repeat)*
      How the Lord loves
      The gates of Zion.
   More than every other dwelling place
   The Lord loves Zion's gates.

3. This one and that one were born in her,
   The Most High will establish her. *(repeat)*
      About Zion
      It shall be said:
   This one and that one were born in her,
   The Most High will establish her.

4. The Lord will count when He registers
   All the people born in Zion.
   The Lord will count when He registers:
   This one was born in her.
      Then those who sing
      And those who play the flute shall say to Him:
   All of my springs of joy are in You,
   All my springs of joy are in You.

56.   Clap your hands, all ye nations

David J. Hadden
Ps 47:5-6

Clap your hands, — all ye na - tions, — shout to God with cries of joy. — Clap your hands, — all ye na - tions, — shout to God — with — joy. 1. God has as - cend - ed — a- mid shouts of joy. — The Lord a - mid _____ the

sound-ing _ of _ the _ trum - pets. _ Sing prai-ses to God, _

_ sing prai - ses to our _ King, _ sing

praise _____ to Him.

2. The Lord most high is King of the earth,
   How awesome is the Lord who rules the heavens.
   Sing praises to God,
   Sing praises to our King,
   Sing praise to Him.

3. Our God is seated on His holy throne,
   And as His rule extends to every nation
   We'll give Him our praise
   And sing our new song,
   Our song of joy.

57.
Come, all you thirsty nations
(Love is waiting here)

Phil Lawson Johnston
Is 55:1; Jn 7:37-38

Liltingly

1. Come, all you thir - sty na - tions,____ Come to the ri - ver side.____ If your foun-tains have run dry then come and be sa - tis - fied.____

Come through to Je - sus,_ The
Lord is wait - ing for you. So come through to
Je - sus,_ the wa - ter is so clear,_
Love is wait - ing here. A stream of ev - er - last - ing

2. How many sons in glory
   Only the Father knows;
   How many will be touched with love
   As the wind of the Spirit blows.

   How many have found freedom,
   How many have found joy,
   Knowing the love that comes from Jesus
   Nothing can destroy,
   Nothing can destroy.

   Come through to Jesus,
   The Lord is waiting for you.
   Come through to Jesus,
   The water is so clear,
   Love is waiting here
   A stream of everlasting life,
   Everlasting life, everlasting life.

58. Come and praise Him, royal priesthood

Andy Carter

1 Pet 2:9

59. Come and praise the living God

Capo 2 (Am)

Mike Kerry
Heb 12:22-28

Come and praise the li-ving God, — come and wor-ship, come and wor-ship.

He has made you priest and king, — come and wor-ship the li-ving God. —

1. We — come not to a moun-tain of fire and smoke,_

not to gloom and dark-ness or trum-pet sound; we come to the new Je-

-ru-sa-lem, the ho-ly ci-ty of God. —

2. By His voice He shakes the earth,
His judgements known throughout the world.
But we have a city that for ever stands,
The holy city of God.

60.

Come bless the Lord

Phil Lawson Johnston
Ps 134:1-2

Come bless the Lord, _____ All you ser-vants of the Lord, _____ Who stand by night in the house of the Lord. _____ Lift up your hands _____ to the ho-ly place and bless _____ the _ Lord. _____ Come bless the Lord, _____ Come bless the Lord, _____ Come bless the Lord.

61.   Come bless the Lord

ALTERNATIVE VERSION
arranged Margaret Evans
Ps 134:1-2

62.

Come let us fill our hearts

Mick Ray

With swing

Verse

1. Come let us fill our hearts and sing a song to the Lord, _____ set a-

side other thoughts and let us sing a song to the Lord. _____ Let us sing,

_____ let us shout _____ and de-clare _ His goodness right out! And

Chorus

fill our hearts and sing a song to the Lord. _____ With

music and dance and a song in our hearts, Lord we praise You, _____ with

music and dance and a song in our hearts, Lord we praise You. _____ Lord we sing,

_____ Lord we shout _____ and de-clare Your good-ness right out! And

fill our hearts and give our praise to You Lord. _____

2. Come let us fill our hearts and give ourselves to the Lord,
With His joy as our strength, let us give ourselves to the Lord.
Let us sing, let us shout and declare His goodness right out!
And fill our hearts and give ourselves to the Lord.

63.
Come let us glorify the Lord

Capo 5 (Am)

Rose Smith

Ps 86:8-13

Come let us glo - ri - fy the Lord, ___ sing Hal - le - lu - jah to the Lord. ___ Come let us wor - ship Him, ___ bow down and wor - ship Him, ___ for He is God ___ and Lord of all. ___

64. Come, let us join our cheerful songs

Capo 3 (G)

NATIVITY

Henry Lahee (1826-1912)

1. Come, let us join our cheer-ful songs with an-gels round the throne; — ten thou-sand thou - sand are their tongues, but all their joys are one.

Alternative tune: LYNGHAM (394)

2. 'Worthy the Lamb that died,' they cry,
   'To be exalted thus.'
   'Worthy the Lamb,' our lips reply,
   'For He was slain for us.'

3. Jesus is worthy to receive
   Honour and power divine:
   And blessings, more than we can give,
   Be, Lord, for ever Thine.

4. Let all that dwell above the sky,
   And air, and earth, and seas,
   Conspire to lift Thy glories high,
   And speak Thine endless praise.

5. The whole creation join in one
   To bless the sacred name
   Of Him that sits upon the throne,
   And to adore the Lamb.

Isaac Watts (1674-1748)

Rev 5: 11-14

65. Come let us kneel before Him

Capo 3 (C)

Pat Ogle
Ps 95: 6; Is 53: 4

1. Come let us kneel before Him,
come let us praise His name;
worship the Lord our God.

2. For He has borne our sorrows,
And He has borne our griefs,
That we might walk redeemed.

3. Wake ye who dwell in Zion,
Sing all ye war-torn lands;
The Prince of Peace is come.

66. Come let us offer

Marlene Bigley
Heb 13: 15

Come let us of-fer a sac-ri-fice of praise,
come let us of-fer a sac-ri-fice of praise. It's the
fruit of our lips giv-ing thanks, the fruit of our lips giv-ing
thanks, so come and of-fer sac-ri-fi-ces,
come and of-fer praise un-to the Lord.

67. Come, let us sing of a wonderful love

Capo 3(C)
WONDERFUL LOVE
Frederick Luke Wiseman (1858-1944)
With a gentle lilt

1. Come, let us sing of a won-der-ful love, ten-der and true;—— out of the heart of the Fa-ther a-bove,—— stream-ing to me and to you:—— won-der-ful love—— dwells in the heart of the Fa-ther a-bove.

2. Jesus, the Saviour, this gospel to tell,
   Joyfully came;
   Came with the helpless and hopeless to dwell,
   Sharing their sorrow and shame;
   Seeking the lost,
   Saving, redeeming at measureless cost.

3. Jesus is seeking the wanderers yet;
   Why do they roam?
   Love only waits to forgive and forget;
   Home, weary wanderer, home!
   Wonderful love
   Dwells in the heart of the Father above.

4. Come to my heart, O Thou wonderful love,
   Come and abide,
   Lifting my life, till it rises above
   Envy and falsehood and pride,
   Seeking to be
   Lowly and humble, a learner of Thee.

   Robert Walmsley (1831-1905)
   Lk 15:11-24; Rom 5:5; 1 Jn 4:10

68. Come now let us reason together

Graham Kendrick
Is 1:16-20

Thoughtfully

Come now let us rea-son to-geth-er, says the Lord, though your sins are as scar-let, they shall be white as snow. 1. A-las sin-ful nat-ion, a peo-ple weighed down with sin, we have a-ban-doned the Lord and

turned   away   from   Him. _____   Our mind is sick and our

heart   is   faint   with - in, _____   we   are

covered in bruises and   sores   and have no   heal - ing. _____

2. So wash yourselves, now take your evil deeds from My sight,
   Cease from evil and turn around to do what is right,
   Reproving the ruthless, defending the helpless and poor,
   Where oppression has ruled, the reign of justice restore.

3. Now if you consent and obey you'll eat from My hand,
   But rebellion will bring a sword to your land.
   For those who forsake the Lord shall be brought to an end,
   But righteousness comes to redeem those who turn again.

69.
Come on and celebrate
(Celebrate)

Patricia Morgan
1 Pet 1: 8-9

Very lively

Come on and cel - e - brate_ His gift of love, we will

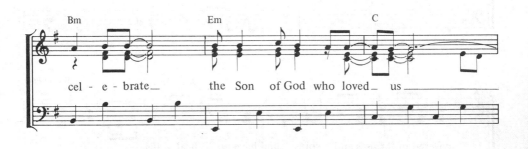

cel - e - brate_ the Son of God who loved_ us_

_ and gave us life. _____ We'll shout Your

praise, O King, _ You give us joy no-thing else can bring,_

70. Come on let us sing to the Lord

Capo 4 (C)

David Williams

Ps 95: 1, 2, 6

Come on ___ let us sing to the Lord, ___

come on ___ let us wor - ship the King, ___

come on ___ let us shout a - loud ___ and

come be - fore Him with thanks-giv - ing. ___

1. We will extol Him with music and with song, we will bow before Him; the Lord He is our God.

2. Let us kneel before our God
In praise and adoration,
He is the King of kings,
He is the Lord of lords.

71.   Come sing a new psalm of David

Daniel Gardner
Ps 100: 4-5

Come sing a new psalm of Dav - id, come sing a song of the Lord, and we'll praise Him with in - stru - ments, praise Him with mus - ic, praise to the One we a - dore. dore. He's the Lord.

72.

Come, walk with me

Pam Ive
1 Pet 2:4-5

2. You are the stones which His love is now shaping,
Lives being made into praise for our God,
See the pure stone that the builders rejected
Now the foundation, the glory of God.
Come dance with me, we're the stones of that city,
Giving the glory to Jesus our King.

73.

Cover me

R. Edward Miller
Ruth 3:9

Tenderly

Cov-er me, _____ cov-er me, _____ ex-tend the bor-der of Thy man-tle ov - er me, Be - cause Thou art _____ my near-est kins - man, _____ Co - ver me, co - ver me, co - ver me. _____

O Lord, open my lips,
  and my mouth will declare your
    praise.
You do not delight in sacrifice, or I
    would bring it;
  you do not take pleasure in burnt
    offerings.
The sacrifices of God are a broken
    spirit;
  a broken and contrite heart,
  O God, you will not despise.

PSALM 51:15–17

74.

Create in me

Dave Fellingham
Ps 51: 7, 10

Create in me a clean heart, O God, and renew a right spirit in me. Create in me a clean heart, O God, and renew a right spirit in me.

Wash me, cleanse me, pur - i - fy me, make my heart as white as snow. Cre - ate in me a clean heart, O ___ God, and re - new a right spi - rit in me. ___

75. Crown Him with many crowns

Capo 2(C)

DIADEMATA

George J. Elvey (1816-93)

1. Crown Him with ma - ny crowns, the Lamb up - on His throne; hark, how the heav'n - ly an - them drowns all mu - sic but its own! A - wake, my soul, and sing of Him who died for thee and hail Him as thy match-less King, through all e - ter - ni - ty.

2. Crown Him the Lord of life,
   Who triumphed o'er the grave,
   And rose victorious in the strife
   For those He came to save:
   His glories now we sing,
   Who died and rose on high;
   Who died eternal life to bring,
   And lives that death may die.

3. Crown Him the Lord of love;
   Behold His hands and side,
   Those wounds yet visible above
   In beauty glorified:
   No angel in the sky
   Can fully bear that sight,
   But downward bends His burning eye
   At mysteries so bright.

4. Crown Him the Lord of peace,
   Whose power a sceptre sways
   From pole to pole, that wars may cease,
   And all be prayer and praise:
   His reign shall know no end,
   And round His piercèd feet
   Fair flowers of paradise extend
   Their fragrance ever sweet.

5. Crown Him the Lord of years,
   The Potentate of time,
   Creator of the rolling spheres,
   Ineffably sublime!
   All hail, Redeemer, hail!
   For Thou hast died for me;
   Thy praise shall never, never fail
   Throughout eternity.

Matthew Bridges (1800-94) & Godfrey Thring (1823-1903)
Lk 24: 36-40; 1 Jn 4: 9-10; Rev 5: 13; 19: 12-13

76.   Dear Lord and Father of mankind

Capo 3 (C)
REPTON

Charles Hubert Hastings Parry (1848-1918)

1. Dear Lord and Fa - ther of man-kind, for - give our fool - ish

ways; re - clothe us in our right-ful mind; in

pur - er lives Thy ser - vice find, in deep-er rev' - rence,

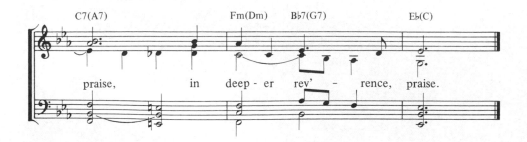

praise, in deep - er rev' - rence, praise.

2. In simple trust like theirs who heard,
   Beside the Syrian sea,
   The gracious calling of the Lord,
   Let us, like them, without a word
   Rise up and follow Thee,
   Rise up and follow Thee.

3. O sabbath rest by Galilee!
   O calm of hills above,
   Where Jesus knelt to share with Thee
   The silence of eternity,
   Interpreted by love,
   Interpreted by love.

4. With that deep hush subduing all
   Our words and works that drown
   The tender whisper of Thy call,
   As noiseless let Thy blessing fall
   As fell Thy manna down,
   As fell Thy manna down.

5. Drop Thy still dews of quietness,
   Till all our strivings cease;
   Take from our souls the strain and stress,
   And let our ordered lives confess
   The beauty of Thy peace,
   The beauty of Thy peace.

6. Breathe through the heats of our desire
   Thy coolness and Thy balm;
   Let sense be dumb, let flesh retire;
   Speak through the earthquake, wind and fire,
   O still small voice of calm,
   O still small voice of calm!

John Greenleaf Whittier (1807-92)

Ex 16:11-15; 1 Kings 19:11-13

77. Delight yourselves in the Lord

Dave Bolton
Ps 37:4; 149:4

Brightly

De - light your-selves in the Lord, _____ de - light your-selves in the Lord, _____ for He de - lights in the prai - ses of His own peo - ple, _____ for He de - lights in the prai - ses of His own peo - ple. Let your well spring up with - in and o - ver-flow to one an - o - ther, let your well spring up with - in and o - ver-flow to the Lord. _____

78.

Draw near to God

Achor
Jas 4.8

Draw near to God and He'll draw near to you,

Draw near to God and He'll draw near to you.

He'll draw near to you. Lift up ho - ly

hands to Him and sing of what He's done, Op - en up your

hearts to Him and praise Him for His Son.

79.

Emmanuel

Bob McGee
Mt 1:23

Em-man - u - el, _____ Em-man - u - el, _____
_____ we call Your name, _____ Em-man - u - el. _____
_____ God with us, _____ re-vealed in us, _____
_____ we call Your name, _____ Em-man - u - el. _____

— □ ▢ □ —

I trust in God's unfailing love
  for ever and ever.
I will praise you for ever for what you
    have done;
  in your name I will hope, for your
    name is good.
  I will praise you in the presence of
    your saints.

PSALM 52:8–9

— □ ▢ □ —

80. Emmanuel

Capo 5(C)

Dave Fellingham
Ps 46; Mt 1:23

God is with us, Em- man-u-el, God is with us. The Lord of Hosts, He is with us, the God of Jac-ob is our strong-hold. The Lord Most High is our ref-uge and strength, God is with us, God is with us. Dwell-ing in the midst of His

81.
Eternal God

Dave Fellingham

Eph 1:20-22; Heb 10:19-20,22

Joyfully with strength

E-ter-nal God, we come to You, we come be-fore Your throne; we ent-er by a new and liv-ing way, with con-fid-ence we come. We declare Your faithfulness, Your promises are true; we will now draw near to wor-ship You.

—— □ ▯ □ ——

*I will praise you, O Lord, among the
  nations;*
  I will sing of you among the peoples.
*For great is your love, reaching to the
  heavens;*
  *your faithfulness reaches to the
  skies.*
Be exalted, O God, above the heavens;
  let your glory be over all the earth.

PSALM 57:9–11

—— □ ▯ □ ——

82.
Every breath that I take

Capo 4(C)

Eddie Espinosa

With life
Verse

1. Ev-'ry breath that I take __ says I __ love You, __

and ev-'ry beat of my heart says I'm Yours. __

Ev-'ry step that I take __ says I __ need __ You __ and I will

bless Your ho - ly name. __

Chorus

You are my Re - deem - er, __ You're the

2. Every day that goes by shows Your mercy,
   And every gift that You give shows You care.
   Every song that I sing says You're worthy
   And I will bless Your holy name.

83.

Every good gift

Capo 3(D)

Steve Young

Jas 1: 17

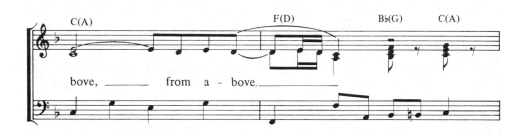

2. So don't you know we need to love the Lord . . . *(etc).*

84.

Every new day that breaks

(For me to live is You)

Dave Bryant

Rom 7:24-8:4,28; Gal 2:20

1. Ev-'ry new day that breaks, the de-ci-sions I make, each breath that I take is You.

Temp-ta-tions that pull, cir-cum-stan-ces that would fool me, I'm see-ing through and find-ing You, just You.

Chorus

For me to live is You, — no long-er torn in two;

— on-ly one life here in me and it's

You, for al-ways You. You. Yes it's

You for al-ways You, Lord it's You.

2. The fun and laughter I wear,
   The pain I bear,
   The love that I share
   Is You.
   The worship I bring,
   The songs that I sing,
   Every single thing
   Lord it's You,
   Just You.

3. The thin line I've been walking on,
   Caught between what's right or wrong,
   Suddenly I find it's gone
   And all that's left is You,
   Just You.

85.

Exalted be the name

Valerie Welch

Is 12: 4-6; Rom 5: 8; 1 Cor 15: 54-57;
2 Cor 5: 17; Eph 1: 13-14; 1 Pet 2: 9

Capo 2 (G)

He has made us whole. Let's give Him our praise to - geth - er in song, for we are His child - ren, _____ to Him we be - long.

D.C. al Fine

Verse 2 — same accompaniment

2. He has won the vic - t'ry o - ver death and all its chains, we can say to - geth - er that our God reigns. The pow - er of His Spi - rit He's giv - en to you, He's with you in ev'ry - thing and in all that you do.

Verse 3 — same accompaniment

3. Cleans'd by His blood _ we have the right to sing, for we are of roy - al - ty, child - ren of the King. The old pass'd a - way, new cre - a - tions in Christ, let our wor - ship to Him be a pleas - ing sac - ri - fice.

86. Exalt the Lord our God

Rick Ridings
Ps 99:5

Ex - alt the Lord our God, _____ ex - alt the Lord our

God, _____ and wor - ship at His foot - stool,

wor - ship at His foot - stool; ho - ly is

He, ho - ly is He. _____

87. Exalt the Lord our God

Capo 2 (C)

Alan Bohling & Sylvia Gallard

Ps 99:9

Triumphantly

Ex - alt the Lord our God _____ who reigns _ high ov - er all. _____ Ho - ly is His name, _____ lov - er of just - ice is He. Praise Him with all your heart, _____ for great _ is His name. _____ We love _ You Lord, _ we love _ You Lord, _ we love You Lord.

88. Facing a task unfinished

Capo 2 (C)
AURELIA
Moderate

Samuel Sebastian Wesley (1810-76)

1. Fac - ing a task un - fin - ish'd, that drives us to our knees, a need that, un - dim - in - ish'd, re - bukes our sloth - ful ease, we who re - joice to know Thee, re - new be - fore Thy throne the sol - emn pledge we owe Thee, to go and make Thee known.

2. Where other lords beside Thee
   Hold their unhindered sway,
   Where forces that defied Thee
   Defy Thee still today;
   With none to heed their crying
   For life, and love, and light,
   Unnumbered souls are dying,
   And pass into the night.

3. We bear the torch that flaming
   Fell from the hands of those
   Who gave their lives proclaiming
   That Jesus died and rose.
   Ours is the same commission,
   The same glad message ours,
   Fired by the same ambition,
   To Thee we yield our powers.

4. O Father who sustained them,
   O Spirit who inspired,
   Saviour, whose love constrained them
   To toil with zeal untired,
   From cowardice defend us,
   From lethargy awake!
   Forth on Thine errands send us
   To labour for Thy sake.

Frank Houghton (1894-1972)

Mt 28: 18-20; Heb 12: 1-3

89.

Father Almighty

Capo 3 (D)

John Johnson

Worshipfully

Fa - ther __ Al-might - y, _____ Mak - er __ and Cre - a -
tor, __ Ru - ler _____ and the on - ly God, we praise Your
ho - ly name, _____ we praise Your name, _____
__ we praise Your __ name, _____ we praise Your
ho - ly name, we praise Your ho - ly name. _____

90.

Father God

Graham Kendrick
Jn 4:23-24

Worshipfully

1. Fa - ther God, we wor - ship You, make us part of all You do. As You move a - mong us now we wor - ship You.

2. Jesus King, we worship You,
   Help us listen now to You.
   As You move among us now
   We worship You.

3. Spirit pure, we worship You,
   With Your fire our zeal renew.
   As You move among us now
   We worship You.

91.

Father God

Capo 3(D)

Jack W. Hayford

———— □ ▢ □ ————

How lovely is your dwelling-place,
* O Lord Almighty!*
My soul yearns, even faints
* for the courts of the Lord;*
my heart and my flesh cry out
* for the living God.*

PSALM 84:1–2

———— □ ▢ □ ————

92.

Father God I wonder
(I will sing Your praises)

Ian Smale

Rom 8: 15-16; Eph 1: 5

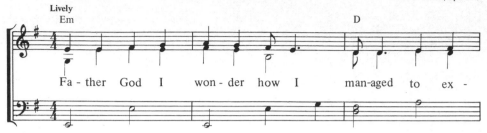

Fa - ther God I won - der how I man - aged to ex -

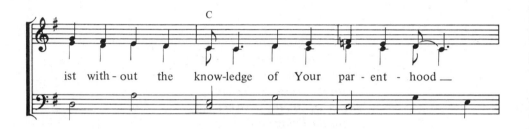

ist with - out the know-ledge of Your par - ent - hood ___

and Your lov - ing care. But now I am Your

son, I am a - dopt - ed in Your fam - i - ly and

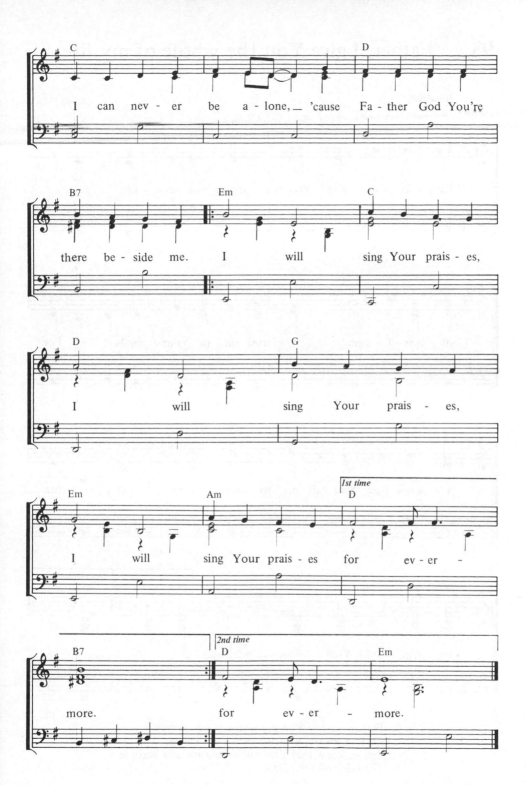

93.   Father, I give You the whole of my life

Thoughtfully

Martin Fakley

1. Fath - er, I give You the whole of my life, all that I am I trust in - to Your hands. For I know that You call me to build with ___ You the king - dom of Your Son. ___

2. Father, we give You the whole of our church,
   All that we are, we trust into Your hands.
   For we know that You call us to grow and become
   The bride of Your Son.

94.   Father, I place into Your hands

Jenny Hewer

Capo 1 (E)

Gently

1. Fa-ther, I place in - to Your hands the things I can - not do.

Fa-ther, I place in - to Your hands—the things that I've been through.

Fa-ther, I place in - to Your hands the way that I should go, For I

know I al - ways can trust You.

2. Father, I place into Your hands
My friends and family.
Father, I place into Your hands
The things that trouble me.
Father, I place into Your hands
The person I would be,
For I know I always can trust You.

3. Father, we love to see Your face,
We love to hear Your voice,
Father, we love to sing Your praises
And in Your name rejoice,
Father, we love to walk with You
And in Your presence rest,
For we know we always can trust You.

4. Father, I want to be with You
And do the things You do.
Father, I want to speak the words
That You are speaking too.
Father, I want to love the ones
That You will draw to You,
For I know that I am one with You.

95. Father make us one

Capo 1 (G)

Rick Ridings
Jn 17:21

Prayerfully

1. Fa - ther make us one, _____
3.

Fa - ther make us _ one, _____ that the

world may know Thou hast sent the Son, _

Fa - ther make us one. _____ 2. Be -

2. Behold how pleasant and how good it is
    For brethren to dwell in unity,
    For there the Lord commands the blessing,
    Life for evermore.

96. Father, we adore You

Capo 3(D)

Terrye Coelho

Rom 12: 1

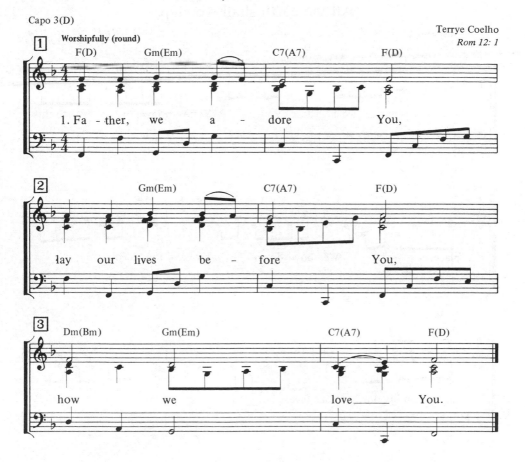

1. Fa - ther, we a - dore You, lay our lives be - fore You, how we love You.

2. Jesus, we adore You. . . *(etc).*

3. Spirit, we adore You. . . *(etc).*

97. Father, we adore You, You've drawn us
(All the earth shall worship)

Carl Tuttle

Ex 15:11; Mt 3:11; Acts 2:3-4;
1 Pet 2:24; 1 Jn 4:19

1. Fa-ther,— we a - dore —You, You've drawn us to this place. We bow down be - fore —You, hum-bly on our face.

Chorus

All the earth shall wor - ship at the throne of the King. Of His great and awe - some power,

2. Jesus we love You,
   Because You first loved us,
   You reached out and healed us
   With Your mighty touch.

3. Spirit we need You,
   To lift us from this mire,
   Consume and empower us
   With Your holy fire.

98.
Father, we love You

Donna Adkins
Jn 12:28

Worshipfully

1. Fa - ther, we love You, we wor - ship and a - dore You,
Glo - ri - fy Your name in all the earth.
Glo - ri - fy Your name, Glo - ri - fy Your name,
Glo - ri - fy Your name in all the earth.

2. Jesus, we love You . . . *(etc.)*
3. Spirit, we love You . . . *(etc.)*

□ □ □

Blessed are those who dwell in your
house;
they are ever praising
you.
Blessed are those whose strength is in
you.

PSALM 84:4–5

□ □ □

99. Father we worship

Dave Bilbrough

Father we wor - ship, — Father we sing, —

Father we love _ You, — You are our King. —

We come to exalt _ You, — our hands we shall raise, —

Yours is the glo - ry _____ Yours is the praise. —

1st time

100.

Father You have loved me
(Dancing Song)

Wayne Drain

Is 63:9

101.
Father Your love is precious
(Your love overwhelms me)

Everett Perry

Capo 3 (D)

102.
Fellowship sweet

Mo Wilkinson & Roy Turner

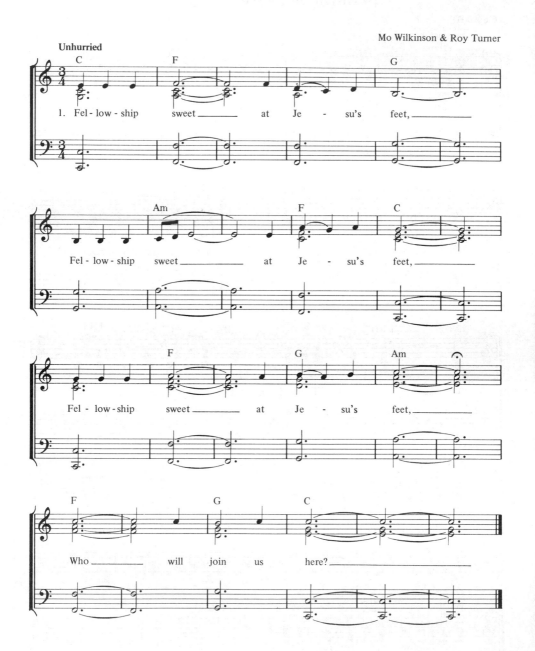

2.   Love we share when Jesus is there, *(three times)*
       . . . Who will join us here?

3.   Money we share when Jesus is there, *(etc.)*

4.   Bread and wine, with Jesus we'll dine, *(etc.)*

5.   We love to sing to Jesus our King, *(etc.)*

103. Fight the good fight

DUKE STREET
John Hatton (d. 1793)

Triumphantly

1. Fight the good fight with all thy might,
Christ is thy strength, and Christ thy right;
lay hold on life, and it shall be thy joy and crown e - ter - nal - ly.

2. Run the straight race through God's good grace,
Lift up thine eyes and seek His face;
Life with its way before thee lies,
Christ is the path, and Christ the prize.

3. Cast care aside, lean on thy Guide;
His boundless mercy will provide;
Lean, and the trusting soul shall prove
Christ is its life, and Christ its love.

4. Faint not, nor fear, His arms are near,
He changeth not, and thou art dear;
Only believe, and thou shalt see
That Christ is all in all to thee.

John Samuel Bewley Monsell (1811-75)

Is 40:29-31; 1 Cor 9:24-27; 1 Tim 1:18; 6:12; Heb 12:1-3

104. Fill Thou my life, O Lord my God
(First tune)

ST FULBERT

Smoothly

Henry John Gauntlett (1805-76)

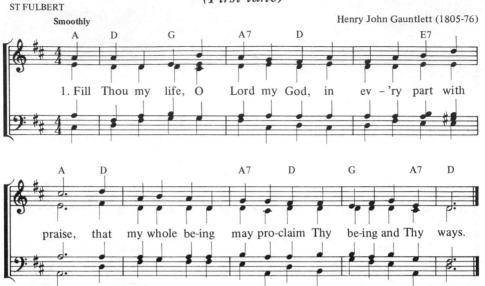

1. Fill Thou my life, O Lord my God, in ev – 'ry part with praise, that my whole be-ing may pro-claim Thy be-ing and Thy ways.

2. Not for the lip of praise alone
   Nor e'en the praising heart,
   I ask, but for a life made up
   Of praise in every part:

3. Praise in the common things of life,
   Its goings out and in;
   Praise in each duty and each deed,
   However small and mean.

4. Fill every part of me with praise;
   Let all my being speak
   Of Thee and of Thy love, O Lord,
   Poor though I be and weak.

5. So shall Thou, gracious Lord, from me
   Receive the glory due;
   And so shall I begin on earth
   The song for ever new.

6. So shall no part of day or night
   From sacredness be free;
   But all my life, in every step,
   Be fellowship with Thee.

Horatius Bonar (1808-89)
Eph 5:19-20; Heb 13:15

Fill Thou my life, O Lord my God

(Second tune)

Capo 3 (D)
RICHMOND

With strength

Thomas Haweis (1732-1820)

1. Fill Thou my life, O Lord my God, in ev-'ry part with praise, that my whole be-ing may pro-claim Thy be-ing and Thy ways.

2. Not for the lip of praise alone
   Nor e'en the praising heart,
   I ask, but for a life made up
   Of praise in every part:

3. Praise in the common things of life,
   Its goings out and in;
   Praise in each duty and each deed,
   However small and mean.

4. Fill every part of me with praise;
   Let all my being speak
   Of Thee and of Thy love, O Lord,
   Poor though I be and weak.

5. So shall Thou, gracious Lord, from me
   Receive the glory due;
   And so shall I begin on earth
   The song for ever new.

6. So shall no part of day or night
   From sacredness be free;
   But all my life, in every step,
   Be fellowship with Thee.

Horatius Bonar (1808-89)

Eph 5:19-20; Heb 13:15

105.

For as truly as I live

Stuart A. Dahl

Num 14:21

Capo 3 (C)

Steadily

For as tru-ly as I live all the earth shall be filled with the glo-ry of the

Lord, For as tru-ly as I live all the earth shall be

filled with the glo-ry of the Lord, The glo-ry, the glo-ry, the

glo-ry of the Lord, For as tru-ly as I live

all the earth shall be filled with the glo-ry of the Lord.

106.

For ever and ever

Mike Kerry
2 Cor 10:17

1. For ev - er __ and ev - er, __ for ev - er __ and ev - er __ my heart __ will boast in Thee. __ Je-sus Christ.is __ my Lord. 2. For all.

2. For Jesus has conquered,
   For Jesus has conquered,
   He's won the victory,
   Jesus is Lord of all.

107. For He is seated on His Father's throne

Dennis Merry

Rom 8: 34; 2 Cor 3: 18;
1 Pet 3:18-22

1. For He is seat - ed on His Fath-er's throne, _____ all foes de - feat - ed by His strength _____ a - lone. He reigns tri - umph - ant ov-er all cre - a - tion, all praise to Him who is on _____ the throne.

This song can be sung with the third verse in D and the fourth verse in E♭.

2. When He had purchased our redemption,
   Giving Himself as the sacrifice,
   He preached the good news to the saints in prison,
   And burst their chains and redeemed their lives.

3. Now as the Lord's Christ, King, Priest and Prophet,
   He intercedes for us always,
   And as we change from glory to glory,
   We'll never cease to give Him praise.

4. For He is seated on His Father's throne,
   All foes defeated by His strength alone.
   He reigns triumphant over all creation,
   All praise to Him who is on the throne.

108.

For His name is exalted

Dale Garratt
Rev 4:8-9

Worshipfully

For His name is ex-alt-ed, _____ His glory above hea-ven and earth. _____ Holy is the Lord God Al-migh-ty, who was and who is and who is to come.

1st time

2nd time sitteth on the throne and who lives for ev-er-more. _____

109. For I'm building a people of power

Dave Richards
Eph 2:21-22

For I'm build-ing a peo-ple of pow-er___ And I'm mak-ing a peo-ple of praise, That will move thro' this land by My Spi-rit,___ And will glo-ri-fy My prec-ious Name. Build Your Church, Lord, Make us strong, Lord, Join our hearts, Lord, through Your Son. Make us one, Lord, in Your Bo-dy, In the King-dom of Your Son.___

110.

For this purpose

Capo 2(C)

Flowing

Intro.

Graham Kendrick

1 Jn 3:8; Rom 6:9-10; 1 Pet 2:24;
Rev 12:10-11

1. For this pur - pose Christ was re - veal'd to de - stroy all the works of the Ev - il One. Christ in us has ov - er - come, _ so with glad-ness we sing _ and wel-come His king- dom in. _

Rhythmic Chorus

Ov-er sin He has con-quer'd, Hal-le-lu-jah, He has con-quer'd. Ov-er
death vic-tor-ious, Hal-le - lu - jah, vic-tor-ious. Ov-er
sick-ness He has tri-umph'd, Hal-le - lu - jah, He has tri-umph'd.
Je - sus reigns ___ ov-er all! _____

2.   In the name of Jesus we stand,
     By the power of His blood
     We now claim this ground.
     Satan has no authority here,
     Powers of darkness must flee,
     For Christ has the victory.

111. For this purpose was the Son of God manifest

Randy Speir

Capo 3 (D)

Col 2: 15; 1 Jn 3: 8

112.
For Thou O Lord art high
(I exalt Thee)

Capo 5 (C)

Pete Sanchez Jnr

Worshipfully with strength

Ps 97:9

For Thou O Lord art high above all the earth, ___

Thou art ex-alt-ed far a-bove all ___ gods.

For Thou O -bove all gods. ___ I ex-

alt Thee, ___ I ex-alt Thee, ___ I ex-alt Thee, ___

O ___ Lord. ___ I ex- Lord. ___

113.
For unto us a child is born

Author unknown
Arr. Margaret Evans
Is 9:6

Joyfully

For unto us a child is born, unto

us a Son is gi - ven. And the gov - ern-ment shall

be up - on His shoulder, and His name shall be called Wonder-

ful Counsel - lor, the Mighty God, the Ev - er - last - ing

Fa - ther, and the Prince of Peace is He.

114.
For we see Jesus

Capo 4 (C)

With majesty

Sue Hutchinson
Rev 4:11

For we see Je - sus___ en - throned on high, Clothed in His right - eous-ness___ we wor - ship Him. Glo - ry and hon - our we give___ un - to You, We see You in Your ho - li-ness and bow be-fore Your throne. You are the Lord,___ Your Name en-dures for ev - er, ___ Je - sus the Name high ov - er all.

115. For Your kingdom is coming, O Lord

For Your king - dom is com - ing, O Lord, — and it shall reign through all the earth. You are pour - ing Your life in - to us, O Lord, and we are tast - ing the prom - is'd new wine.

—— □ ▢ □ ——

I will praise you, O Lord my God,
with all my heart;
I will glorify your name for ever.
For great is your love towards me;
you have delivered my soul from
the depths of the grave.

PSALM 86:12–13

—— □ ▢ □ ——

116.

For Zion's sake
(Royal diadem)

Graham Kendrick
Is 62:1-3

Lightly with increasing pace

1. For Zion's sake I will not keep si - lent, for Jer-u-sa-lem I will not keep qui - et, till her right-eousness goes forth like brightness, like a flam-ing torch her sal-va - tion. _____ You will be a crown of beauty in the hand of the Lord, _____ you will be a roy - al di-a-dem in the

CODA

hand of your God.

2. The
3. So
4. For

2. The nations will see your righteousness,
    And all kings will see your glory,
    And you will be called by a new name
    Which the mouth of the Lord will choose.

3. So take no rest for yourselves,
    All you who remind the Lord,
    And give Him no rest until He makes
    Jerusalem a praise in the earth.

4. *As verse 1.*

117. Fountain, fountain
(His love has found a home in me)

Phil Lawson Johnston
Jn 7:37-38

Capo 3 (C)

1. Foun-tain, foun-tain, spring from the earth, So man-y thirst and cry. ___ Your li-ving wa-ters owe their birth to One who chose to die. ___ Ri-ver, ri-ver, flow to the sea, Some may pass you by, ___ But you've be-come a home to me and I'm no long-er li-ving dry, ___ I'm no long-er li-ving dry. ___ 'Cause I've been

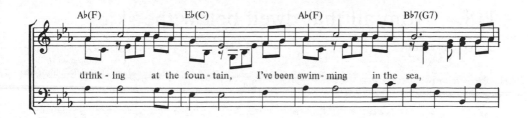

drink - ing   at the foun - tain,   I've been swim - ming   in the   sea,

Je-sus led me to that   moun-tain stream, _____   His   love   has found a   home in

me, _____ ____ O yes His   love   has found a home in   me.

2. Water, water, flow through my heart,
    So many souls are dry,
    Lead me on from ankle deep
    To bathe in the ocean wide.
    Mountain, mountain, reach to the sky,
    Holy hands are raised,
    Before the Father's throne we bow
    In wonder, love and praise,
    In wonder, love and praise.

118. From all that dwell below the skies

LASST UNS ERFREUEN

Geistliche Kirchengesang
Cologne (1623)

Jubilant
Verse

1. From all that dwell be-low the skies let
the Cre - a - tor's praise a - rise: Al - le -
lu - ia! Al - le - lu - ia! Let
the Re - deem-er's name be sung through
ev - 'ry land, by ev - 'ry tongue: Al - le -

Harmonized by Ralph Vaughan Williams (1872-1958)
from the English Hymnal by permission of Oxford University Press.

lu - ia! Al - le - lu - ia! Al - le - lu - ia! Al - le -

lu - ia! Al - le - lu - ia!

2. Eternal are Thy mercies, Lord;
   Eternal truth attends Thy word:
   Alleluia! Alleluia!
   Thy praise shall sound from shore to shore,
   Till suns shall rise and set no more.

3. Your lofty themes, ye mortals, bring
   In songs of praise divinely sing:
   Alleluia! Alleluia!
   The great salvation loud proclaim,
   And shout for joy the Saviour's name.

4. In every land begin the song;
   To every land the strains belong.
   Alleluia! Alleluia!
   In cheerful sounds all voices raise,
   And fill the world with loudest praise.

Isaac Watts (1674-1748)

Ps 113:1-3; Phil 2:10-11

119. From before the earth's foundations

Dennis Merry
1 Cor 15: 24-28; Eph 1: 4;
Col 1: 15-20

With strength

From be - fore the earth's foun - da - tions and cre -

a - tion came to be, ___ God de - clar'd Christ rule ___ ov - er

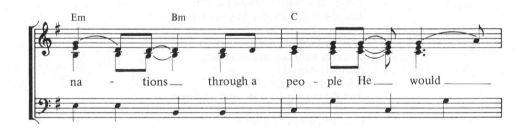

na - tions ___ through a peo - ple He ___ would ___

free. It was God's e - ter - nal pur - pose that the

sons of God should rise, hand-ing ov - er all things to

Je - sus, whose glo - ry fills the skies.

And when Christ re - ceives the king - dom He will

bow be - fore God's throne and de - liv - er up to the

Fa - ther all that He has won.

120.
From heaven You came
(The Servant King)

Graham Kendrick

Capo 3(C)

Phil 2:4-8; Mt 26:39;
Is 53:7; Eph 6:7

King, He calls us now to fol-low Him, to bring our lives as a dai-ly off-er-ing of wor-ship to the Ser-vant King. King.

2. There in the garden
   Of tears,
   My heavy load
   He chose to bear;
   His heart with sorrow
   Was torn,
   'Yet not my will
   But Yours,' He said.

3. Come see His hands
   And His feet,
   The scars that speak
   Of sacrifice,
   Hands that flung stars
   Into space
   To cruel nails
   Surrendered.

4. So let us learn
   How to serve,
   And in our lives
   Enthrone Him;
   Each other's needs
   To prefer,
   For it is Christ
   We're serving.

121.
From the rising of the sun

Capo 3 (C)

Paul S. Deming

Ps 113:1-3

122. Give thanks to the Lord

Patricia Morgan

123. Glorious things of thee are spoken

Capo 3(C)

AUSTRIA

Franz Joseph Haydn (1732-1809)

1. Glo - rious things of thee are spo - ken, Zi - on, cit - y of our God! He whose word can-not be bro - ken, form'd thee for His own a - bode. On the Rock of A - ges foun - ded, what can shake thy sure re - pose? With sal - va - tion's walls sur - round - ed, thou may'st smile at all thy foes.

2. See! The streams of living waters,
Springing from eternal love,
Well supply thy sons and daughters,
And all fear of want remove;
Who can faint, whilst such a river
Ever flows their thirst to assuage?
Grace which, like the Lord, the Giver,
Never fails from age to age.

3. Round each habitation hovering,
See the cloud and fire appear!
For a glory and a covering,
Showing that the Lord is near.
He who gives them daily manna,
He who listens when they cry:
Let Him hear the loud hosanna
Rising to His throne on high.

4. Saviour, if of Zion's city
I, through grace, a member am,
Let the world deride or pity,
I will glory in Thy name.
Fading is the worldlings pleasure,
All his boasted pomp and show,
Solid joys and lasting treasure
None but Zion's children know.

John Newton (1725-1807)

Ex 13:21-22; 16:4; Ps 18:2; 87; Eph 2:11-13; Rev 22:1-3

124. Glory and honour and power to You

Leonard E. Smith Jnr.
Rev 5:12

Glo - ry _ and hon - our _ and pow-er _ to

You, O _ Lamb of God _ for sin - ners _

slain. Rich - es _ and bless - ings _ be-

long to You, O _ King of kings, _ I

bless Your name. 1. When I think a-bout all those things You've
done for me, And I think a-bout _
who it is You _ are to me, I sing:

2. When I think about how You came into the earth,
When I think about the holiness of Your humble birth,
I sing:

3. What a glorious plan You had to rescue me,
What a glorious price You paid to purchase me;
I sing:

4. You are my Redeemer and the Lord to me,
You are quite the giver and a friend indeed;
I sing:

125. Glory be to Jesus

Capo 5(C)

CASWALL

F. Filitz (1804-1876)

Thoughtfully

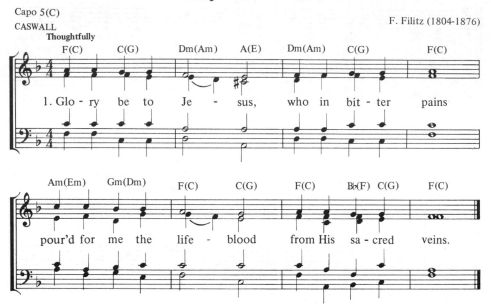

1. Glo-ry be to Je - sus, who in bit - ter pains pour'd for me the life - blood from His sa - cred veins.

2. Grace and life eternal
   In that blood I find;
   Blessed be His compassion,
   Infinitely kind.

3. Blessed through endless ages
   Be the precious stream,
   Which from endless torments
   Did the world redeem.

4. Abel's blood for vengeance
   Pleaded to the skies;
   But the blood of Jesus
   For our pardon cries.

5. Oft as it is sprinkled
   On our guilty hearts,
   Satan in confusion
   Terror-struck departs.

6. Oft as earth exulting
   Wafts its praise on high,
   Angel-hosts rejoicing
   Make their glad reply.

7. Let us lift our voices;
   Praise and thank our God,
   Louder still and louder
   For the precious blood.

Italian
Tr. Edward Caswall (1814-1878)

Gen 4: 10; Eph 1: 7; Heb 9: 11-15; 12: 23-24

———— □ ▢ □ ————

Sing to the Lord a new song;
  sing to the Lord, all the earth.
Sing to the Lord, praise his name;
  proclaim his salvation day after
    day.
Declare his glory among the nations,
  his marvellous deeds among all
    peoples.

PSALM 96:1–3

———— □ ▢ □ ————

126.

God forgave my sin
(Freely, freely)

Capo 3(C)

Carol Owens
Mt 10: 8; 28: 18-20; Jn 3: 3

1. God for-gave my sin in Je - sus' name, I've been born a - gain in Je - sus' name; and in Je - sus' name I come to you to share His love as He told me to.

2. All power is given in Jesus' name,
   In earth and heaven in Jesus' name;
   And in Jesus' name I come to you
   To share His power as He told me to.

127.
God has ascended

Capo 2(Am)

Graham Kendrick

Triumphantly (with a brass sound)

Ps 47:5-8; Eph 1:20-23; 4:8-10; Heb 2:7-9

1. God has a-scend-ed a-mid shouts of joy, the Lord a-mid the sound-ing of trum-pets. O how awe-some is the Lord most high, the great King ov-er all the earth. Praise to our King, sing prai - ses,

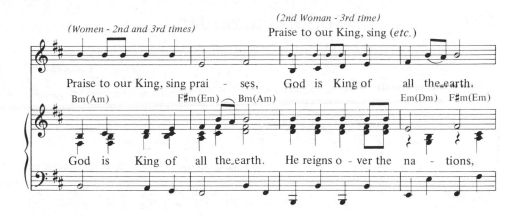

(Women - 2nd and 3rd times)

(2nd Woman - 3rd time)
Praise to our King, sing (etc.)

Praise to our King, sing prai - ses, God is King of all the earth.

Bm(Am)   F#m(Em)   Bm(Am)   Em(Dm)   F#m(Em)

God is King of all the earth. He reigns o - ver the na - tions,

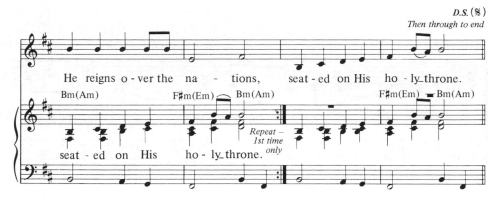

D.S. (%)
Then through to end

He reigns o - ver the na - tions, seat - ed on His ho - ly throne.

Bm(Am)   F#m(Em)   Bm(Am)   F#m(Em)   Bm(Am)

Repeat –
1st time
only

seat - ed on His ho - ly throne.

Last time

Seat - ed on His ho - ly throne.

Last time

F#m(Em)   Bm(Am)

Seat - ed on His ho - ly throne.

2. Christ has ascended to the highest place,
    The Lord amid the sound of our praises.
    Far above all rule and authority
    With all things underneath His feet.

    Praise to our King sing praises,
    Christ is King of all the earth.
    He reigns over the nations
    Seated on His holy throne.

*The chorus is sung in unison for the first time, the second time as a two-part canon between men and women and the third time as a three-part canon between the men and two groups of women.

128. God has a garden

Tony Gemmell

Slowly, building to a climax

1. God has a garden _____ and He calls it praise, _____ and He bids us to

en-ter, _____ to walk through the maze. _____ Well it's like an

oc-ean _____ so vast and so free, _____ and God said He

made it _____ for You and for me. _____ So I will ex -

-alt Him ___ with all of my being; _____ I will ex -

tol Him ___ with all that I am. _____ And if I should

fal - ter, ___ all na-ture will praise Him. _____ So I will now

glo-ri-fy _____ His pre-cious name, _____ So I will now

Last time only

glo-ri-fy _____ His pre-cious name. _____

2. And in that garden there's freedom from sin;
   There's no condemnation to those who walk in.
   Because of the keeper there's love all around,
   There's healing and blessing on His glory ground.

129.
God has exalted Him

Austin Martin

Phil 2:9-10

God has ex-alt-ed Him to the high-est place, gi-ven Him the name that is a-bove ev-'ry name. And ev-'ry knee shall bow and ev-'ry tongue con-fess that Je-sus Christ is Lord to the glo-ry of God the Fa-ther.

130.   God has spoken to His people

Stuart Baugh

Mk 2:21-22

1. God has spo - ken to His peo - ple, through His pro - phets long a-go, of the days — in which we're liv-ing, and the things — His church should know. Lis-ten then — you sons of Zi - on, lend your ears — to what God says, then res - pond — in full o - be-di-ence, gladly walk in all His ways.

2. These are times of great refreshing
Coming from the throne in heaven,
Times of building and of shaking,
When God rids His church of leaven.
Not a patching up of wineskins,
Or of garments that are old,
But a glorious restoration,
Just exactly as foretold.

3. Reign on, O God victorious,
Fulfil Your promises.
Seed of Abraham remember
You will see all nations blessed.
Powers of darkness, we remind you
Of Christ's victory on the cross.
Hear the truth we are declaring,
Jesus won and you have lost.

131.

God is good

Graham Kendrick
Ps 100:5; Heb 4:16

God is good, we sing and shout it, God is good, we cel-e - brate.

God is good, no more we doubt it, God is good, we know it's

true. And when I think of His love for me my heart fills with praise and I

feel like danc-ing. For in His heart there is room for me and I run with arms op-en'd

wide. we know it's true. Hey!

———— □ ▢ □ ————

Ascribe to the Lord the glory due to
his name;
bring an offering and come into
his courts.
Worship the Lord in the splendour
of his holiness;
tremble before him, all the earth.

PSALM 96:8–9

———— □ ▢ □ ————

132.

God is our Father

Alex Simons & Freda Kimney

God is our Fa - ther, — for He has made us His own, —

made Je - sus our bro - ther, — and hand in hand we'll

grow to - geth-er as one.   Sing praise   to the Lord —

— with the tambourine,   sing praise   to the Lord —

133. God is the strength of my life
(Show us Your strength)

Graham Kendrick

Ps 68:28; 80:1-3; 118:14;
Is 61:1

1. God is the strength of my life, my joy, my song,
I will sing prai-ses to Him and re-joice.
He has done great things for me out of His mer-cy,
O that the na-tions might see that He is Lord!

With strength
Chorus

Show us Your strength, O God,

sum-mon now Your pow'r, O Lord. Show us Your strength, O

God, may Your king-dom come, O Lord.

Lord.

2. Stir up Your strength, O God,
   Come near to save.
   Let Satan's strongholds fall down
   In Jesus' name.
   Come set the prisoners free,
   Bring joy and gladness,
   Now let Your enemies see
   That Christ is Lord.

134. God is working His purpose out

Capo 5(C)

BENSON

Millicent Douglas Kingham (1866-1927)

1. God is working His purpose out, as year succeeds to year; God is working His purpose out, and the time is drawing near; nearer and nearer draws the time, the time that shall surely be, when the earth shall be fill'd with the glory of God, as the waters cover the sea.

2. From utmost East to utmost West,
   Where'er man's foot hath trod,
   By the mouth of many messengers
   Goes forth the voice of God;
   Give ear to Me, ye continents,
   Ye isles, give ear to Me,
   That the earth may be filled
   With the glory of God,
   As the waters cover the sea.

3. March we forth in the strength of God
   With the banner of Christ unfurled,
   That the light of the glorious gospel of truth
   May shine throughout the world:
   Fight we the fight with sorrow and sin,
   To set their captives free,
   That the earth may be filled
   With the glory of God,
   As the waters cover the sea.

4. All we can do is nothing worth,
   Unless God blesses the deed;
   Vainly we hope for the harvest-tide
   Till God gives life to the seed;
   Yet nearer and nearer draws the time,
   The time that shall surely be,
   When the earth shall be filled
   With the glory of God,
   As the waters cover the sea.

Arthur Campbell Ainger (1841-1919)
Is 13: 2-3; 24: 14-16; Hab 2: 14; Jn 5: 19; Eph 1: 11

135. God moves in a mysterious way

Capo 2 (C)
LONDON NEW

Melody from *Scottish Psalter* (1635)
Adapted in J. Playford's *Psalms and Hymns* (1671)

Not too slow

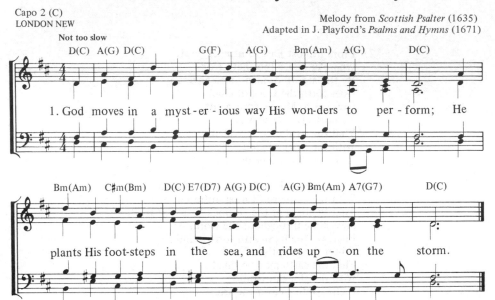

1. God moves in a myst-er-ious way His won-ders to per-form; He plants His foot-steps in the sea, and rides up-on the storm.

2. Deep in unfathomable mines
   Of never-failing skill
   He treasures up His bright designs,
   And works His sovereign will.

3. Ye fearful saints, fresh courage take,
   The clouds ye so much dread
   Are big with mercy, and shall break
   In blessings on your head.

4. Judge not the Lord by feeble sense,
   But trust Him for His grace;
   Behind a frowning providence
   He hides a smiling face.

5. His purposes will ripen fast,
   Unfolding every hour;
   The bud may have a bitter taste,
   But sweet will be the flower.

6. Blind unbelief is sure to err,
   And scan His work in vain;
   God is His own interpreter,
   And He will make it plain.

William Cowper (1731-1800)

Ecc 3: 17; Is 14: 27; Rom 8: 28; 11: 33; Eph 3: 8-9

—————————— □ ☐ □ ——————————

Shout for joy to the Lord, all the
*   earth,*
*   burst into jubilant song with*
*   music;*
make music to the Lord with the
*   harp,*
*   with the harp and the sound of*
*   singing,*
with trumpets and the blast of the
*   ram's horn –*
*   shout for joy before the Lord, the*
*   King.*

PSALM 98:4–6

—————————— □ ☐ □ ——————————

136.
God of glory

Capo 2 (C)

Dave Fellingham
1 Tim 1:17

Brightly with strength and feeling

God of glo - ry, we ex-alt Your name,

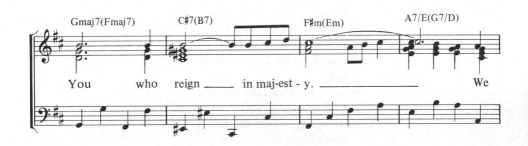

You who reign ___ in maj-est - y. ___ We

lift our hearts to You ___ and we will wor - ship, praise and

mag-ni-fy Your ho - ly name. ___ In power res-

(Descant)

In power res - plend - ent _ You reign in glo - ry, _

- plend - ent _____ You reign in glo - ry, _____ e - ter-nal

Bm(Am)   F#m(Em)

e - ter-nal King, You reign _ for ev - er. _____

King, _____ You reign for ev - er. _____ Your word is

Em(Dm)   A(G)

Your word is might - y, _ re leas-ing cap - tives,

might - y, _____ re - leas-ing cap - tives, _____ Your love is

Bm(Am)   F#m(Em)

Your love is gra - cious, You are my God. _____

gra - cious, _____ You are my God. _____

Em(Dm)   A7(G7)   D(C)   G(F)   D(C)

137.
God will keep you

Betty Lou Mills
Is 26:3

Capo 3 (G)

Slow

God will keep you in per - fect peace _____ if your mind is stayed on Him. God will keep you in per - fect peace if your mind is stayed on Him. Stayed on God, per - fect peace, Stayed on God, fears de - crease. God will

138.

Gracious Father

Capo 1 (D)

Dave Bilbrough
Arr. G. Wilson
Jn 13:34-35

Gracious Fa-ther, take us fur-ther in-to ___ Your love; join us to-geth-er, build us in love. ___ Draw us clo-ser to one an-oth-er, as we dis-cov-er Your love. ___ We be-long to-geth-er, we were made to ___ love. ___

139.

Great and marvellous

Bob Pitcher
Rev 15:3-4

Great and_ mar-vel-lous are Thy works, O Lord God the Al - might - y,

Right-eous and true are Thy_ ways, O Thou King of the na - tion.

Who will not fear, O Lord,_____ And glo - ri - fy Thy name?___ For

Thou a - lone art ho - ly and all the na -tions will come be - fore_ Thee and

wor - ship, wor - ship, wor - ship be - fore_ Thee, And

wor - ship, wor - ship, wor - ship be - fore_ Thee.

140.
Great and wonderful

Stuart Dauermann
Rev 15:3-4

Thou a - lone. All the nations shall come and worship Thee, _

for Thy glo - ry shall be re - veal - èd. Hal - le - lu - jah, _ Hal - le - lu - jah, _

Hal - le - lu - jah, A - . men. Lai-lai-lai - lai - lai, lai-lai-lai-

lai - lai-lai, _ lai-lai-lai - lai - lai, lai-lai-lai - lai - lai - lai, _ lai-lai-lai-

lai - lai, lai-lai-lai - lai - lai - lai, lai-lai-lai - lai - lai, - lai lai-lai-lai - lai.

141.

Great is the Lord

Robert Ewing
Ps 48:1-2; Eph 4:45

142.   Great is the Lord and mighty in power

Capo 3 (Am)

With strength

Dale Garratt

Ps 147:5-20

Great is the Lord and might-y in pow-er, His und-er-stand-ing has no lim-it. The Lord delights in those who fear Him, who put their hope in His unfailing love. He strengthens the bars of your gates, He grants you peace in your borders, He re-veals His word to His peo-ple, He has done this for no other na-tion. Great is the Lord and might-y in pow-er, His under-stand-ing has no lim-it. Ex-tol the Lord, O Je-rus-a-lem, praise your God, O people of Zi - on.

143. Great is Thy faithfulness

RUNYAN

Worshipfully

William M. Runyan (1870-1957)

1. Great is Thy faith - ful - ness, O God my Fa - ther,
there is no sha - dow of turn - ing with Thee;
Thou chang - est not, Thy com - pa - ssions, they fail not;
As Thou hast been Thou for - ev - er wilt be.

Chorus

Great is Thy faith-ful - ness! Great is Thy faith-ful-ness!

Morn-ing by morn-ing new mer-cies I see; all I have need-ed Thy hand hath pro-vi-ded, great is Thy faith-ful-ness, Lord, un-to me!

2. Summer and winter, and springtime and harvest,
   Sun, moon and stars in their courses above,
   Join with all nature in manifold witness
   To Thy great faithfulness, mercy and love.

3. Pardon for sin and a peace that endureth,
   Thine own dear presence to cheer and to guide;
   Strength for today and bright hope for tomorrow,
   Blessings all mine, with ten thousand beside!

Thomas O. Chisholm (1866-1960)
Gen 8: 22; Ps 89: 1-37; Lam 3: 22-24

144. Guide me, O Thou great Jehovah

CWM RHONDDA

John Hughes (1873-1932)

Boldly

1. Guide me, O Thou great Jehovah, pil-grim through this bar-ren land; I am weak, but Thou art migh-ty, hold me with Thy power-ful hand: Bread of hea-ven, Bread of hea-ven, feed me now and e-ver-more, feed me now and e-ver-more.

(e-ver-more)

2. Open Thou the crystal fountain
   Whence the healing stream doth flow;
   Let the fiery, cloudy pillar
   Lead me all my journey through:
   Strong Deliverer, strong Deliverer,
   Be Thou still my strength and shield,
   Be Thou still my strength and shield.

3. When I tread the verge of Jordan
   Bid my anxious fears subside;
   Death of death, and hell's destruction,
   Land me safe on Canaan's side:
   Songs of praises, songs of praises,
   I will ever give to Thee,
   I will ever give to Thee.

William Williams (1717-91)
Tr. Peter Williams (1727-96)

Ex 13: 21-22; Josh 3; Ps 31: 3-5; 78: 24-25; Jn 6: 32-35; 7: 37; Rev 22: 1-2

145. Hail, Thou once despisèd Jesus

LUX EOI

Arthur Seymour Sullivan (1842-1900)

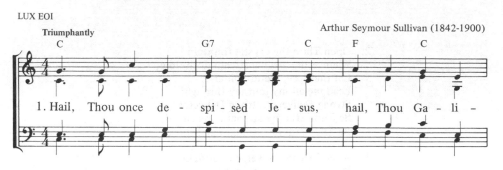

1. Hail, Thou once de - spi - sèd Je - sus, hail, Thou Ga - li -

le - an King! Thou didst suf - fer to re - lease us,

Thou didst free sal - va - tion bring. Hail, Thou ag - on -

iz - ing Sa - viour, bear - er of our sin and shame,

by Thy me-rits we find fa-vour, life is giv-en through Thy name.

Alternative tune: HYFRYDOL (266)

2. Paschal Lamb, by God appointed,
   All our sins on Thee were laid.
   With almighty love anointed
   Thou hast full atonement made.
   All Thy people are forgiven
   Through the virtue of Thy blood:
   Opened is the gate of heaven,
   Man is reconciled to God.

3. Jesus, hail! enthroned in glory,
   There for ever to abide;
   All the heavenly hosts adore Thee,
   Seated at Thy Father's side:
   There for sinners Thou art pleading,
   There Thou dost our place prepare,
   Ever for us interceding,
   Till in glory we appear.

4. Worship, honour, power and blessing
   Thou art worthy to receive:
   Loudest praises, without ceasing,
   Right it is for us to give;
   Come, O mighty Holy Spirit,
   As our hearts and hands we raise,
   Help us sing our Saviour's merits,
   Help us sing Immanuel's praise.

John Bakewell (1721-1819)

Is 53: 4-10; 2 Cor 5: 17-21; Heb 2: 9; 7: 25

146. Hail to the Lord's Anointed

CRÜGER

Johann Crüger (1598-1662)

Majestically

1. Hail to the Lord's A - noint - ed, great Da - vid's great - er Son! Hail in the time ap - point - ed, His reign on earth be - gun! He comes to break op - pres - sion, to set the cap - tive free, to take a - way trans - gres - sion, and rule in e - qui - ty.

2. He comes, with succour speedy,
    To those who suffer wrong;
    To help the poor and needy,
    And bid the weak be strong;
    To give them songs for sighing,
    Their darkness turn to light,
    Whose souls, condemned and dying,
    Were precious in His sight.

3. He shall come down like showers
    Upon the fruitful earth;
    Love, joy, and hope, like flowers,
    Spring in His path to birth;
    Before Him, on the mountains,
    Shall peace, the herald, go;
    And righteousness, in fountains,
    From hill to valley flow.

4. Kings shall fall down before Him,
    And gold and incense bring;
    All nations shall adore Him,
    His praise all people sing;
    To Him shall prayer unceasing
    And daily vows ascend,
    His kingdom still increasing,
    A kingdom without end.

5. O'er every foe victorious,
    He on His throne shall rest;
    From age to age more glorious,
    All-blessing and all-blessed.
    The tide of time shall never
    His covenant remove;
    His name shall stand for ever,
    His changeless name of Love.

James Montgomery (1771-1854)
Ps 72

147. Hallelujah, for the Lord our God
(Hallelujah ... our God reigns)

Dale Garratt
Rev 19:6-7

148.

Hallelujah, Hallelujah
(Hallelujah . . . the Lord reigns)

Capo 5 (C)

Dave Fellingham
Ps 93:1-2

With strength

(Men) F(C)   C7(G7)

The Lord ___ reigns ___

(Together/Women)

Hal - le - lu - jah,   Hal - le -

F(C)

___ in maj - est - y, ___   the Lord has

lu - jah,   Hal - le - lu -

C7(G7)   F(C)

clothed ___ Him-self with strength. ___

jah,   Hal - le - lu - jah!   I will

149. Hallelujah my Father

Tim Cullen

Is 53:4,5

Worshipfully

Hal-le-lu-jah my Father for giving us Your Son;
send-ing Him in-to the world to be gi-ven up for men.
Know-ing we would bruise Him and smite Him from the earth. Halle-
lu-jah my Father, in His death is my birth; Halle-
lu-jah my Father, in His life is my life.

150. Hallelujah, praise the name of the Lord

Andy Carter

Capo 4 (C)

151. Hallelujah! sing to Jesus

Capo 5 (C)
HALLELUJAH

Samuel Sebastian Wesley (1810-76)

1. Hal - le - lu - jah! sing to Je - sus; His the scep - tre, His the throne; Hal - le - lu - jah! His the tri - umph, His the vic - to - ry a - lone. Hark, the songs of ho - ly Zi - on thun - der like a migh - ty flood: 'Je - sus out of ev - 'ry _ na - tion hath re - deem'd us by His blood.'

Alternative tune: HYFRYDOL (266)

2. Hallelujah! not as orphans
   Are we left in sorrow now;
   Hallelujah! He is near us,
   Faith believes, nor questions how.
   Though the clouds from sight received Him
   When the forty days were o'er,
   Shall our hearts forget His promise,
   'I am with you evermore'?

3. Hallelujah! Bread of heaven,
   Thou on earth our food, our stay;
   Hallelujah! here the sinful
   Flee to Thee from day to day.
   Intercessor, Friend of sinners,
   Earth's Redeemer, plead for me
   Where the songs of all the sinless
   Sweep across the crystal sea.

4. Hallelujah! sing to Jesus;
   His the sceptre, His the throne;
   Hallelujah! His the triumph,
   His the victory alone.
   Hark, the songs of holy Zion
   Thunder like a mighty flood:
   'Jesus out of every nation
   Hath redeemed us by His blood.'

William Chatterton Dix (1837-98)

Mt 28: 20; Jn 6: 35; Acts 1: 9; Rom 8: 15-16; Eph 1: 7; Heb 1: 8; 7: 25

152.
Happy are the people

Mick Ray
Ps 89:15-18

Triumphantly

1. Hap-py are the people ____ who have learned to acclaim You Who walk, O Lord, in the light of Your presence. ____ In Your name ____ they shall re - joice all the day long Your righteousness shall lift them up. ____

Chorus

Hal - le - lu - jah! Hal - le - lu - jah! Hal - le - lu - jah! Hal - le - lu - jah! ____

2. You are Yourself the strength in which we glory
   Through Your grace we hold our heads up high
   The Lord our God, He is our strength and shield
   The Holy One of Israel is our King.

—□ □ □—

Shout for joy to the Lord, all the earth.
Serve the Lord with gladness;
come before him with joyful songs.

PSALM 100:1–2

—□ □ □—

153. Have Thine own way, Lord

Capo 3(D)
THINE OWN WAY, LORD!
Prayerfully

George C. Stebbins (1846-1945)

1. Have Thine own way, Lord, have Thine own way; Thou art the Pot - ter, I am the clay. Mould me and make me, af - ter Thy will, while I am wait - ing yield - ed and still.

2. Have Thine own way, Lord,
   Have Thine own way;
   Search me and try me,
   Master today.
   Whiter than snow, Lord,
   Wash me just now,
   As in Thy presence
   Humbly I bow.

3. Have Thine own way, Lord,
   Have Thine own way;
   Wounded and weary,
   Help me, I pray.
   Power, all power,
   Surely is Thine;
   Touch me and heal me,
   Saviour divine.

4. Have Thine own way, Lord,
   Have Thine own way;
   Hold o'er my being
   Absolute sway.
   Fill with Thy Spirit
   Till all shall see
   Christ only, always,
   Living in me.

A.A. Pollard (1862-1934)

Ps 51:7; Jer 18:6; Rom 9:2; 2 Cor 3:18

154.

Hear my cry

Phil Rogers

Ps 61:1-4

Capo 4 (C)

Hear my cry, O Lord, lis - ten
to my prayer. Lead me to the Rock that is
high-er than I, lead me to Je - sus' throne. For
You are my ref - uge, You are my strength, a strong tow'r a-gainst the en-e-
my. So let me for ev - er dwell in Your house and take

1st time   *Last time only*

refuge in the sha - dow_ of Your wings. wings.

———— □ ▢ □ ————

Enter his gates with thanksgiving
and his courts with praise;
give thanks to him and praise his
name.

PSALM 100:4

———— □ ▢ □ ————

155.
Hear my cry, O Lord
(In the shelter of His wings)

Phil Lawson Johnston

Ps 61:1-4

Hear my cry, O Lord, Lis-ten to my prayer. From the end of the earth I cry to Thee When my heart is faint. Lead Thou me to the rock That is higher than I. Thou hast been a re-fuge for

me ____ a - gainst the en - e - my, ____ Thou hast been a

re - fuge for me ____ a - gainst the en - e - my.

Let me dwell in Thy house for

e - ver. O to be safe in the shel-ter of Thy wings. ____

____ O to be safe in the shel-ter of Thy wings. ____

156. Heavenly Father, I appreciate You

author unknown
arranged Margaret Evans

1. Hea-ven-ly Fa-ther, I app-re-ci-ate You. Hea-ven-ly Fa-ther, I app-re-ci-ate You. I love You, a-dore You, I bow down be-fore You, Hea-ven-ly Fa-ther, I app-re-ci-ate You.

2. Son of God, what a wonder You are,
   Son of God, what a wonder You are.
   You cleansed my soul from sin,
   You set the Holy Ghost within,
   Son of God, what a wonder You are.

3. Holy Ghost, what a comfort You are,
   Holy Ghost, what a comfort You are.
   You lead us, You guide us,
   You live right inside us,
   Holy Ghost, what a comfort You are.

157.

He gave me beauty
(Beauty for ashes)

Capo 3 (D)

Robert Whitney Manzano

Is 61:3

He gave me beau-ty for ashes, — the oil of joy for
mourning, — the gar-ment of praise for the
spi-rit of heav-i-ness. That we might be trees of
right-eous-ness, — the plant-ing of the Lord, that
He might be glor-i-fied. —

158. He holds the key

Joan Parsons

Steady pace

1. He holds the key to sal - va - tion, Je - sus is o - ver all. He is the Lord of cre - a - tion:

Chorus

Al - le - lu, Al - le - lu - ia.

Al - le - lu, Al - le - lu - ia Lord.

2.   He is the Rock ever standing,
      No man could break Him down.
      He is the Truth everlasting:

3.   He is a Light in the darkness,
      All men shall see His face.
      He breaks all chains to redeem us:

4.   All power to Him who is mighty,
      All praise to Him who is God.
      All glory now and for ever:

159.   He is Lord

Marvin V. Frey
Phil 2:10-11

Triumphantly

He is Lord, He is Lord, He is ri-sen from the dead and He is Lord. Ev-'ry

knee shall bow, ev-'ry tongue con - fess that Je - sus Christ is Lord.

160.

He is our peace

Kandela Groves

Eph 2:14; 1 Pet 5:7

Capo 4(C)

He is our peace, who has bro-ken down ev-ery wall;
He is our peace, He is our peace.
peace. Cast all your cares on Him, for He cares for
you; He is our peace, He is our
peace. Cast all your peace.

*The Lord is good and his love endures
for ever;
his faithfulness continues through
all generations.*

PSALM 100:5

161.

Here I am

Capo 4 (C)

Thoughtfully

Chris A. Bowater

Josh 24:15; Is 6:8; Mt 5:13-16; Jn 4:35

Chorus E(C)   D♯dim7(G7)   C♯m(Am)   E7(C7)

Here   I   am,   whol - ly   a -

A(F)   G♯dim7(C)   F♯m(Dm)   B7(G7)

vail - a - ble.

E(C)   G♯7(E7)   A(F)   Am/F♯(Dm)

As   for   me,   I   will

E/B(C)   B7(G7)   **To repeat or continue** E(C)   A/B(F) B7(G7)

serve   the   Lord.   (1. The)

Last time only E(C)   *Fine*   **Verse** E(C)   B(G)

Lord.   fields   are white un - to

har - vest _____ but O, the lab'-rers are so

few, _____ so Lord I give my-self to help the

D.C. al Fine

reap - ing, to ga-ther pre-cious souls un-to You.

2. The time is right in the nation
For works of power and authority;
God's looking for a people who are willing
To be counted in His glorious victory.

3. As salt are we ready to savour,
In darkness are we ready to be light,
God's seeking out a very special people
To manifest His truth and His might.

162. Here we are gathered together
(Go ahead)

Wayne Drain

With pace

Here we are gath-ered to-geth-er, ___ there could-n't be a

time that was bet - ter ___ to lift our voice. ___

It's time to rise and be count - ed, ___ no need to

1st and last time

Fine

ques-tion or doubt ___ it, ___ for He is our choice. ___

2nd time only

So go a-head __ and let __ your __ feel-ings show, _____ just lift your heart __ and let __ the __ prais-es flow. _____ It's time to pour __ out __ our heart and soul, and praise the One __ who loves us so. _____

D.C. al Fine

163. His name is higher

author unknown
arranged Margaret Evans
Is 9:6

─────────── □ ▢ □ ───────────

In the beginning you laid the
   foundations of the earth,
   and the heavens are the work of your
      hands.
They will perish, but you remain;
   they will all wear out like a
      garment.
Like clothing you will change them
   and they will be discarded.
But you remain the same,
   and your years will never end.

PSALM 102:25–27

─────────── □ ▢ □ ───────────

164.

His voice is the sea
(Jesus is Lord)

Bill Anderson
Phil 2: 9-11; Rev 1: 14-16

Capo 3 (D)

With breadth

1. His voice is the sea and the sound-ing of the trum-pets; and the call-ing of the Shep-herd is so sweet. His face is the sun, bright-er than the morn-ing; and all cre-a-tion bows down at His feet.

Chorus

Je - sus is Lord, and all the earth a -

2. His mouth is a sword
   That rules o'er the nations,
   And His sword will draw His children to His side.
   His eyes are a fire
   That burns throughout the kingdom,
   And the burning purifies the Master's bride.

165.

Hold me Lord

Danny Daniels

Is 41: 13

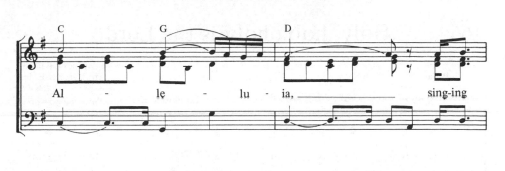

Al - le - lu - ia, _____ sing-ing

Al - le - lu - ia, _____ sing-ing Al - le - lu -

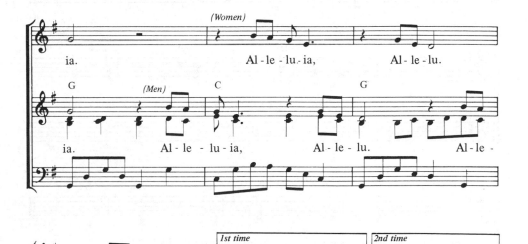

ia.   (Women) Al - le - lu - ia,   Al - le - lu.

ia.   (Men) Al - le - lu - ia,   Al - le - lu.   Al - le -

1st time   2nd time

Al - le - lu - ia,   Al - le - lu.   Al - le - lu.

lu - ia,   Al - le - lu.   -lu.

166. Holy, holy, holy is the Lord

Author unknown
Arr. Margaret Evans
Rev 4:8

2. Worthy, worthy, worthy is . . . (*etc*).

3. Jesus, Jesus, Jesus is . . . (*etc*).

4. Glory, glory, glory to . . . (*etc*).

167.   Holy, Holy, Holy is the Lord of hosts

Nolene Prince

Is 6:3

168. Holy, holy, holy, Lord God Almighty!

Capo 2 (C)
NICAEA

(First tune)

John Bacchus Dykes (1823-76)

1. Ho - ly, ho - ly, ho - ly, Lord ___ God Al - migh - ty! Ear - ly in the morn - ing our song shall rise to Thee: ho - ly, ho - ly, ho - ly, mer - ci - ful and migh - ty, God in three Per - sons, bless - èd Tri - ni - ty!

Holy, holy, holy! Lord God Almighty!

2. Holy, holy, holy! all the saints adore Thee,
   Casting down their golden crowns
   Around the glassy sea;
   Cherubim and seraphim falling down before Thee,
   Who were, and are, and evermore shall be.

3. Holy, holy, holy! though the darkness hide Thee,
   Though the eye of sinful man
   Thy glory may not see;
   Only Thou art holy, there is none beside Thee
   Perfect in power, in love and purity.

4. Holy, holy, holy, Lord God Almighty!
   All Thy works shall praise Thy name,
   In earth, and sky, and sea;
   Holy, holy, holy, merciful and mighty,
   God in three Persons, blessèd Trinity!

Reginald Herber (1783-1826)

Is 6: 3; Rev 4: 8-11

Holy, holy, holy, Lord God Almighty!
(Second tune)

TERSANCTUS

Gordon Frederick James Hartless (1913-)

2. Holy, holy, holy! all the saints adore Thee,
   Casting down their golden crowns
   Around the glassy sea;
   Cherubim and seraphim falling down before Thee,
   Who were, and are, and evermore shall be.

3. Holy, holy, holy! though the darkness hide Thee,
   Though the eye of sinful man
   Thy glory may not see;
   Only Thou art holy, there is none beside Thee
   Perfect in power, in love and purity.

4. Holy, holy, holy, Lord God Almighty!
   All Thy works shall praise Thy name,
   In earth, and sky, and sea;
   Holy, holy, holy, merciful and mighty,
   God in three Persons, blessèd Trinity!

Reginald Herber (1783-1826)

Is 6: 3; Rev 4: 8-11

169.

Holy is the Lamb
(Worthy is the Lamb)

Capo 5(C)

Paula Diesel

Rev 5: 12

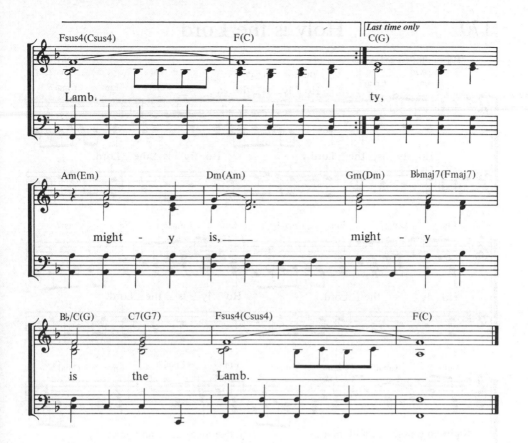

2. Worthy is the Lamb. . . *(etc).*

3. Jesus is the Lamb. . . *(etc).*

4. Mighty is the Lamb,
   Mighty is the Lamb
   That was raised, raised.
   Mighty is the Lamb,
   Mighty is the Lamb,
   Mighty, mighty is,
   Mighty is the Lamb.

170. Holy is the Lord

Majestically (Men and women in canon)

Kelly Green
Rev 15:3-4

Copyright © 1982 Mercy Publishing.
Administered in Europe by Thankyou Music, P.O. Box 75, Eastbourne BN23 6NW.

171.
Holy is the Lord, O holy

Bruce Clewett
Lam 3:22-23; Heb 13:8; Rev 4:8

1. Ho-ly is the Lord, O ho - ly is ___ the Lord of hosts. ___

There is no un-right-eous - ness in all ___ You do. ___

You've re-fused to com-pro-mise ___ on truth, in You are found no lies, ___ all

hea-ven joins us now in praise ___ to You. ___

Chorus

1. Ho - ly, O ___ ho - ly, yes - ter -
2. Wor - thy,

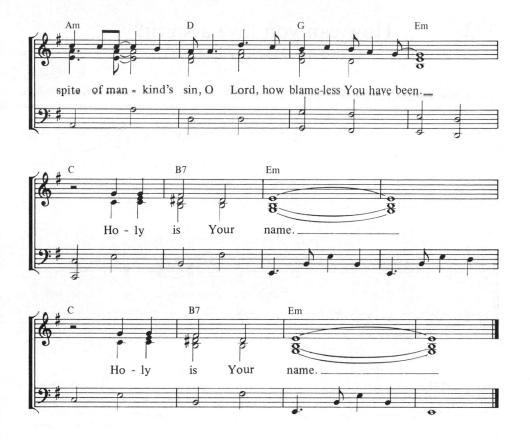

spite of man - kind's sin, O Lord, how blame-less You have been.—

Ho - ly is Your name.——————

Ho - ly is Your name.——————

2. Worthy is the Lord,
   O worthy is the Lord of hosts.
   Your loving kindness is every morning new.
   Through holding to Your righteousness
   You've been merciful to us,
   All heaven joins us now in praise to You.

   Worthy, O Worthy . . . (etc).

172.

How can you love a spirit?
(Love me, love my brother)

Bob Gillman
1 Jn 4:12

With pace

1. How can you love a spirit, How can you touch it with your hand? So how can you touch the Lord your God? Just give your-self to His com - mand.

Chorus

Love me, love my bro-ther, That's the way God says it has to be. His Spi-rit is made flesh in His peo-ple, so you can love the Lord now in me.

2. It's easy to say we love Father,
   For He ain't hard to live with day by day.
   But it doesn't mean much to Him if we're neglecting
   To love one another come what may.

3. Have you ever felt you wanted to touch Jesus,
   But you never feel that you are getting through?
   Well here's a way that you can meet God surely,
   Just touch that brother sitting next to you.

173.

How great is our God

author unknown
arranged Margaret Evans
Ex 14:21; Deut 31:6

Capo 3(D)

Joyfully

How great is our God, ___ How great is His name, ___

___ How great is His love ___ for ev - er the

same. ___ He rolled back the wa - ters ___

___ of the might - y Red Sea, ___ And He said, I'll nev-er

leave you, ___ put your trust in Me. ___

174.

How I love You
(You are the One)

Keith Green
Jn 14: 6

1. I was so lost
   But You showed the way,
   'Cause You are the Way.
   I was so lost
   But You showed the way to me!

2. I was lied to
   But You told the truth,
   'Cause You are the Truth.
   I was lied to
   But You showed the truth to me!

3. I was dying
   But You gave me life,
   'Cause You are the Life.
   I was dying
   And You gave Your life for me!

   How I love You,
   You are the One,
   You are the One.
   How I love You,
   You are the One,
   God's risen Son.
   You are the One for me!

4. Hallelujah!
   You are the One,
   You are the One.
   Hallelujah!
   You are the One for me!

175. How lovely is Thy dwelling place

Author unknown
Arr. Margaret Evans
Ps 84:1-2, 10-11

Capo 5 (C)

Joyfully

How love-ly is Thy dwell-ing place, O Lord of

hosts, My soul longs and yearns for Your courts,

And my heart and flesh sing for joy to the liv-ing God.

One day in Thy pre - sence is far bet-ter to me than

176.

How lovely on the mountains
(Our God reigns)

Leonard E. Smith Jnr.

Is 52:7-10

Capo 1 (A)

Triumphantly with pace

1. How love - ly on the moun-tains are the feet of Him

Who brings good news, good news,

Pro - claim - ing peace, an - nounc - ing news of hap-pi - ness,

[orig. version] An - nounc - ing peace, pro - claim - ing news of hap-pi - ness,

Our God reigns Our God reigns.

[orig. version] Saying to Zi - on: Your God reigns.

Our God reigns Our God reigns

[orig. version] Your God reigns Your God reigns

Our God reigns _____ Our God reigns. _____

[orig. version]   *Your God   reigns*   *Your God   reigns.*

Popular Version.

2. You watchmen lift your voices joyfully as one,
    Shout for your King, your King.
    See eye to eye the Lord restoring Zion:
    Your God reigns, your God reigns!

3. Waste places of Jerusalem break forth with joy,
    We are redeemed, redeemed.
    The Lord has saved and comforted His people:
    Your God reigns, your God reigns!

4. Ends of the earth, see the salvation of your God,
    Jesus is Lord, is Lord.
    Before the nations He has bared His holy arm:
    Your God reigns, your God reigns!

Original Version.

2. He had no stately form, He had no majesty,
    That we should be — drawn to Him.
    He was despised and we took no account of Him,
    Yet now He reigns — with the Most High.
        Chorus: Now He reigns   *(three times)*
            With the Most High!

3. It was our sin and guilt that bruised and wounded Him,
    It was our sin — that brought Him down.
    When we like sheep had gone astray, our Shepherd came
    And on His shoulders — bore our shame.
        Chorus: On His shoulders   *(three times)*
            He bore our shame.

4. Meek as a lamb that's led out to the slaughterhouse,
    Dumb as a sheep — before its shearer,
    His life ran down upon the ground like pouring rain,
    That we might be — born again.
        Chorus: That we might be   *(three times)*
            Born again.

5. Out from the tomb He came with grace and majesty,
    He is alive — He is alive.
    God loves us so — see here His hands, His feet, His side,
    Yes, we know — He is alive.
        Chorus: He is alive!   *(four times)*

6. How lovely on the mountains are the feet of Him
    Who brings good news, good news,
    Announcing peace, proclaiming news of happiness:
    Our God reigns, our God reigns.
        Chorus: Our God reigns!   *(four times)*

177.

How precious, O Lord

Capo 3 (C)

Phil Rogers
Ps 36:7-9

How pre-cious, O Lord, is Your un-fail-ing love; we find re-fuge in the shadow of Your wings. We feast, Lord Je-sus, on the a-bund-ance of Your house and drink from Your

178. How sweet the name of Jesus sounds

ST PETER

Gently   Alexander Robert Reinagle (1799-1877)

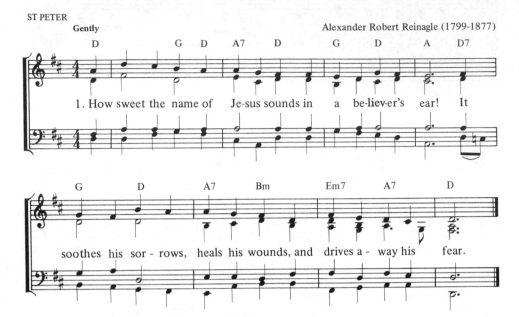

1. How sweet the name of Je-sus sounds in a be-liev-er's ear! It soothes his sor-rows, heals his wounds, and drives a-way his fear.

2. It makes the wounded spirit whole,
   And calms the troubled breast;
   'Tis manna to the hungry soul,
   And to the weary, rest.

3. Dear name, the rock on which I build,
   My shield and hiding place,
   My never-failing treasury, filled
   With boundless stores of grace!

4. Jesus! My Shepherd, Saviour, Friend,
   My Prophet, Priest and King,
   My Lord, my Life, my Way, my End,
   Accept the praise I bring.

5. Weak is the effort of my heart,
   And cold my warmest thought;
   But when I see Thee as Thou art,
   I'll praise Thee as I ought.

6. Till then I would Thy love proclaim
   With every fleeting breath;
   And may the music of Thy name
   Refresh my soul in death.

John Newton (1725-1807)

Acts 4:12; 10:43; Rom 10:13; Rev 22:4-5

Praise the Lord, O my soul;
*   all my inmost being, praise his*
*   holy name.*
Praise the Lord, O my soul,
*   and forget not all his benefits.*

PSALM 103:1–2

179.

I am a new creation

Dave Bilbrough

Rom 5: 1-2; 8: 1; 2 Cor 5: 17; 1 Pet 1: 8

Capo 3 (C)

180.
I am confident

Phil Rogers
Phil 1:6

As Scottish folkdance
Not too fast

I am con-fi-dent that He who be-gan a good work in me will

car-ry it through to com-ple-tion _ un-til the day of Christ. So I'll

work out _ my own sal-va-tion with fear and trem-bling, _ for

God is at work _ in me.

*Praise the Lord, you his angels,
   you mighty ones who do his
      bidding,
   who obey his word.
Praise the Lord, all his heavenly
      hosts,
   you his servants who do his will.
Praise the Lord, all his works
   everywhere in his dominion.*

PSALM 103:20–22

181. I am joined to the perfect life of Jesus
(More than a conqueror)

Dave Bilbrough

Jn 8: 32; 15: 5; Rom 8: 37; 2 Cor 5: 17

1. I am joined __ to the per - fect life __ of Je - sus, all the old of my - self __ has pass'd __ a - way. __ In this truth __ I've found __ the key __ to ex - press __ the Christ __ in me, __ and I am more __ than a con - quer-or, more than a con-

quer-or,   more   than   a   con - quer - or,   through   the

life _____ He lives _ in   me. _____

2. I'm a branch of the vine that stands for ever,
   And as I yield He will bear His fruit in me.
   And the truth that sets me free
   Is this glorious mystery,
   That I am more than a conqueror,
   More than a conqueror,
   More than a conqueror,
   Through the life He lives in me.

3. I am part of a kingdom that's eternal,
   Whose hope is its calling from above.
   Joined with others I will sing
   Of the Christ that dwells within;
   We are more than conquerors,
   More than conquerors,
   More than conquerors,
   Through the life that He lives.

182. I am the bread of life

Capo 3 (G)

S. Suzanne Toolan
Jn 6:35-58

1. I am the bread of life, ____ he who comes to Me shall not hun-ger, he who be-lieves in Me shall not thirst. No one can come to Me ____ un-less the ____ Fa-ther draw him, and I will raise ____ him up, and I will

raise _____ him up, and I will raise _____ him

up__ on the last _____ day. 2. The day.
3. Un
5. Yes

2. The bread that I will give
   Is My flesh for the life of the world,
   And he who eats of this bread,
   He shall live for ever,
   He shall live for ever.

3. Unless you eat
   Of the flesh of the Son of man
   And drink of His blood,
   And drink of His blood,
   You shall not have life within you.

4. I am the resurrection,
   I am the life,
   He who believes in Me,
   Even if he die,
   He shall live for ever.

5. Yes Lord we believe
   That You are the Christ,
   The Son of God
   Who has come
   Into the world.

183. I am trusting Thee, Lord Jesus

BULLINGER
Flowing

Ethelbert William Bullinger (1837-1913)

1. I am trust-ing Thee, Lord Je-sus, trust-ing on - ly Thee! Trust-ing Thee for full sal - va - tion, great and free.

2. I am trusting Thee for pardon,
   At Thy feet I bow;
   For Thy grace and tender mercy,
   Trusting now.

3. I am trusting Thee for cleansing
   In the crimson flood;
   Trusting Thee to make me holy,
   By Thy blood.

4. I am trusting Thee for power,
   Thine can never fail;
   Words which Thou Thyself shalt give me
   Must prevail.

5. I am trusting Thee to guide me,
   Thou alone shalt lead;
   Every day and hour supplying
   All my need.

6. I am trusting Thee, Lord Jesus;
   Never let me fall;
   I am trusting Thee for ever,
   And for all.

Frances Ridley Havergal (1836-79)
Is 30:21; Jn 1:12; 1 Tim 4:9-10; Heb 9:13

─────────── □ ▢ □ ───────────

I will extol the Lord with all my
heart
in the council of the upright and
in the assembly.

PSALM 111:1

─────────── □ ▢ □ ───────────

184.

I bless You, Lord

Carl Tuttle
Deut 6:5

2. I thank You Lord, I thank You Lord,
   I kneel down before You.
   I thank You Lord, I thank You Lord,
   I lift my hands to You.

3. I worship You, I worship You,
   I fall down before You.
   I worship You, I worship You,
   I fall down before You.

185.   I cannot tell

la - bour'd, __ and so the Sa-viour, Sa-viour of the world, is come.__

2. I cannot tell how silently He suffered,
   As with His peace He graced this place of tears,
   Or how His heart upon the cross was broken,
   The crown of pain to three-and-thirty years.
   But this I know, He heals the broken-hearted,
   And stays our sin, and calms our lurking fear,
   And lifts the burden from the heavy-laden,
   For yet the Saviour, Saviour of the world, is here.

3. I cannot tell how He will win the nations,
   How He will claim His earthly heritage,
   How satisfy the needs and aspirations
   Of East and West, of sinner and of sage
   But this I know, all flesh shall see His glory,
   And He shall reap the harvest He has sown,
   And some glad day His sun shall shine in splendour,
   When He the Saviour, Saviour of the world, is known.

4. I cannot tell how all the lands shall worship,
   When, at His bidding, every storm is stilled,
   Or who can say how great the jubilation
   When all the hearts of men with love are filled.
   But this I know, the skies will thrill with rapture,
   And myriad, myriad human voices sing,
   And earth to heaven, and heaven to earth, will answer:
   'At last the Saviour, Saviour of the world, is King!'

William Young Fullerton (1857-1932)
Lk 2:5-7,39-40; 4:18-19; 8:24; 23:44-46; Phil 2:6-11; 1 Thess 4:16

186. I delight greatly in the Lord

Capo 5 (C)

Chris A. Bowater
Is 61:10

I de-light greatly in the Lord, my soul re-joices in my God. I delight greatly in the Lord, my soul re-joices in my God. For He has clothed me with garments of sal-va-tion and arrayed me in a robe of righteousness; He has clothed me with garments of sal-va-tion and a-rrayed me in a robe of righteousness.

— □ ▢ □ —

Let the name of the Lord be praised
both now and for evermore.
From the rising of the sun to the
place where it sets
the name of the Lord is to be
praised.

PSALM 113:2–3

— □ ▢ □ —

187.

If there be any love
(Be kind)

Pete & Dai Roe
Jn 13:34-35; Eph 4:32

If there be an-y love be-tween us, let's keep this in mind:

Be kind, be kind,

And if there's an-y un-der-stand-ing be-tween us let's keep this in

mind, Be kind, Be

kind, Be kind.

Verse

Am · Em · F · C

1. For a new com-mand-ment ____ I give un-to you, That you

Em · C · F · G

love one an-oth-er ev-en as I have loved you.

C · Em · F · C

Then all will know ____ that you are My ___ dis-ci-ples ____ If

Em · C · Dm7 · G · *D.S. al Fine*

you love ____ one an-oth-er. ____ So if there's

2. Love one another – that's what Jesus said,
So let's be kind and tenderhearted –
   to our brother who is our friend.
Let's live together – working out life in love,
Let's be sure our love endures – to the end.

3. Sometimes love can hurt us –
   and the pain of the truth is real,
But let's remember that our Father –
   is building His people with steel,
We are sons and daughters – children of the King,
So let's lay down our lives and feelings
   for our friends.

188. If your heart is right with my heart

Capo 5 (C)

Graham Perrins
Gal 2:9

1. If your heart is right with my — heart — give me your hand.

— If your heart is right with my heart — give me your hand. —

— The right hand of fel-low - ship, The right hand of co - ve - nant; If your

heart is right with my — heart — give me your hand. —

2. If your heart is right with my heart,
   Then we shall love;
   If your heart is right with my heart,
   Then we shall love.
   We shall love in word and deed,
   And be open to each need;
   If your heart is right with my heart
   Then we shall love.

3. If your heart is right with my heart,
   We shall be one;
   If your heart is right with my heart,
   We shall be one.
   One in heart and mind and soul,
   One in purpose and in goal;
   If your heart is right with my heart
   We shall be one.

―――――――― □ ▢ □ ――――――――

Let the people of Zion be glad in
   their King.
Let them praise his name with
   dancing
and make music to him with
   tambourine and harp.

PSALM 149:2–3

―――――――― □ ▢ □ ――――――――

189. I get so excited, Lord
(I'm forgiven)

Capo 2 (G)

With pace and swing

Mick Ray
Eph 1:7

1. I get so ex-cit-ed, Lord, ev-'ry time I re-a-lize ____ I'm for-gi - ven, ____ I'm for-gi-ven,

Je-sus Lord, You've done it all, You've paid the price. ____ I'm for-gi - ven, ____ I'm for-gi-ven.

Chorus

Hal-le-lu-jah, Lord, my heart just fills with praise, ____

2. Living in Your presence, Lord, is life itself.
    I'm forgiven, I'm forgiven.
    With the past behind, grace for today
        and a hope to come.
    I'm forgiven, I'm forgiven.

190.

I give thanks, O Lord

Phil Lawson Johnston
Ps 138:1-2

1. I give thanks, O____ Lord, with my whole__ heart be-fore the gods I sing Thy praise.____ I bow down to Thy ho-ly__ tem-ple and give____ thanks to Thy name,_____ and give____ thanks to Thy name.

For Thy stead-fast love and faith-ful - ness, Thy stead-fast love and

faith - ful - ness, I give Thee thanks, O ___ Lord. ___

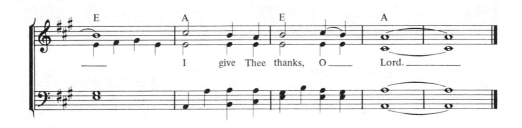

___ I give Thee thanks, O ___ Lord. ___

2. For Thou hast exalted above everything
   Thy name and Thy word on high,
   On the day I called, Thou didst answer me,
   My strength of soul Thou didst increase
   My strength of soul Thou didst increase.

3. Thou dost stretch out Thy hand against my foes,
   Thy right hand delivers me.
   The Lord will fulfil His purpose for me,
   Thy steadfast love endures for ever
   Thy steadfast love endures for ever.

191.

I give You all the honour

(I worship You)

Carl Tuttle

1 Chron 16:25-27; Lk 4:18-21

2. As Your Spirit moves upon me now
   You meet my deepest need,
   And I lift my hands up to Your throne,
   Your mercy, I've received.

3. You have broken chains that bound me,
   You've set this captive free,
   I will lift my voice to praise Your name
   For all eternity.

192. I have been crucified

Phil Rogers
Gal 2:20

Joyfully

I have been cru-ci-fied, cru-ci-fied with Christ, and I live, no long-er I, but Christ _ lives in me. And the life I now live, I live by _ faith, by the faith of the Son of God who loved _ me, loved _ me and gave Him-self for me, _____ who _ loved _ me, loved _ me and gave Himself for me.

193.
I have built in My people
(I'm building a city)

Joan Parsons
1 Pet 2:5

194.

I have loved you
(Arise, arise)

Yvonne Gale & Maureen Smith
Jer 31:3-6

Capo 3 (C)

1. I have loved you with an ev - er - last - ing love ____ ____ And have cont - in - ued My faith-ful - ness ____ to you. ____ A - gain I will build ____ you and you shall be built, And I will be your God, says the Lord. ____ So a -

rise, a - rise and let's go up to Zi - on. A - rise, a - rise and let's go up to Zi - on. A - rise to the Lord our___ God.____ 2. A - God.____

2.   Again you'll adorn yourself with the timbrels,
     And go forth in the dance of the merrymakers,
     So plant your vineyards and you'll enjoy the fruit
     And I will be your God, says the Lord.

195.
I have made a convenant

Karen Barrie
Ps 89:1-6

1. I have made a cov-e-nant — with — My cho-sen, — giv-en My ser-vant My word. — I have made Your name — to last — for ev-er, built to out-last — all time. —

I will cel-e-brate Your love for-ev-er, Yah-weh, age on age —

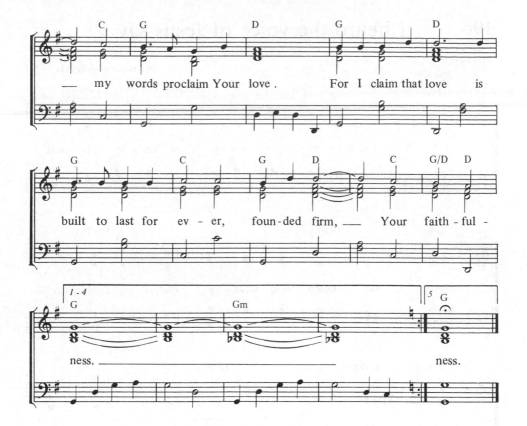

my words proclaim Your love. For I claim that love is built to last for ev - er, foun-ded firm, ___ Your faith - ful - ness. ___ ness.

2. Yahweh, that assembly of those who love You
   Applaud Your marvellous word.
   Who in the skies can compare with Yahweh?
   Who can rival Him?

3. Happy the people who learn to acclaim You,
   They rejoice in Your light.
   You are our glory and You are our courage,
   Our hope belongs to You.

4. I have revealed My chosen servant
   And He can rely on Me,
   Given Him My love to last for ever,
   He shall rise in My name.

5. He will call to Me, 'My Father, my God!'
   For I make Him My firstborn Son.
   I cannot take back My given promise,
   I've called Him to shine like the sun.

196. I heard the voice of Jesus say
(First tune)

Capo 3 (Em)
VOX DELECTI

John Bacchus Dykes (1823-76)

Peacefully

1. I heard the voice of Jesus say: 'Come unto Me and rest; lay down, thou weary one, lay down thy head upon My breast.' I came to Jesus as I was weary and worn and sad, I found in Him a resting place, and He has made me glad.

2. I heard the voice of Jesus say:
   'Behold, I freely give
   The living water, thirsty one,
   Stoop down and drink and live.'
   I came to Jesus, and I drank
   Of that life-giving stream;
   My thirst was quenched, my soul revived,
   And now I live in Him.

3. I heard the voice of Jesus say:
   'I am this dark world's Light;
   Look unto Me, thy morn shall rise,
   And all thy day be bright.'
   I looked to Jesus, and I found
   In Him my Star, my Sun;
   And in that light of life I'll walk,
   Till travelling days are done.

Horatius Bonar (1808-89)
Mt 11: 28-30; Jn 7: 37-38; Rev 21: 23-24

I heard the voice of Jesus say
(Second tune)

KINGSFOLD

Joyfully

Traditional English melody

1. I heard the voice of Jesus say: 'Come unto Me and rest; lay down, thou weary one, lay down thy head upon My breast.' I came to Jesus as I was, weary and worn and sad, I found in Him a resting place, and He has made me glad.

Arranged and harmonized by Ralph Vaughan Williams (1872-1958)
from the English Hymnal by permission of Oxford University Press.

2.   I heard the voice of Jesus say:
      'Behold, I freely give
      The living water, thirsty one,
      Stoop down and drink and live.'
      I came to Jesus, and I drank
      Of that life-giving stream;
      My thirst was quenched, my soul revived,
      And now I live in Him.

3.   I heard the voice of Jesus say:
      'I am this dark world's Light;
      Look unto Me, thy morn shall rise,
      And all thy day be bright.'
      I looked to Jesus, and I found
      In Him my Star, my Sun;
      And in that light of life I'll walk,
      Till travelling days are done.

Horatius Bonar (1808-89)
Mt 11: 28-30; Jn 7: 37-38; Rev 21: 23-24

197.   I hear the sound of rustling

Ronnie Wilson

Ps 45:1

With pace

1. I hear the sound of rust - ling in the leaves of the trees, The

Spi - rit of the Lord has come down on the earth. The

Church that seemed in slum - ber has now ris - en from its knees And

dry bones are res - pond-ing with the fruits of new birth. Oh

this is now a time for dec - la - ra - tion, ___ The

word will go to all men ev-'ry-where, _____ The Church is here for heal-ing of the na-tions, _____ Be-hold the day of Je-sus draw-ing near. _____ My tongue will be the pen of a rea-dy wri-ter, _____ And what the Fa-ther gives to me I'll sing, _____ I on-ly want to be His breath, _____ I on-ly want to glo-ri-fy the King. _____

2. And all around the world the body waits expectantly,
   The promise of the Father is now ready to fall.
   The watchmen on the tower all exhort us to prepare
   And the church responds — a people who will answer the call.
   And this is not a phase which is passing,
   It's the start of an age that is to come.
   And where is the wise man and the scoffer?
   Before the face of Jesus they are dumb.

3. A body now prepared by God and ready for war,
   The prompting of the Spirit is our word of command.
   We rise, a mighty army, at the bidding of the Lord,
   The devils see and fear, for their time is at hand.
   And children of the Lord hear our commission
   That we should love and serve our God as one.
   The Spirit won't be hindered by division
   In the perfect work that Jesus has begun.

198. I hear the sound of the army of the Lord

199. I just want to praise You

Capo 5(C)

Arthur Tannous

200. I know not why God's wondrous grace

I KNOW WHOM I HAVE BELIEVÈD   James McGranahan (1840-1907)

1. I know not why God's wondrous grace to me hath been made known; nor why unworthy as I am He claim'd me for His own. But I know whom I have believ-ed; and am persuaded that He is able to keep that which I've committed unto Him against that day.

2. I know not how this saving faith
   To me He did impart;
   Or how believing in His word
   Wrought peace within my heart.

3. I know not how the Spirit moves,
   Convincing men of sin;
   Revealing Jesus through the Word,
   Creating faith in Him.

4. I know not what of good or ill
   May be reserved for me,
   Of weary ways or golden days
   Before His face I see.

5. I know not when my Lord may come;
   I know not how, nor where;
   If I shall pass the vale of death,
   Or meet Him in the air.

D. W. Whittle (1840-1901)

Jn 3:8; Rom 8:28; Eph 2:4-5; 1 Thess 4:16-17; 2 Tim 1:12

201.

I lift my hands
(Most of all)

Eddie Espinosa

Capo 2(C)

With feeling

1. I lift my __ hands, ___ I raise my __ voice, ___ I give my heart to You my Lord ___ and I re-joice. There are man - y, man-y rea-sons why I do the things I do, O but most of all, I

praise You, most of all I praise You, Je - sus,

most of all I praise You be-cause You're You.

1st and 2nd times

Last time only

2. I lift my ___ You.

2. I lift my hands,
   I raise my voice,
   I give my life to You my Lord,
   And I rejoice.
   There are many, many reasons why I do the things I do,
   O but most of all, I love You,
   Most of all I love You,
   Jesus, most of all I love You because You're You.

3. I lift my hands,
   I raise my voice,
   I give my love to You my Lord,
   And I rejoice.
   There are many, many reasons why I love You like I do,
   O but most of all, I love You,
   Most of all I love You,
   Jesus, most of all I love You because You're You.

202.

I live

Rich Cook

203.

I love You, Lord

Capo 3 (C)

Laurie Klein

With feeling

I love You, Lord, and I lift my voice To

wor - ship You, O my soul re - joice. Take

joy, my King, in what You hear, { May it be a / Let me

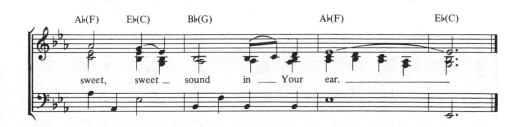

sweet, sweet sound in Your ear.

204.
I love You my Lord

Capo 1 (G)

Dave Fellingham
Rom 1:17; 5:9-11; 8:1-2, 37;
10:9; 16:20

I love You my Lord for giv-ing to me ____ Your
great __ sal-va-tion, set-ting me free from
sin and death and the king-dom of Sa-tan's de-struc-
tion. There's pow'r in the blood to cleanse all my sin, ____
__ I know I'm for-gi-ven, I'm reigning in

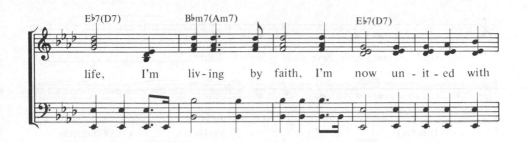

life, I'm liv-ing by faith, I'm now un-it-ed with

1st part

Christ. I con-fess with my mouth that

2nd part

Christ. I con-fess with my mouth _____

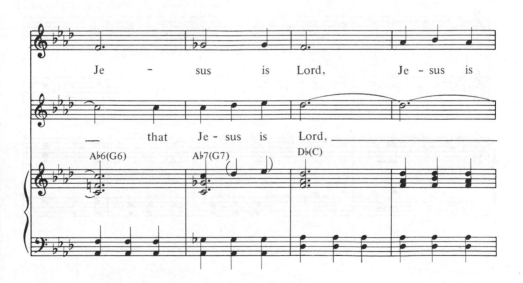

Je - sus is Lord, Je - sus is

_____ that Je - sus is Lord, _____

205. I love you with the love of the Lord

James M. Gilbert

I __ love you with the love __ of the Lord, _____

__ yes I love you with the love __ of the Lord. _____

__ I can see in you the glo-ry of my

King, and I love you with the love __ of the Lord. _____

206. I'm expecting great things of You

Mick Gisbey

Ps 62:5; 2 Cor 3:17-18

I'm ex-pect-ing great things of You, my Lord, my Lord, for You've shown me the pow-er that's in You, my Lord, my sov'reign Lord. Re-veal-ing all the gifts You've gi - ven to me, and by Your Ho-ly Spi-rit You've gi-ven me lib-er - ty to grow and to be made com-plete for You.

207. I'm gonna dance and sing

Dale Garratt
Ps 149: 2-3; Eph 2: 8; Heb 4: 12

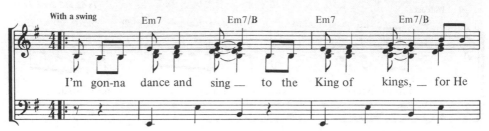

I'm gon-na dance and sing — to the King of kings, — for He

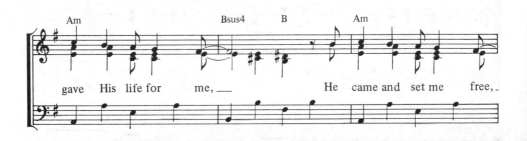

gave His life for me, — He came and set me free, —

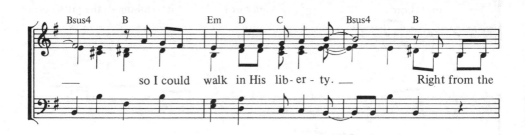

— so I could walk in His lib-er-ty. — Right from the

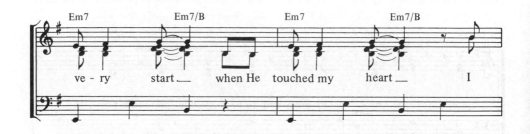

ve-ry start — when He touched my heart — I

208.   I'm gonna give Him all the thanks

John Kennett

Eph 1:3

209.   I'm gonna thank the Lord

Dave Bilbrough
Rom 8: 2

2.   I'm gonna clap my hands and stamp my feet... *(etc).*

3.   I'm gonna sing and shout aloud for joy... *(etc).*

4.   I'm gonna raise my hands in victory... *(etc).*

May the praise of God be in their
mouths
and a double-edged sword in their
hands.

PSALM 149:6

210.　Immortal, invisible

ST DENIO

Welsh hymn melody

1. Im - mor - tal, in - vis - i - ble,— God on - ly wise, in light in ac - cess - i - ble — hid from our eyes, most bless - èd, most glor - ious the An - cient of Days, Al - migh - ty, vic - tor - ious Thy — great name we praise.

2. Unresting, unhasting, and silent as light,
   Nor wanting, nor wasting, Thou rulest in might;
   Thy justice like mountains high soaring above
   Thy clouds which are fountains of goodness and love.

3. To all life Thou givest, to both great and small;
   In all life Thou livest, the true life of all;
   We blossom and flourish as leaves on the tree,
   And wither and perish; but naught changeth Thee.

4. Great Father of glory, pure Father of light,
   Thine angels adore Thee, all veiling their sight;
   All laud we would render: O help us to see
   'Tis only the splendour of light hideth Thee.

5. Immortal, invisible, God only wise,
   In light inaccessible hid from our eyes,
   Most blessèd, most glorious, the Ancient of Days,
   Almighty, victorious, Thy great name we praise.

Walter Chalmers Smith (1824-1908)

1 Tim 1:17; 6:15-16

211.

I'm redeemed

Tony Humphries

Rev 5:9

— ▫ ◻ ▫ —

Praise God in his sanctuary;
praise him in his mighty heavens.
Praise him for his acts of power;
praise him for his surpassing
greatness.

PSALM 150:1–2

— ▫ ◻ ▫ —

212. I'm saved by the grace of God

Ian Traynar
Rom 6:4-11

1. I'm saved by the grace of God,
Root-ed and fixed in love, and I'm fi - nished

with my old life. I'm a - live in a brand new

way And it's ea - sy to live now, I've gi - ven my

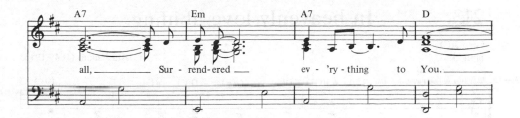

all, _____ Sur - rend-ered _____ ev - 'ry-thing to You. _____

_____ I have no rights on my life, _____

_____ O Je - sus, _____ You are my Lord. _____

2. I know I have died to sin,
   Baptised into His glorious death;
   I've been raised up into newness of life,
   I'm no longer a slave to sin.

3. I live now by the law of God
   Written on my heart,
   And the Spirit and my brothers
   Are showing me where I've got to change.

4. My life is hid with Christ in God,
   I know I am secure
   And nothing can separate me
   From the love which is in Christ.

213.

In heavenly love abiding

Capo 2(C)

PENLAN

David Jenkins (1849-1915)

1. In heav'n - ly love a - bid - ing, ____ no change my heart shall fear; ____ and safe is such con - fid - ing, ____ for no - thing chang - es here: ____ the storm may roar with - out me, ____ my heart may low be laid; ____

but God is round a - bout me,

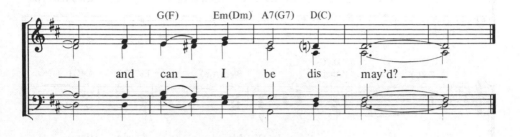

and can I be dis - may'd?

2. Wherever He may guide me,
No want shall turn me back;
My Shepherd is beside me,
And nothing can I lack:
His wisdom ever waketh,
His sight is never dim;
He knows the way He taketh,
And I will walk with Him.

3. Green pastures are before me,
Which yet I have not seen;
Bright skies will soon be o'er me,
Where darkest clouds have been;
My hope I cannot measure,
My path to life is free;
My Saviour has my treasure,
And He will walk with me.

Anna Laetitia Waring (1820-1910)

Ps 23

214.

In Him we have redemption

Dave Fellingham

Eph 1: 6-8

This song has been written to lead into 'Blessed be', song no. 42.

215.

In Him we live and move

Randy Speir

Ps 66: 1-4; Acts 17: 28

In Him we live and move and have our being, ___ in Him we live and move and have our being. ___ being. ___

Make a joy _ ful noise, sing un-to _ the Lord, tell Him of _ your love, dance be -fore Him. Make a joy - ful noise, sing un-to _ the Lord, tell Him of _ your love: Hal-le - lu - jah! In Him we

216.

In my life, Lord

(Lord, be glorified)

Bob Kilpatrick

2. In Your church, Lord,
    Be glorified, be glorified.
    In Your church, Lord,
    Be glorified today.

217. In the Lord is goodness and mercy

Pete Lawry

Ex 34: 6; 1 Chron 16:11-12; Is 49:13;
Mal 3:3; Rom 8:1-2,14

In the Lord is good-ness and mer-cy, in the Lord __ is
wis-dom and strength. __ 1. Seek the Lord __ in all His full-ness, see __ if He's not
faith-ful to __ the word He gives; for He prom-is-es to
com-fort them_that mourn, and those who trust_in Him shall live.

2. God is challenging His people
   To release their hold on everything but Him;
   Let Him have His way to break you
   And remake you, so you'll trust in Him alone.

3. Jesus take our lives, we give ourselves to You,
   And thus we share Your victory.
   No more condemnation, we have been forgiven,
   Sons of God we are set free!

218. In the name of Jesus

Author unknown
Arr. Margaret Evans
Lk 10: 17

Capo 1(D)

Lively

In the name of Je-sus, in the name of Je-sus, we have the vic-tor-y.

In the name of Je-sus, in the name of Je-sus, de-mons will have to flee. Who can tell what God can do? Who can tell of His love for you? In the name of Je-sus, Je-sus, we have the vic-tor-y!

219. In the presence of the Lord

Capo 2(G)

Chris A. Bowater

Ps 16: 11; 2 Cor 3: 17

In the pres-ence of the Lord there is full - ness of joy, and

where His Spi - rit reigns there is lib - er - ty, and

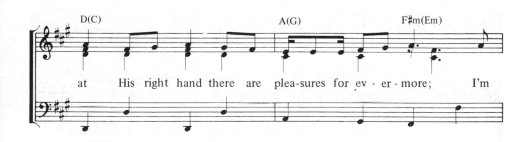

at His right hand there are plea-sures for ev - er - more; I'm

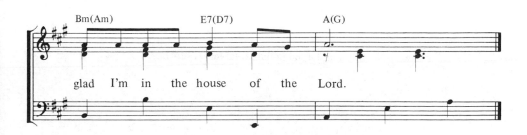

glad I'm in the house of the Lord.

220.
In the presence of Your people
(Celebration song)

Brent Chambers

Ps 22: 3, 25

Capo 5 (Am)

'Hebrew' style

1. In the pre-sence of Your peo-ple I will praise Your name,
for a-lone You are ho-ly, en-thron'd on the prais-es of Is - ra - el.
Let us cel-e-brate Your good-ness and Your stead-fast love,
may Your name be ex-alt - ed here on earth and in heav'n a-bove.

2. Lai, lai, lai-lai-lai-lai-lai-lai. . . (*etc*).

221.

In these last days

Tony Humphries

Is 2:2

Peacefully

In these last days   I'll be with my child-ren,

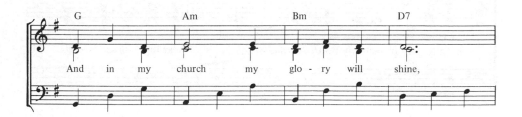

And in my church   my glo-ry will shine,

They all shall be   my ve-ry own re-flec-tion,

And all the earth shall know that they are mine.

222.

In through the veil

Bruce Clewett
Ps 141:2; Eph 5:1-2 Heb 6:19-20

In through the veil now we en-ter, 'bold-ly ap-proach-ing Your throne, bear-ing a sac-ri-fice of fra-grance sweet;— the fruit of some seeds You have sown.— From our lips we of-fer these prais-es,— may You be bless'd as we sing.— Lord we a-dore—You, like in-cense be-fore—You our

223.

In Thy presence

Mike Kerry
Ps 16:8-9

In Thy presence there's full-ness of joy, full-ness of joy, full-ness of joy.

At Thy right hand are pleasures for ev-er, pleasures for ev-er-more. more.

I keep the Lord be-fore me, I shall not be moved. My heart is glad and my

soul re-joi-ces; I shall dwell in safe-ty. And in Thy presence there's

— □ ▢ □ —

Praise him with the sounding of the
*   trumpet,*
* praise him with the harp and*
*   lyre,*
praise him with tambourine and
*   dancing,*
* praise him with the strings and*
*   flute,*
praise him with the clash of
*   cymbals.*

PSALM 150:3–5

— □ ▢ □ —

224.   I only want to love You

Eddie Espinosa

2. I only want to praise You... *(etc).*

3. I only want to serve You... *(etc).*

225.

I receive You

John Lai
Ex 15: 26; Mk 6: 56; Lk 11: 13

Capo 3(G)

Flowing

1. I re - ceive You, O _ Spi - rit of love, how I need Your healing from a - bove, I re - ceive You, I re - ceive You, I re - ceive Your heal-ing from a - bove.____ 2. I can feel Your pow-er on me now, I can feel Your pow-er on me now.

2. I can feel You, touching me right now,
   Come reveal Your power on me now,
   I can feel You, I can feel You,
   I can feel Your power on me now,
   I can feel Your power on me now.

226.

I receive Your love

Paul Armstrong
Rom 5:5

1. I re-ceive Your love, I re-ceive Your love, In my heart I re-ceive Your love, O Lord. I re-ceive Your love by Your Spi-rit with-in me, I re-ceive, I re-ceive Your love.

2. I confess Your love,
   I confess Your love,
   From my heart I confess Your love, O Lord.
   I confess Your love
   By Your Spirit within me,
   I confess, I confess Your love.

227.
I see the Lord

author unknown
arranged Margaret Evans
Is 6:1-3; Rev 4:8

With warmth

I see the Lord, __ I see the Lord, __ He is
high and lift-ed up and His train fills the tem-ple, __ He is
high and lift-ed up __ and His train fills the tem-ple. __ The
an-gels cry, Ho-ly, __ the an-gels cry, Ho-ly, __ the
an-gels cry, Ho-ly is the Lord. __

228.

Isn't He beautiful?

John Wimber

Is 9: 6

Capo 2 (G)

Isn't He beau-ti-ful, beau-ti-ful, is-n't-He? Prince of Peace, Son of God, Is-n't He? _____ Is-n't He won-der-ful, won-der-ful, is-n't He? Coun-sel-lor, Al-might-y God, is-n't He, is-n't He, is-n't He? _____

229. I stand before the presence

Capo 5 (C)

Mavis Ford
Mt 27:51

Thoughtfully

I stand be-fore the pres-ence of the Lord God of hosts, A
child of my Fath-er and an heir of His grace, For
Je-sus paid the debt for me, the veil was torn in two, And the
Ho-ly of Ho-lies has be-come my dwel-ling place.

230.   It is a good thing to give thanks unto the Lord

Capo 3 (C)

Judy Horner

Ps 92:1

It is a good thing to give thanks un-to the Lord, it is a good thing to give thanks un-to the Lord and to sing prais-es ___ un-to Thy name, O Most High. ___

231. It is God who trains my hands for battle
(Battle song)

Dale Garratt
Ps 18:34-35

ry, the Lord of hosts gives

F   C7   F

bronze. _____ He gives me His shield of vic - to - ry, my

vic - to - ry. Praise be to my

D7   Gm   B♭6   Bdim7

en - e - mies fall at my feet. Praise be to my

Rock! He is the Lord of hosts!

F/C   D7   Gm7   C7   F   B♭/C   F

Rock! He is the Lord of hosts!

232.
It is good for me

Tim Blomdahl
Ps 73:25-26

Joyfully with pace

It is good for me to draw near un - to God;__ Lord I

put my trust in Thee, _____ that I may de-clare __ all Thy

works, O my God,_Lord I put my trust in Thee. __ My flesh and my heart_they

fail_me, _____ but God is the strength_of my life. You are my portion both

now and ever - more,_ there is none that I de-sire but Thee.

233. It is no longer I that liveth

Sally Ellis
Gal 2:20

234.

It's so good, my Lord

Mick Ray
Mt 11:30

The price all paid,_____ Things that came be-tween

us are now all e - rased._____ O it's so

Final chorus

good, my Lord,_____ Yes, it's so good, my Lord,_____

Yes, it's so good, my Lord. _____

2. Knowing I'm loved, Lord, standing in Your grace,
   Reigning in life, running the race.

235. It's so good to thank You, Lord

Brook Trickett
1 Chron 23:30

It's so good to thank You, Lord, It's so good to thank You, It's good to give You our thanks for ev-'ry-thing. —

1. thanks un-to the King.

So I'll thank You — in the morn-ing — and I'll thank You — a-gain at night, — I'll thank You — for Your kind-ness — and I'll thank You for Your faith-ful-ness. —

236.
It's the presence of Your Spirit, Lord, we need

Len Magee
Jn 14:16-17

1. It's the pre - sence of Your Spi - rit, Lord, we need, _____ it's the pre - sence of Your Spi - rit, Lord, we need. _____ So help us, Lord, _____ to wor - ship You. It's the pre - sence of Your Spi - rit, Lord, we need. _____

2. It's the presence of Your Spirit, Lord, we love . . . *etc.*

3. For the moving of Your Spirit, Lord, we pray . . . *etc.*

237. I've found it hard, Lord

Mick Ray
Jn 6:63

Verse thoughtfully
Chorus with strength

1. I've found it hard, _ Lord, _ I've been perplexed, _ trying to get it all right, _ Lord, _ by conforming to the text. _ But Lord it's fresh-ly dawn-ing, _ Your word has life with-in, _ in-stead of work-ing at _ it, _ I'm gonna let it in. _ And I'll say,

Be it un-to me, Lord, ac-cording to Your word,

be it un-to me, Lord, ac-cording to Your word. And I'll say

1st time

2nd time ac-cor-ding to Your word.

2. Tired of getting nowhere,
   Active yet standing still,
   Doing instead of believing,
   Struggling to work out Your will.
   But Lord it's freshly dawning,
   Your word has life within.
   Instead of working at it,
   I'm gonna let it in.

238.
I waited patiently

Capo 3 (C)

Phil Rogers
Ps 40:1-3

I wait - ed pat - ient-ly _____ for the Lord, _____ He in - clined to me _____ and heard my cry. _____ He drew me up from a des - o - late pit, _____ out of the mi - ry

239.

I walk with God

Dave Fellingham
Rom 8:1, 31-39; Eph 5:8-10

I walk with God in the light _ of the liv - ing, You have de - liv - er'd me from sin and death. Now there is no - thing _ that can sep - ar - ate me from God's migh - ty love which I have _ in Christ. _____ This I

240. I wanna be more than words
(More than words)

Capo 2(C)

Noel Richards
1 Cor 4: 20

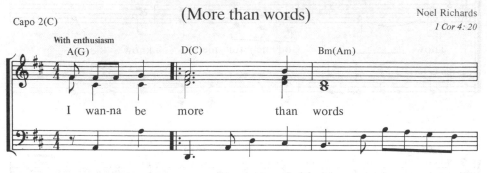

I wan-na be more than words

and emp-ty spec-u-la tion, the time to start is

now, Lord lift my ex-pec-ta-tion. _____ To

mor-row _____ quick-ly turns to yes-ter-day, _____

241. I wanna dance, I wanna sing

Dale Cox & Wayne Drain

1. I wan-na dance, I wanna sing, I wan-na show You what You mean to me, _

I wan-na do something now_ to show_You somehow_how I feel. _

I wan-na live, I wanna love like I nev - er have done be-fore _

and as I do I want You Lord to fill_ me up more and more. _

I wanna

2. I wanna pray, I wanna shout,
   I wanna tell Him about my plan,
   And that's to pray and to sing
   And to shout till we all understand.
   So with that goal in my eye
   I'm gonna do it or die trying.
   I want this whole world to know
   That this light in my heart has to show.

   It's not for my own glory,
   For I might seem like a fool,
   But somehow what's inside my heart
   Has got to get to you.

I wanna sing

Dave Reneham

With pace and strength

1. I___ wanna sing, ___ wanna sing, ___
I ___ wanna sing, ___ wanna sing ___ for Jesus, for Je - sus, for Je sus. Oh I___
___ wanna sing ___ for ___ Him.

2. I wanna clap. . . *etc.*

3. I wanna dance. . . *etc.*

4. I wanna praise. . . *etc.*

5. I wanna work. . . *etc.*

6. I wanna love. . . *etc.*

7. I wanna live. . . *etc.*

243. I want to learn to appreciate You

John Kennett

Gal 5:16

Capo 3 (C)

With pace and swing

I want to learn to ap - pre - ci - ate You Lord in ev - 'ry way,

I want to learn to walk with You Lord

day by day, With You al - ways

there to guide me, Hand in hand there be - side me,

Walk-ing in the Spi - rit day by day.

Often sung colloquially *I wanna learn to . . .* etc.

244. I want to sing about my Jesus
(As eternity begins)

Phil Lawson Johnston/Penny Somerville

1 Pet 2:9

Chorus

Glo-ry, Glo-ry, Glo-ry, Glo-ry, How I love the King of glo-ry, We sing of Je-sus and His

Glo-ry, Glory, Hal-le-lu-jah, Ho-ly, Holy, Ho-ly, Holy, Ho-ly is the King of glo-ry. We sing of

Je-sus and His love, _____ love, _____ love, _____

love. _____ ___ Sing of His love. _____

2. I want to meet Him on the mountain;
I want to stand before His throne.
He has asked me to His table
To share the beauty of His home.

We are welcome, we are chosen,
Children in His family.
I never cease to gaze in wonder
At what He has revealed to me.

So, can I share with you my Jesus;
Share with you my precious Lord.
Let me lead you to the Kingdom.
He is the way, He is the
'Door, door, door, door.'

245. I want to sing a song

Brightly

Joe Price
Rom 8:28

I want to sing a song to say __ how much You mean to me, for You are in my life each day, Your hand in all __ I see. Be-cause I know that You are here and work-ing in my life, then I can give my all to praise Your name. __

246. I want to sing until I am lost in Your love

Malcolm du Plessis
Ez 2:2; Hos 11:3-4

With feeling

I want to sing ___ un - til I am lost in Your

love, till I am found in Your pres - ence,

wor-ship - ping be-fore Your throne. ___ Mov'd by Your

Spi - rit, en-ter - ing in - to His flow, ___

___ how pre-cious these mo-ments, Lord I want You to know: ___

247.

I want to worship the Lord

Robert Cameron

1 Thess 5:18

I want to wor - ship the Lord with all of my heart, give Him my all, not just a part, lift up my hands to the King of kings, praise Him in ev - 'ry - thing.

248. I was once in darkness

Two-part round

Joan Parsons

1 Thess 4:17

I was once in darkness, Now my eyes can see, I was lost but Jesus sought and found me. O what love He offers, O what peace He gives, I will sing for evermore, He lives.

Hallelujah Jesus! Hallelujah Lord! Hallelujah Father, I am shielded by His word. I will live for ever, I will never die, I will rise up to meet Him in the sky.

249. I will bless the Lord at all times

Vep Ellis
Ps 34:1-4

Joyfully

I will bless the Lord at all times, His praise shall con-tin-u-ally be in my mouth. My soul shall make her boast in Thee, Lord, the hum-ble shall hear there-of and be glad. O mag-ni-fy the Lord with me, and let us ex-alt His name to-geth-er! I sought the Lord and He heard me and de-liv-ered me from all my fears.

———————— □ ▢ □ ————————

Heaven is my throne
  and the earth is my footstool.
Where is the house you will build for
    me?
  Where will my resting place be?
Has not my hand made all these things,
  and so they came into being?

ISAIAH 66:1–2

———————— □ ▢ □ ————————

250.

I will call

Capo 2(C)

Steadily (men and women in canon)

(Women 8va lower)

Victor Rubbo
Ps 18: 3

I will call

I will call . . . (etc).

up - on the

Lord,

who is wor - thy

to be

prais'd.

I will call

up-on the

Lord,

who is wor - thy

to be

G(F)   *(Together)*   F♯m(Em)

prais'd.   So shall I   be —

G(F)   F♯m(Em)

sav'd,   so shall I   be —

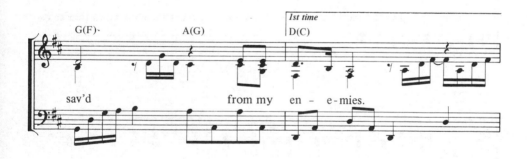

G(F)·   A(G)   **1st time**
                                                D(C)

sav'd   from my en – e-mies.

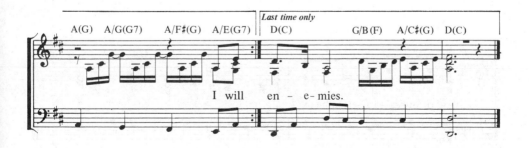

A(G) A/G(G7)   A/F♯(G) A/E(G7) **Last time only**
                                   D(C)   G/B(F) A/C♯(G) D(C)

I will en – e-mies.

251. I will call upon the Lord

Michael O'Shields
Ps 18:3

(Ladies) I will call. . .

(Men) I will call up-on the Lord, who is worthy to be

(Ladies) Who is worthy. . .   (Ladies) So shall I. . .   (Together)

praised. So shall I be saved from mine en -e - mies. The

Lord liv-eth, and bless-ed be my Rock and may the God of my sal-va-tion be ex-

alt - ed. The Lord liv-eth, and bless-ed be my Rock and may the

God of my sal - va - tion be ex - alt - ed.

252.

I will enter His gates

Leona von Brethorst

Capo 3 (C)

Ps 92:4; 100:4; 118:24

With pace and swing

I will en-ter His gates with thanks-giv-ing in my heart, I will en-ter His courts with

praise, I will say this is the day that the Lord has made, I will re-joice for He has made me

glad. He has made me glad, He has made me glad, I

will re-joice for He has made me glad. ____ He has made me glad,

He has made me glad, I will re-joice for He has made me glad.

253.

I will extol You

Capo 5 (C)

Sue Hutchinson & Wendy Churchill

Ps 145:1-4, 7, 21

Brightly

I will ex-tol You, my God and my King, I will bless Your Name for ev-er and ev-er. Ev-'ry day will I bless You, O Lord, I will glo-ri-fy Your Name for ev-er-more. For You are great and high-ly to be praised, We shall de-clare Your mighty acts, We shall tell of Your good-ness and kind-ness to us, Our mouths shall speak the praise of our God.

— □ ⧠ □ —

The Lord will roar from Zion
and thunder from Jerusalem;
the earth and the sky will
tremble.
But the Lord will be a refuge for
his people,
a stronghold for the people of
Israel.

JOEL 3:16

— □ ⧠ □ —

254. I will give thanks to Thee

Capo 3 (G)

Brent Chambers

Ps 57:9-11

With steady strength

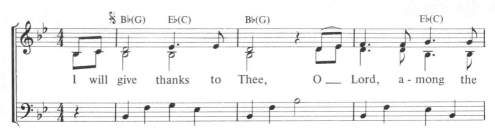

I will give thanks to Thee, O __ Lord, a - mong the

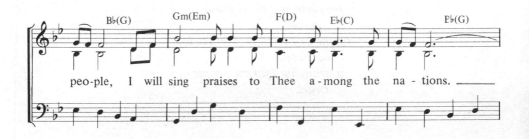

peo - ple, I will sing praises to Thee a - mong the na - tions. _____

__ For Thy stead - fast love is great, is __ great to the

hea - vens, and Thy faith - ful - ness, Thy __ faith - ful - ness to __ the clouds. _____

255.

I will give You praise

Tom Walker
Ex 15: 11; Is 9: 6;
Mt 9: 29-30; 28: 20

Capo 2(C)

With strength

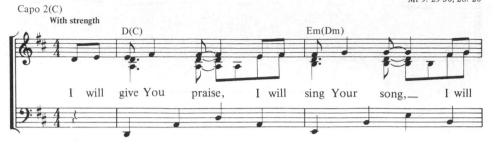

I will give You praise, I will sing Your song,— I will

bless Your ho - ly name; — for there is

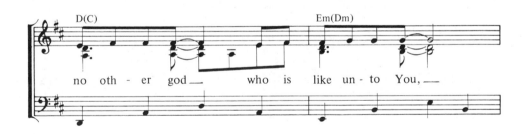

no oth - er god — who is like un - to You, —

You're the on - ly way. — On - ly You —

256.

I will give You thanks

Susie Hare
Ps 86: 11-12 15

I will give You thanks,
O Lord my God, with all ___ my heart.
I will glor - i - fy Your name ___ for
ev - er - more. ___ 1. Slow to ang - er
and a - bound-ing in stead - fast love; ___

257. I will magnify Your name, O Lord

Dave Bolton
Ps 34:3; Jn 4:14

Brightly

1. I will mag-ni-fy Your name, O Lord, Hal - le - lu - jah! I will
drink of the well of Your love, Hal - le - lu - jah! I will
wor-ship You to the end of my days, Hal - le - lu - jah! With a
heart that is full of praise_____ Hal - le - lu - jah!

2. I will magnify Your name, O Lord, Hallelujah!
I will drink of the well of Your love, Hallelujah!
With instrument and with voice, Hallelujah!
My spirit in You shall rejoice, Hallelujah!

3. I will magnify Your name, O Lord, Hallelujah!
I will drink of the well of Your love, Hallelujah!
With the timbrel and the dance, Hallelujah!
My love for You I shall express, Hallelujah!

4. I will magnify Your name, O Lord, Hallelujah!
I will drink of the well of Your love, Hallelujah!
I will worship You to the end of my days, Hallelujah!
With a heart that is full of praise, Hallelujah!

258. I will praise Thee, O Lord my God

Charles F. Munroe
Ps 86:12-13

Brightly

I will praise Thee, O Lord my God, _____ with all my heart, ___ with all my heart, ___ and I will glo-ri-fy Thy name for ev-er- more with all my heart. For great is Thy mer-cy toward me, and Thou hast de-liv-ered my soul from the lowest hell..I will praise Thee, O Lord my God, __ with all my heart, __ with all my heart.

259.   I will rejoice in You and be glad

Author unknown
Arr. Margaret Evans
Song 1:4

With swing

I will re - joice _____ in You and be glad, —

I will ex - tol _ Your love more than wine. _

Draw me af - ter You and let us run to - geth - er,

I will re - joice _____ in You and be glad.

260.   I will rejoice, I will rejoice

Capo 3 (Em)

Dave Fellingham
Ps 23:5-6

With pace

I will re-joice, I will re-joice, I will re-joice in the Lord with my whole heart. I will re-joice, I will re-joice, I will re-joice in the Lord. You a-noint my head with oil, and my cup sure-ly o-ver-flows. Good-ness and love shall fol-low me all the days that I dwell in Your house.

261. I will rise and bless You, Lord

Capo 5 (C)

Diane Fung

Rom 8:39

Joyfully

I will rise and bless You, Lord, — lift my hands and

shout Your praise. — I will tell of the mar - vel-lous things You have done — and de-

clare Your faith-ful - ness. I will rise and

bless You, Lord, — lift You high — and dance for joy. — Oh —

nothing can sep-ar - ate me — from Your wonderful, won-der-ful love.

262.
I will run after You

Anne Denton
Ps 42:1

263. I will sing about Your love

Phil Potter
Ps 59:16

─────────── □ ▢ □ ───────────

Though the fig-tree does not bud
    and there are no grapes on the
      vines,
though the olive crop fails
    and the fields produce no food,
though there are no sheep in the
    pen
and no cattle in the stalls,
yet I will rejoice in the Lord,
    I will be joyful in God my
    Saviour.

HABAKKUK 3:17–18

─────────── □ ▢ □ ───────────

264.

I will sing a song

Capo 4 (C)

Paul Kyle

Lk 1: 49; 1 Cor 13: 11-12; Eph 4: 11-15;
1 Jn 2: 12-14

1. I will sing a song, a song to my God, He has done great things of which we are glad. For the sake of Jesus His Son He's for-giv-en our sins, and as a Fa-ther He's draw-ing us up from child-ren to men. And He's mak-ing me strong, put-ting His word in my life, mak-ing me

one who ov-er-comes the en - e - my._____ So by Your

grace Lord keep on, ___ get me where You want me to be, ___ then the

world will see Je-sus the man in me. _____ (No)

2. No weakness, no strength that's just show, but strong in the Lord,
   No impersonation of God but expressing His word,
   Not punching the air but laying the enemy low,
   As His dominion gives way to the victory God's sons only know.

265. I will sing of the love of the Lord for ever

Phil Potter
Ps 89: 14-16

'Hebrew' style

I will sing of the love _ of the Lord for ev - er, de-clare _ Your love stands

firm. I will pro-claim Your faith - ful-ness,

with my mouth _ I will _ sing. _____ Bless - èd are they _ who have

learn'd to praise _ You, _ bless-èd are they _ who be-lieve. _____ Blessèd are they _ who have

learn'd to acc-laim _ You, _ for they be-lieve _ the Lord reigns. _____ I will

— □ ☐ □ —

God is spirit, and his worshippers
must worship in spirit and in truth.

JOHN 4:24

— □ ☐ □ —

266. I will sing the wondrous story

Capo 5 (C)
HYFRYDOL

Rowland Hugh Prichard (1811-87)

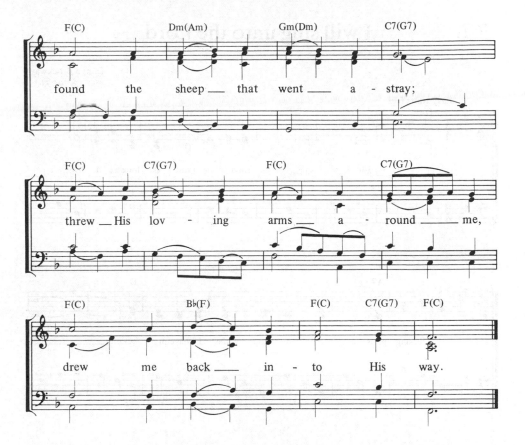

found the sheep ___ that went ___ a - stray;

threw ___ His lov - ing arms ___ a - round _____ me,

drew me back ___ in - to His way.

2. I was bruised but Jesus healed me,
   Faint was I from many a fall;
   Sight was gone, and fears possessed me,
   But He freed me from them all.
   Days of darkness still come o'er me;
   Sorrow's paths I often tread,
   But the Saviour still is with me,
   By His hand I'm safely led.

3. He will keep me till the river
   Rolls its waters at my feet,
   Then He'll bear me safely over,
   All my joys in Him complete.
   Yes, I'll sing the wondrous story
   Of the Christ who died for me;
   Sing it with the saints in glory,
   Gathered by the crystal sea.

Francis Harold Rawley (1854-1952)

Ps 23: 4; Lk 15: 11-21; Jn 10: 14-15; Phil 2: 8; Rev 22: 1-5

267.   I will sing unto the Lord

Donya Brockway
Ps 104:33-35

268.

I will worship You

Capo 3 (D)

Worshipfully

Heather Hunter

I will wor - ship You my God, give You the praise and ad-or-a - tion of my heart; I stand com-mit-ted to the love shown on the cross, re-deem'd by the blood of Je - sus.

269. Jesus Christ is risen today

EASTER HYMN

Joyfully

Melody from *Lyra Davidica* (1708)

1. Jesus Christ is ris'n to-day;— Hallelujah!
   Our triumphant holy day;— Hallelujah!
   Who did once up-on the cross; Hallelujah!
   Suffer— to re-deem our loss; Hallelujah!

2. Hymns of praise then let us sing; Hallelujah!
   Unto Christ our heavenly King; Hallelujah!
   Who endured the cross and grave; Hallelujah!
   Sinners to redeem and save: Hallelujah!

3. But the pains, which He endured; Hallelujah!
   Our salvation have procured; Hallelujah!
   Now above the sky He's King; Hallelujah!
   Where the angels ever sing: Hallelujah!

Charles Wesley (1707-88)
Mt 28: 7; Heb 12: 2

270. Jesus Christ our Great Redeemer

Capo 2(Am)

Strongly

Peter & Diane Fung

Job 19:25: Eph 1:7-8

Je-sus Christ our— Great Re-deem-er, Might-y Vic-tor and Strong De-liv-erer, King of kings and— Lord of lords we praise You, praise Your name. Hal-le-lu-jah, Hal-le-lu-jah, King of kings and Lord of lords, Hal-le-lu-jah, Hal-le-lu-jah, Your vic-t'ry is ass-ur'd.

271. Jesus, come closer now to me

Pat Bilbrough

272.

Jesus, come to me

David Barcham
Ps 51: 10; 1 Pet 5: 7

1. Je-sus, come to me now that I need You,

bring Your good-ness in, cleanse my heart a - new.

2. Take away my doubt,
   Take away my fear,
   Cause my heart to know
   That You're ever near.

3. Simply now I cry:
   'Lay Your hand on me.'
   Meet, O Master dear,
   Every need in me.

4. Lord, I reach to You,
   Though my faith is small,
   Trusting that Your love
   Knows no bounds at all.

5. Jesus, change my ways,
   Make me hear and see,
   Teach me deeper things,
   Show Your ways to me.

— □ □ □ —

Peace I leave with you; my peace I give you. I do not give to you as the world gives. Do not let your hearts be troubled and do not be afraid.

JOHN 14:27

— □ □ □ —

273.

Jesus has sat down

Jonathan Wallis
Is 9:6-7; Lk 4:18-19

Capo 5 (C)

1. Je-sus has sat down at God's right hand, He is reign-ing now on Dav-id's throne. God has placed all things be-neath His feet, His en-e-mies will be His footstool. For the gov-ern-ment is now up-on His shoul-der, for the gov-ern-ment is

now up-on His shoul-der, _____ and of the in-crease of His

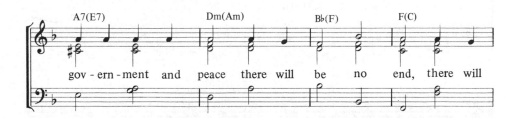

gov-ern-ment and peace there will be no end, there will

be no end, there will be no end. _____

2. God has now exalted Him on high,
   Given Him a name above all names.
   Every knee will bow and tongue confess
   That Jesus Christ is Lord.

3. Jesus is now living in His church,
   Men who have been purchased by His blood.
   They will serve their God, a royal priesthood,
   And they will reign on earth.

4. Sound the trumpets, good news to the poor,
   Captives will go free, the blind will see,
   The kingdom of this world will soon become
   The kingdom of our God.

274. Jesus, how lovely You are

Dave Bolton
Rev 22:16

Je - sus,___ how love-ly You are.___ You are so gen-tle so pure and kind.___

You___ shine as the morn-ing star.___ Je - sus, how love-ly You are.___

1. Hal - le-lu - jah, Je - sus is my Lord and King.___

Hal - le-lu - jah, Je - sus is___ my ev - 'ry - thing.

2.   Hallelujah, Jesus died and rose again;
Hallelujah, Jesus forgave all my sin.

3.   Hallelujah, Jesus is meek and lowly;
Hallelujah, Jesus is pure and holy.

4.   Hallelujah, Jesus is the Bridegroom;
Hallelujah, Jesus will take His Bride soon.

275.

Jesus I come

Tony Humphries

Je-sus I come and I fall at Your feet to kiss those deep wounds borne for me. I feel my heart sing at Your pres-ence so sweet, my lips trem-ble in mel-o-dy. Come and fill me a-new, let me dwell in You too, Make me one in the Spi-rit with Thee. As I call on Your name I am so glad You came and died, rose a-gain and saved me.

276.   Jesus is changing me

Capo 5(C)

Alison Huntley
Mal 3:2-3

Chorus
Brightly

Je - sus is chang-ing me, Je - sus is chang - ing me, The work of the re - fin - er's fire. To __ be as pure gold in the house of the Lord, To give right off - er - ings to

1st and 2nd times   *To verse* | *Last time only*   *Fine*

Him.   1. To Him.

Verse

Him I give all my ____ love and praise, With
joy I draw near to Him. ____ The
Son of right-eous-ness ri - ses o - ver me With
heal - ing in His ____ wings. ____

D.C. al Fine

2. Then shall the blessing of the Lord come down,
   When we give all to Him;
   And we shall go forth in holiness
   Delighting ourselves in God.

277.

Capo 5 (C)

Jesus is King

Wendy Churchill
Heb 4:14-16

1. Je - sus is King and I will ex - tol Him,
give Him the glo - ry and hon - our His name.
He reigns on high, en - throned in the hea - vens,
Word of the Fa - ther, ex - alt - ed for us.

2. We have a hope that is steadfast and certain,
Gone through the curtain and touching the throne.
We have a Priest who is there interceding,
Pouring His grace on our lives day by day.

3. We come to Him, our Priest and Apostle,
Clothed in His glory and bearing His name,
Laying our lives with gladness before Him;
Filled with His Spirit we worship the King.

4. O holy One, our hearts do adore You;
Thrilled with Your goodness we give You our praise.
Angels in light with worship surround Him,
Jesus, our Saviour, for ever the same.

278.

Jesus is Lord!

Capo 1 (G)

With majesty

David Mansell
Phil 2:5-11

1. Je-sus is Lord! Cre-a-tion's voice pro-claims it, For by His power each tree and flower was planned and made. Je-sus is Lord! the un-i-verse de-clares it, Sun, moon and stars in hea-ven cry

Chorus

'Je-sus is Lord!' Je-sus is Lord! Je-sus is Lord! Praise Him with Ha-lle-lu-jahs for Je-sus is Lord!

2. Jesus is Lord! yet from His throne eternal
In flesh He came to die in pain
On Calv'ry's tree.
Jesus is Lord! from Him all life proceeding,
Yet gave His life a ransom
Thus setting us free.

3. Jesus is Lord! o'er sin the mighty conqueror,
From death He rose, and all His foes
Shall own His Name.
Jesus is Lord! God sent His Holy Spirit
To show by works of power
That Jesus is Lord.

279.

Jesus is Lord of all

Marilyn Baker

Rom 16:20; 1 Cor 15:25;
Eph 1: 22

Majestically

1. Je - sus is Lord of all, — Sa - tan is un - der His feet, — Je - sus is reign-ing on high — and all pow'r is giv - en to Him in heav'n and earth. Him.

2. We are joined to Him,
Satan is under our feet,
We are seated on high
And all authority is given
To us through Him.

3. One day we'll be like Him,
Perfect in every way,
Chosen to be His bride,
Ruling and reigning with Him
For evermore.

280.

Jesus is the Lord

Dennis Merry
Phil 2:11

281.

Jesus is the name I love

Bob Brogan

Capo 2 (C)

Acts 4: 12; Phil 2: 9-11

Je - sus is the name I love, I love the name of Je - sus. Just to hear with Spi - rit's ear the love - ly name of Je - sus. Just to speak with tongue so weak the match - less name of Je - sus. Je - sus is the name I love, I love the name of Je - sus.

282.

Jesus, I worship You

Capo 5(C)

Chris A. Bowater

283. Jesus, Jesus Christ in majesty You reign

Pete Lawry

Rom 16:20; Eph 1:19-22; 2:6;
Rev 1:12-16; 7:12; 12:11

Capo 3 (C)

Majestically

1. Jesus, Jesus Christ, in majesty You reign, — high above the pow'rs opposing heav'nly rule; — 'All things subject to the Father once again,' — is the vision You have promis'd to fulfil. _____ With a sound like thunder Your voice is heard, — cleaving

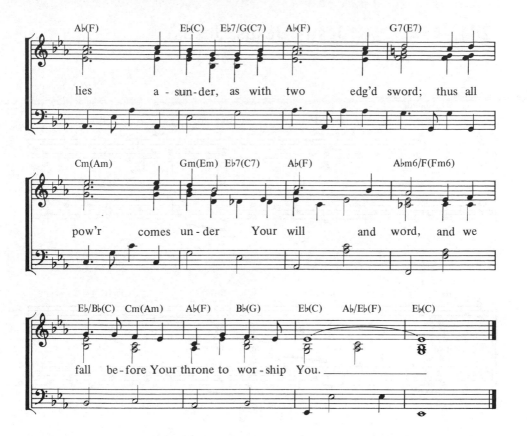

lies a-sun-der, as with two edg'd sword; thus all
pow'r comes un-der Your will and word, and we
fall be-fore Your throne to wor-ship You. _____

2. Jesus, Jesus Christ, Your face is like the Sun,
   Burning brilliant at the zenith of the sky;
   Blazing fire is in Your eyes, O Holy One,
   Making spirit leap, but causing flesh to die.
   Though we fear, Almighty, our hearts rejoice,
   For we see Your glory and we hear Your voice,
   And Your word is mighty, at work in us,
   And we fall before Your throne to worship You.

3. Glory, wisdom, thanks and praise are Yours, O God,
   And all honour, power, righteousness and strength.
   You have saved us by Your blood and mighty word,
   And we reign with You above the powers of death.
   For we're seated with You beside the throne,
   Taking strongholds for You, facing Satan's own;
   All the power comes from You to tread him down,
   And we fall before Your throne to worship You.

284.

Jesus, Jesus, Jesus

Capo 3 (G)

Chris A. Bowater

Worshipfully

Je - sus, Je - sus, Je - sus, Your love has mel - ted my heart.

Je - sus, Je - sus, Je - sus, Your love has mel - ted my heart.

—————— □ ▯ □ ——————

*Father, I want those you have given me
to be with me where I am, and to see
my glory, the glory you have given me
because you loved me before the
creation of the world.*

JOHN 17:24

—————— □ ▯ □ ——————

285.

Jesus, Lord of everything

Martyn Perry

Capo 5(C)

Gen 1:27; Rom 6:18; 1 Cor 15:22;
Col 1:15-17; 1 Thess 4:16-17

Hymn like

1. Je-sus, Lord of ev-'ry-thing, be-fore cre-a-tion's light, pre-sent in the Fa-ther, Your glo-ry shin-ing bright. Made us in Your im-age so to live with You, Je-sus we're Your slaves, Your blood has brought us through.

Chorus

Je-sus Lord of ev-'ry-thing, turn our hearts to You, for

ev - er You're en - thron'd a-bove, we seek Your work to do.

2. Man desired to break the bond
   Of fellowship with You.
   So ungrateful for our life,
   Doomed to wandering?
   No! Your love was greater still,
   So it is today,
   On Calvary You set us free.
   For ever now we say:

3. Blood-bought and Spirit-filled,
   Born from above.
   Walking in Your world with You,
   Help us share Your love.
   Countless lost and dying ones
   Suffering from their sin,
   Must be told You're coming back
   For the church You live within.

286.

Jesus, lover of my soul

ABERYSTWYTH
Majestically

Joseph Parry (1841-1903)

1. Je - sus, __ lov - er of my soul, let me to Thy
bo - som fly, while the __ near - er wa - ters roll,
while the __ temp - est still is high; hide me, O my
Sa - viour, __ hide, till the storm of life is __ past;
safe in - to the ha - ven guide, O re - ceive __ my soul at last.

2. Other refuge have I none,
   Hangs my helpless soul on Thee;
   Leave, ah, leave me not alone,
   Still support and comfort me.
   All my trust on Thee is stayed,
   All my help from Thee I bring;
   Cover my defenceless head
   With the shadow of Thy wing.

3. Thou, O Christ, art all I want;
   More than all in Thee I find;
   Raise the fallen, cheer the faint,
   Heal the sick, and lead the blind.
   Just and holy is Thy name,
   I am all unrighteousness;
   False and full of sin I am,
   Thou art full of truth and grace.

4. Plenteous grace with Thee is found,
   Grace to cover all my sin;
   Let the healing streams abound,
   Make and keep me pure within.
   Thou of life the fountain art;
   Freely let me take of Thee;
   Spring Thou up within my heart,
   Rise to all eternity.

Charles Wesley (1707-88)

Ps 46:1-7; Mt 8:23-27; Jn 1:16-17; Rev 22:1-2

287.

Jesus my Lord

Pete Gilgan

Acts 17:7; Rom 12:1-2

Capo 5 (C)

Prayerfully

Je - sus my Lord, You are my King. You are the One to make my heart sing. I'll give You ev - 'ry - thing that's mine to give. Lord, my whole life is Yours; use me as You will.

288.   Jesus, Name above all names

Naida Hearn
Mt 1:23; Phil 2:9

Jesus, Name a-bove all names, Beau-ti-ful Sav-iour, Glo-ri-ous Lord; Em-man-u-el, God is with us, Bless-ed Re-deem-er, Liv-ing Word.

289.

Capo 3(D)
RIMINGTON

Jesus shall reign
(First tune)

Francis Duckworth (1862-1941)

1. Je - sus shall reign wher - e'er the sun doth his suc - ces - sive

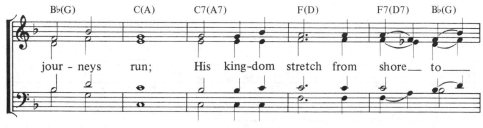

jour - neys run; His king-dom stretch from shore___ to___

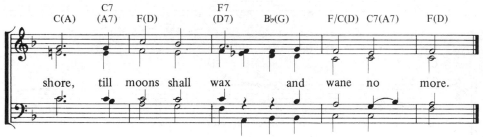

shore, till moons shall wax and wane no more.

2. For Him shall endless prayer be made,
   And praises throng to crown His head;
   His name like sweet perfume shall rise
   With every morning sacrifice.

3. People and realms of every tongue
   Dwell on His love with sweetest song,
   And infant voices shall proclaim
   Their early blessing on His name.

4. Blessings abound where'er He reigns;
   The prisoner leaps to lose his chains;
   The weary find eternal rest,
   And all the sons of want are blessed.

5. Let every creature rise and bring
   Peculiar honours to our King;
   Angels descend with songs again,
   And earth repeat the loud Amen!

Isaac Watts (1674-1748)

Ps 72:5-19

Jesus shall reign
(Second tune)

TRURO

Psalmodia Evangelica (1789)

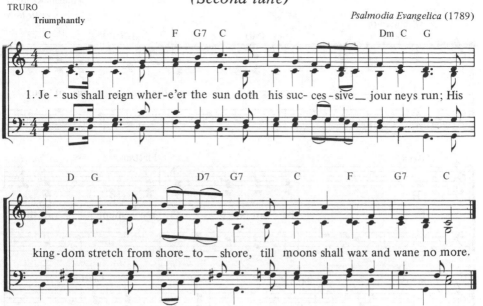

1. Je - sus shall reign wher-e'er the sun doth his suc- ces - sive— jour neys run; His king-dom stretch from shore— to— shore, till moons shall wax and wane no more.

2. For Him shall endless prayer be made,
And praises throng to crown His head;
His name like sweet perfume shall rise
With every morning sacrifice.

3. People and realms of every tongue
Dwell on His love with sweetest song,
And infant voices shall proclaim
Their early blessing on His name.

4. Blessings abound where'er He reigns;
The prisoner leaps to lose his chains;
The weary find eternal rest,
And all the sons of want are blessed.

5. Let every creature rise and bring
Peculiar honours to our King;
Angels descend with songs again,
And earth repeat the loud Amen!

Isaac Watts (1674-1748)

Ps 72:5-19

290.

Jesus, stand among us

Graham Kendrick

Capo 3 (C)

Mt 18:20

With warmth

1. Je - sus, stand a - mong us __ at the meet - ing of our lives, be our sweet a - gree - ment at the meet - ing of our eyes; O, Je - sus, we love You, so we ga - ther here, join our hearts in un - i - ty __ and

1st time take a - way __ our fear.

Last time our fear.

(Optional verse for communion)

2. So to You we're gathering
    Out of each and every land,
    Christ the love between us
    At the joining of our hands;
    O, Jesus, we love You . . . *(etc.)*

3. Jesus stand among us
    At the breaking of the bread,
    Join us as one body
    As we worship You, our Head.
    O, Jesus, we love You . . . *(etc.)*

291. Jesus, stand among us in Thy risen power

(First tune)

NORTH COATES

Timothy Richard Matthews (1826-1910)

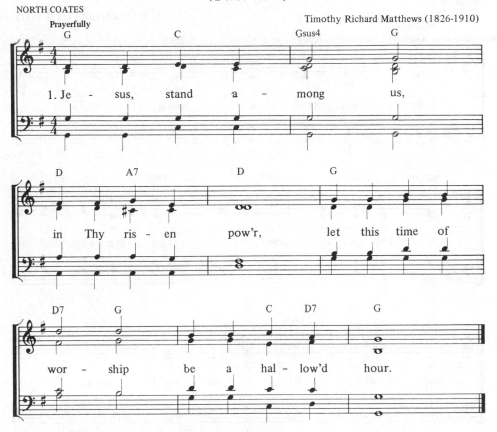

1. Je - sus, stand a - mong us, in Thy ris - en pow'r, let this time of wor - ship be a hal - low'd hour.

Alternative tune: CASWALL (125)

2. Breathe Thy Holy Spirit
   Into every heart,
   Bid the fears and sorrows
   From each soul depart.

3. Thus with quickened footsteps
   We'll pursue our way,
   Watching for the dawning
   Of eternal day.

   William Pennefather (1816-73)

   Mt 18: 20; Jn 20: 22; 1 Thess 5: 1-6

Jesus, stand among us in Thy risen power
(Second tune)

Capo 2 (C)
QUIETUDE

Harold Green (1871-1931)

2. Breathe Thy Holy Spirit
   Into every heart,
   Bid the fears and sorrows
   From each soul depart.

3. Thus with quickened footsteps
   We'll pursue our way,
   Watching for the dawning
   Of eternal day.

   William Pennefather (1816-73)
   Mt 18: 20; Jn 20: 22; 1 Thess 5: 1-6

*Therefore, since we have been
justified through faith, we have peace
with God through our Lord Jesus
Christ, through whom we have gained
access by faith into this grace in
which we now stand. And we rejoice in
the hope of the glory of God.*

ROMANS 5:1–2

292.

Jesus take me as I am

Capo 4 (C)

Dave Bryant

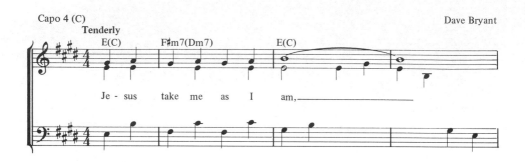

Je - sus take me as I am, _____

I can come no oth-er way. _____

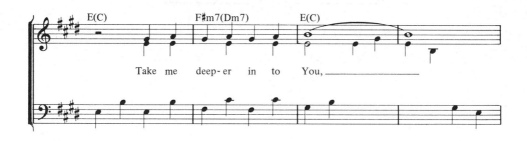

Take me deep-er in to You, _____

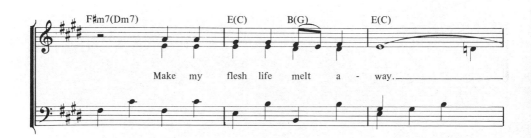

Make my flesh life melt a - way. _____

293.

Jesus, thank You, Jesus

Fred Chedgey

With Simplicity

Je - sus,_____ thank You, Je - sus,_____ for all You

are to me, for all the things You do._____ But I

thank You_____ most of all, Lord,_____ For show-ing

me how much I mean to You._____

---□ ⬜ □---

*There is now no condemnation for those
who are in Christ Jesus, because
through Christ Jesus the law of the
Spirit of life set me free from the
law of sin and death.*

ROMANS 8:1–2

---□ ⬜ □---

294.   Jesus! the name high over all

LYDIA

Thomas Phillips (1735-1807)

Triumphantly

1. Je - sus! the name____ high o - ver____ all,

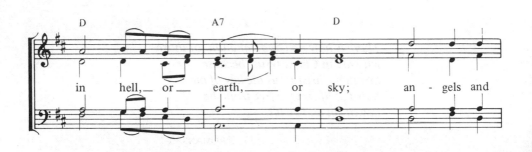

in hell,__ or__ earth,____ or sky; an - gels and

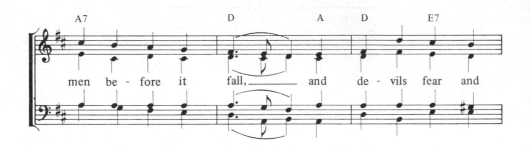

men be - fore it fall,____ and de - vils fear and

fly,_____ and de - vils__ fear__ and__ fly.

2. Jesus! the name to sinners dear,
   The name to sinners given;
   It scatters all their guilty fear,
   It turns their hell to heaven,
   It turns their hell to heaven.

3. Jesus! the prisoners' fetters breaks,
   And bruises Satan's head;
   Power into strengthless souls it speaks,
   And life into the dead,
   And life into the dead.

4. O that the world might taste and see
   The riches of His grace!
   The arms of love that compass me
   Would all mankind embrace,
   Would all mankind embrace.

5. His only righteousness I show,
   His saving grace proclaim;
   'Tis all my business here below
   To cry: 'Behold the Lamb!'
   To cry: 'Behold the Lamb!'

6. Happy if with my latest breath
   I might but gasp His name;
   Preach Him to all, and cry in death:
   'Behold, behold the Lamb!'
   'Behold, behold the Lamb!'

Charles Wesley (1707-88)

Ps 34:8; Lk 4:18; Jn 1:29; Rom 16:20; 1 Cor 1:30-31; Phil 2:9-11

295. Jesus, the very thought of Thee

ST AGNES
Smoothly

John Bacchus Dykes (1823-76)

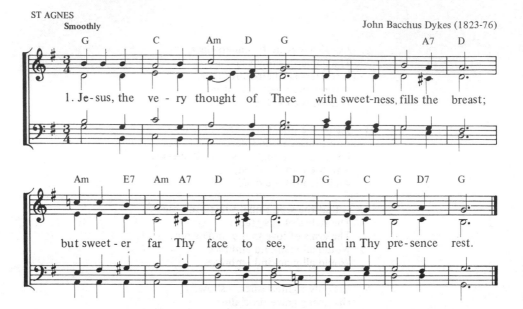

1. Je-sus, the ve - ry thought of Thee with sweet-ness, fills the breast;
but sweet - er far Thy face to see, and in Thy pre - sence rest.

2. Nor voice can sing, nor heart can frame,
   Nor can the memory find
   A sweeter sound than Thy blessed name,
   O Saviour of mankind!

3. O hope of every contrite heart,
   O joy of all the meek,
   To those who fall how kind Thou art,
   How good to those who seek!

4. But what to those who find? Ah, this
   Nor tongue nor pen can show:
   The love of Jesus, what it is
   None but His loved ones know.

5. Jesus, Thy mercies are untold
   Through each returning day;
   Thy love exceeds a thousandfold
   Whatever we can say.

6. Jesus, our only joy be Thou,
   As Thou our prize wilt be;
   Jesus, be Thou our glory now,
   And through eternity.

Bernard of Clairvaux (1091-1153)
Tr. Edward Caswall (1814-78)

Ps 27:8; Mt 5:3-10; 2 Cor 3:18

296. Jesus, Thou joy of loving hearts

Capo 3(C)
MARYTON

Henry Percy Smith (1825-98)

2. Thy truth unchanged hath ever stood;
   Thou savest those that on Thee call;
   To them that seek Thee Thou art good,
   To them that find Thee, all in all.

3. We taste Thee, O Thou living Bread,
   And long to feast upon Thee still;
   We drink of Thee, the Fountain-head,
   And thirst our souls from Thee to fill.

4. Our restless spirits yearn for Thee,
   Where'er our changeful lot is cast;
   Glad when Thy gracious smile we see,
   Blessed when our faith can hold Thee fast.

5. O Jesus, ever with us stay;
   Make all our moments calm and bright;
   Chase the dark night of sin away;
   Shed o'er the world Thy holy light.

12th Century Latin
Tr. Ray Palmer (1808-87)

Ps 36:9; 55:16; Jn 6:35

Number
as 343

Jesus, we enthrone You

Capo 2 (G)

With reverence

Paul Kyle
Ps 22:3

Lord Je - sus,__ we en - throne__ You,__

ALTERNATIVE

Je - sus we en -

we pro - claim You our King,__

Stand - ing here__ in the midst of us__

we raise You up__ with our

297.

Jesus, You are changing me

Marilyn Baker
Jer 18: 6; 2 Cor 3: 18

Capo 3 (C)

Prayerfully

Je - sus, _____ You are chang - ing me, _____ by Your Spi - rit You're mak - ing me like You. _____ Je - sus, _____ You're trans - form - ing me, _____ that Your love - li - ness may be seen in all I do. _____

298. Jesus, You are the radiance

Capo 5(C)

Dave Fellingham

Heb 1:1-3

Je - sus, You are the rad - iance of the Fath - er's glo - ry, You are the Son, the ap - poin - ted heir, through whom all things are made._____ You are the One who sus - tains all things by Your pow-er-ful

299.
Jesus, You are worthy

Capo 3(D)

With strength

Phil Holmes

Is 9:6-7; 1 Tim 1:17

Je - sus, You are wor - thy of all our praise and ad-or - a - tion. Je - sus, we want to lift up Your name and hon-our You as King. Of the in-crease of Your gov -ern-ment — there shall be no end. Praise the King, praise the King, — praise the King, praise the King, — praise the King.

*For you did not receive a spirit that
makes you a slave again to fear, but
you received the Spirit of sonship.
And by him we cry, 'Abba, Father.'*

ROMANS 8:15

300.
Jesus, You rule in authority

Capo 4 (C)

David Barcham
Eph 1: 18-21

Je - sus, You rule in au - thor - i - ty,

far a - bove an - y ___ pow'r, ___

far a - bove ev - 'ry dom - in - ion,

Name a - bove ev - 'ry ___ name. ___

1. O what a glor - ious in - her - i - tance, ___

what _____ a hope He calls us to. _____

O the im - meas - 'ra - ble great - ness of _____ His

pow'r, His _____ pow'r in _____ us who be - lieve. _____

2. Now that we live He has raised us up,
   And made us sit with Him;
   That He might show us the riches of His grace,
   In kindness towards us in Christ.

301. Join all the glorious names

ST GODRIC

John Bacchus Dykes (1823-76)

Moderate

1. Join all the glo-rious names of wis-dom, love, and

pow'r, that e-ver mor-tals knew, that

an-gels e-ver bore: all are too mean to

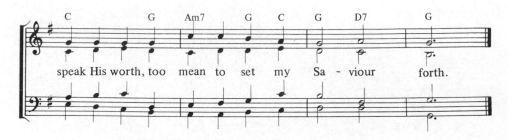

speak His worth, too mean to set my Sa-viour forth.

Alternative tunes: DARWALL'S 148th (627) & GOSPAL (463)

2. Great Prophet of my God,
   My tongue would bless Thy name:
   By Thee the joyful news
   Of our salvation came:
   The joyful news of sins forgiven,
   Of hell subdued and peace with heaven.

3. Jesus, my great High Priest,
   Offered His blood, and died;
   My guilty conscience seeks
   No sacrifice beside:
   His powerful blood did once atone,
   And now it pleads before the throne.

4. My Saviour and my Lord,
   My Conqueror and my King,
   Thy sceptre and Thy sword,
   Thy reigning grace I sing:
   Thine is the power; behold, I sit
   In willing bonds beneath Thy feet.

5. Now let my soul arise,
   And tread the tempter down:
   My Captain leads me forth
   To conquest and a crown:
   March on, nor fear to win the day,
   Though death and hell obstruct the way.

6. Should all the hosts of death,
   And powers of hell unknown,
   Put their most dreadful forms
   Of rage and malice on,
   I shall be safe; for Christ displays
   Superior power and guardian grace.

Isaac Watts (1674-1748)

Josh 5: 13-15; Acts 3: 22; Rom 8: 35-39; Eph 1: 20-21; Col 2: 3;
Heb 4: 14-16; Rev 2: 26-27

302.

Join our hands with Yours
(Jesus make us one)

David Williams

Jn 17: 22-23

With life

Verse

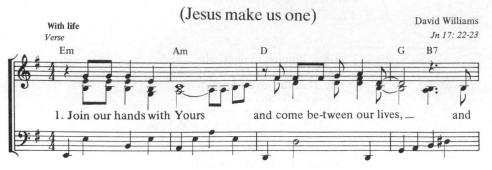

1. Join our hands with Yours and come be-tween our lives, — and

join our hearts in love — as we meet with You. —

Chorus

Je - sus make us one, — by the strength of Your

hand ac - com - plish ev-'ry-thing that You say,

ev-'ry-thing that You are.   ev-'ry-thing that You are.

2. And as we live in Your way,
   And travel step by step,
   We stand secure in Your life,
   We feel secure in Your love.

3. And in our future lives,
   May we share Your joy,
   And breathe the life that You give,
   Until we see Your face.

303.

Jubilate, everybody
(Jubilate Deo)

Fred Dunn
Ps 100:1-2

*Oh, the depths of the riches of the
wisdom and knowledge of God!
How unsearchable his judgments,
and his paths beyond tracing out!*

ROMANS 11:33

304.

Just as I am
(First tune)

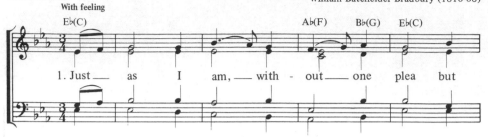

Capo 3(C)
JUST AS I AM
With feeling

William Batchelder Bradbury (1816-68)

1. Just __ as I am, __ with - out __ one plea but

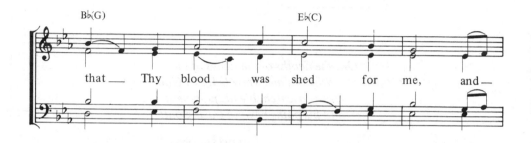

that __ Thy blood __ was shed for me, and __

that Thou bid'st __ me come to Thee, __ O

Lamb of God, __ I come, I come. __

2. Just as I am, and waiting not
To rid my soul of one dark blot,
To Thee, whose blood can cleanse each spot,
O Lamb of God, I come.*

3. Just as I am, though tossed about
With many a conflict, many a doubt,
Fightings and fears within, without,
O Lamb of God, I come.

When singing to JUST AS I AM sing 'I come' twice.

4. Just as I am, poor, wretched, blind;
   Sight, riches, healing of the mind,
   Yea, all I need, in Thee to find,
   O Lamb of God, I come.

5. Just as I am, Thou wilt receive,
   Wilt welcome, pardon, cleanse, relieve,
   Because Thy promise I believe,
   O Lamb of God, I come.

6. Just as I am, Thy love unknown
   Has broken every barrier down;
   Now to be Thine, yea, Thine alone,
   O Lamb of God, I come.

7. Just as I am, of that free love
   The breadth, length, depth, and height to prove,
   Here for a season, then above,
   O Lamb of God, I come.

Charlotte Elliott (1789-1871)

Just as I am
(Second tune)

Capo 3(C)
MISERICORDIA

Henry Smart (1813-79)

305. King of kings and Lord of lords

Hebrew folk melody
Words by: Sophie Conty & Naomi Batya
Rev 17:14

Capo 3 (Em)
Round

Brightly with increasing pace

King of kings and Lord of _ lords, _ Glo-ry, Hal - le - lu-jah!

Je - sus, Prince of Peace, _ Glo-ry, Hal - le - lu-jah!

306. Lead us, heavenly Father, lead us

Capo 4(C)
MANNHEIM

Adapted from F. Filitz's *Choralbuch* (1847)

1. Lead us, heav'n-ly Fa-ther, lead us o'er the world's tem-pes-tuous sea;
guard us, guide us, keep us, feed us, for we have no help but Thee;
yet pos-sess-ing ev-'ry bless-ing if our God our Fa-ther be.

2. Saviour, breathe forgiveness o'er us;
   All our weakness Thou dost know,
   Thou didst tread this earth before us,
   Thou didst feel its keenest woe;
   Tempted, taunted, yet undaunted,
   Through the desert Thou didst go.

3. Spirit of our God, descending,
   Fill our hearts with heavenly joy,
   Love with every passion blending,
   Pleasure that can never cloy;
   Thus provided, pardoned, guided,
   Nothing can our peace destroy.

James Edmeston (1791-1867) alt.

Ps 32:8; Lk 4:1-13; Jn 14:26-27

307.

Led like a lamb
(You're alive)

Graham Kendrick
Is 53:7; Rev 5:12-13

Verse **thoughtfully**
Chorus **triumphantly**

1. Led like a lamb to the slaugh-ter in si-lence and shame, there on Your back You _ car-ried a world of vio-lence and pain.

Bleeding, — dy-ing, — bleeding, —

For the antiphonal Alleluias the congregation divide into three parts.

2. At break of dawn, poor Mary,
   Still weeping she came,
   When through her grief she heard Your voice
   Now speaking her name.
   Mary, Master, Mary, Master.

3. At the right hand of the Father
   Now seated on high
   You have begun Your eternal reign
   Of justice and joy.
   Glory, glory, glory, glory.

308.

Let God arise

Ian Smith
Ps 68:1, 32-35

Let God a - rise u - pon this ho - ly moun - tain, Come sing to Him O king - doms of the earth. He gives power and strength un - to His peo - ple, Sing praise to Him, Sing prai - ses to His name.

— □ ▢ □ —

For from him and through him and
to him
are all things.
To him be the glory for ever!
Amen.

ROMANS 11:36

— □ ▢ □ —

309.

Let God arise

Graham Kendrick
Ps 68:1,3-4

Let God a - rise, and let His en - e - mies be sca - ttered; and

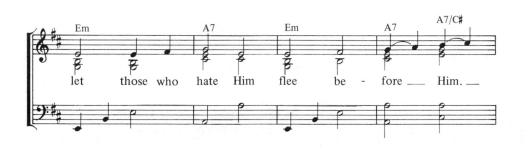

let those who hate Him flee be - fore ___ Him. ___

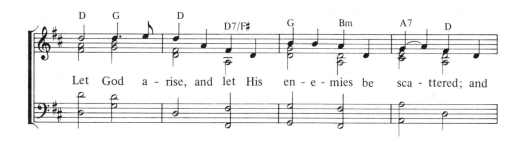

Let God a - rise, and let His en - e - mies be sca - ttered; and

let those who hate Him flee a - way. ___

310.

Let God arise, let His

Graeme Southern
Ps 68:1,4,7-9

Him. _____ He rides on the clouds, His name is the Lord:

ex - alt be-fore Him! _____

D.C. al Fine

Verse 2 – use verse 1 accompaniment

2. Be-fore Your peo - ple You went forth, through the

wil - der - ness; _____ the heav-ens pour'd and the

ho - ly mount-ain shook at the pres-ence of God. _____

D.C.

Verse 3

3. You shed a - broad_ a plen - ti-ful rain, O God of

Is - ra - el; _____ Your in - her-i-tance You have re-stor'd,

_____ a dwell-ing place for Your flock. _____

D.C. al Fine

311.

Let God speak

Ian Smale
1 Sam 3:10

Let God speak and I will lis - ten, __

let God speak, there's things I'm needing to put right. Let God speak and I will

o-bey what He says, please God I want to hear Your voice to-night.

1st time

Last time only *Fine* night.

Lord I want to hear Your voice, _ Lord I want to hear Your voice, _

D.C. al Fine

Lord I want to hear Your voice to- night, _____ to - night. _____

312. Let Me have My way among you
(Do not strive)

Graham Kendrick
Col 3:15

Thoughtfully

1. Let Me have My way a - mong __ you, do not strive, do not strive. strive. For Mine is the pow - er and the glo - ry for ev - er and ev - er the same. Let Me have My way a - mong __ you, do not strive, do not strive.

2. We'll let You have Your way among us,
   We'll not strive, we'll not strive. (*Repeat.*)
   For Yours is the power and the glory
   For ever and ever the same.
   We'll let You have Your way among us,
   We'll not strive, we'll not strive.

3. Let My peace rule within your hearts,
   Do not strive, do not strive. (*Repeat.*)
   For Mine is the power and the glory
   For ever and ever the same.
   Let My peace rule within your hearts,
   Do not strive, do not strive.

4. We'll let Your peace rule within our hearts,
   We'll not strive, we'll not strive. (*Repeat.*)
   For Yours . . . (*etc.*)

313. Let our praise to You be as incense

Brent Chambers
Ps 141: 2

Let our praise to You be as in - cense,____ let our

praise to You be as pil - lars of Your throne.

Let our praise to You be as in - cense,____ as we

come be - fore You and wor - ship You a - lone.

314. Let the high praise of God

Philip Lawson Johnston
Ps 149: 6-9

1. Let the high praise of God be in our mouths, may the two-edg'd sword be in our hands, let the en-e-my fear, for God is on the move, let the fire with-in our hearts begin to burn.

High prais-es to Je-sus, His splen-dour we pro-

claim, high prais-es to Je-sus, for the glor-ies of His name. High prais-es to Je-sus, the King up-on His throne, we pro-claim the high prais-es of God.

2. Let the high wind of God blow through our midst,
   Let it fan the flames of zeal and purify.
   Let the Spirit proclaim that God is in control,
   May His kingdom rule be seen in all our lives.

3. Let the high places where we long to dwell,
   Let the most holy place become our home.
   May our praise be mountain high, our love be ocean deep,
   Lifting hands in celebration to the sky.

315. Let's give Him all the glory

Bob Gillman

Let's give Him all the glo - ry, let's give Him all the praise. Let's give Him all the hon - our that He de - serves to - day. Let's lift our hearts in wor - ship, let's lift our hands in praise. Let's give Him all the glo - ry that He de - serves to - day.

316. Let's praise the Lord together

Capo 5 (C)

Pete & Dai Roe

Brightly with pace

Let's praise the Lord_ to - geth - er, let's bless His ho-ly name, _ for
He will be _ what He will be, His good-ness we'll pro - claim. _ Let's
sing and dance and bless the Lord, _ His gov-ern-ment de - clare. _ With
thank-ful hearts we'll sing a - new of all we have to share, _ with
thank-ful hearts we'll sing a - new of all we have to share. _

317. Let there be glory and honour

James & Elizabeth Greenelsh
Is 9:2

318.   Let there be love

Dave Bilbrough

1 Jn 4:7

Let there be love shared a- mong us, let there be love in our eyes, May now Your love sweep this na- tion, Cause us O Lord _____ to a - rise. Give us a fresh un- der- stand- ing of bro- ther- ly love that is real, Let there be love shared a - mong us, Let there be love. _____

319.   Let there be singing

Author unknown
Arr. Margaret Evans
Ps 100:2

Let there be singing, _____ let there be joy, _____

let there be praise _____ in the house of the

Lord. _____ Let there be mer - cy, _____

_ re - joice, _ re - joice, _____ we're build-ing to-

ge - ther _____ the house of the Lord. _____

320.

Let us adore

Julius Chajes

Capo 3 (Am)

and es-tab-lish-èd the earth, and whose

earth, and whose glo - ry

glo - ry is re-veal'd in the hea-vens a-bove, and whose

is re-veal'd in the hea-vens a-bove, _____ and whose great-ness _____

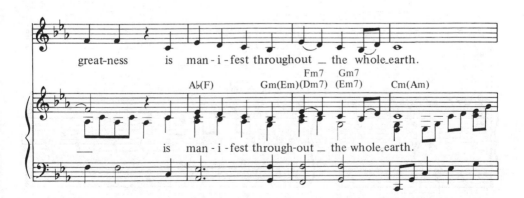

great-ness is man - i - fest throughout _ the whole_earth.

is man - i - fest through-out _ the whole_earth.

321.
Let us be grateful

Capo 3 (Am)
Two-part round

Phil Rogers
Heb 12:28-29

322. Let us consecrate our lives

Reverently

Martin F. Ball
Rom 12:1

1. Let us con-se-crate our lives be-fore the Lord ___ as we wor-ship Him ___ in truth. ___ So our lives will ___ be a sac-ri-fice, both ho - ly and pure, ___ as be-fit-ting a per - fect ___ God ___ who has made us like His Son. ___

2. Lord we empty our lives of all our wrong
As You cleanse us with Your blood
And You bathe our wounds with healing love
And purify with fire,
To be vessels that pour Your love,
Giving life to everyone.

———————— □ ▯ □ ————————

I urge you, brothers, in view of God's mercy, to offer your bodies as living sacrifices, holy and pleasing to God—which is your spiritual worship.

ROMANS 21:1

———————— □ ▯ □ ————————

323.   Let us open up ourselves

Pat Bilbrough
1 Pet 4:8

each pos-sess a prec-ious part _ of our Fa-ther's na - ture, And to -ge - ther we'll be - come that per - fect whole. _____ So let us

2.   And God shall surely build His living temple
       Of people set completely free,
       Loving and appreciating one another,
       Enjoying life in its entirety.

3.   Many shall be drawn to us and wonder
       At the peace and the love and the joy that will never die;
       They will drink from that stream of living water
       Flowing out from the fulness of our lives.

4.   So help us to understand each other in a new and living way,
       Not just accepting words that are spoken in themselves,
       But by speaking more freely and listening more clearly
       We shall understand the spirit that's within.

324. Let us with a gladsome mind

Capo 1(A)
MONKLAND

John Antes (1740-1811)
Arranged by John Wilkes (1785-1869)

1. Let us with a glad-some mind praise the Lord, for He is kind:

For His mer-cies shall en-dure, ev-er faith-ful, ev-er sure.

2. Let us blaze His name abroad,
   For of gods He is the God:

3. He, with all-commanding might,
   Filled the new-made world with light:

4. He the golden-tressèd sun,
   Caused all day his course to run:

5. And the silver moon by night,
   'Mid her spangled sisters bright:

6. He His chosen race did bless
   In the wasteful wilderness:

7. All things living He doth feed,
   His full hand supplies their need:

8. Let us then with gladsome mind
   Praise the Lord, for He is kind:

John Milton (1608-74)

Ps 136

325. Lifted high, exalted Father God

Peter & Diane Fung

Is 6:1-3

Not too slowly

1. Lift-ed high, _ ex-alt-ed Fa-ther God, _____ in ho-li-ness a-dorned with light_You reign. _____ O lift us high,_now let our spi-rits soar, _ that we might know_Your love pour'd out_a - gain. _____ Lift-ed high,_You are lift-ed high,_ we come to worship and a-dore._ Lifted high,_You are lifted high,_we come to wor-ship and a-dore. _____ 2. We

2. We crown You now the source of all our joy,
The life You pour on us is rich and free.
In truth we come, just as we are, to You,
To sing Your praise throughout eternity.

326.

Lift Jesus higher

author unknown
arranged Margaret Evans
Jn 12:32

Lift Je-sus high-er, Lift Je-sus high-er, Lift Him up for the world to see. ___ He said if I be lift-ed up from the earth I will draw all men un-to Me. ___

327.
Lift up your hands
(Worship the Lord)

Capo 3(D)

Steadily

Steve Young

Ps 50: 15; 95: 6; 143: 6. Jas 4: 10

2. Humble yourself
   And worship the Lord. . .*(etc).*

3. Call on His name
   And worship the Lord. . .*(etc).*

4. Fall on your knees
   And worship the Lord. . .*(etc).*

328.
Lift up your heads

Capo 1 (G)

Steven L. Fry
Lk 21:28

May the God of hope fill you with all joy and peace as you trust in him, so that you may overflow with hope by the power of the Holy Spirit.

ROMANS 15:13

329. Lift up your heads, O ye gates
(The King of glory)

Capo 2(C)

Terry Manship
Ps 24: 3-4, 7-10

(Women)

2. Who shall ascend the hill,
   The hill of the Lord?

(Men)
Even he that hath clean hands
And a pure heart with which to praise his God.

330.

Lion of Judah

Ted Sandquist

Rev 19:16

1. Li - on of Ju - dah on the throne, I shout Your name, let it be known that You are the King of kings, You are the Prince of Peace, may Your king - dom's reign never cease. Hail to the King!

Hail to the King!

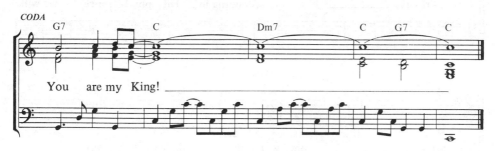

You are my King!

2. Lion of Judah come to earth,
   I want to thank You for Your birth,
   For the living Word,
   For Your death on the tree,
   For Your resurrection victory.
   Hallelujah! Hallelujah!

3. Lion of Judah, come again,
   Take up Your throne Jerusalem.
   Bring release to this earth
   And the consummation
   Of Your kingdom's reign, let it come!
   Maranatha! Maranatha!

4. Lion of Judah on the throne,
   I shout Your name, let it be known
   That You are the King of kings,
   You are the Prince of Peace,
   May Your kingdom's reign never cease.
   Hail to the King!
   Hail to the King!
   You are my King!

331.   Living under the shadow of His wing

David J. Hadden & Bob Silvester

Ps 91:4

2. Bowed in adoration at His feet
    We dwell in harmony.
    Voices joined together that repeat,
    Worthy, worthy, worthy is the Lamb.

3. Heart to heart embracing in His love
    Reveals His purity.
    Soaring in my spirit like a dove.
    Holy, holy, holy is the Lord.

———— □ ☐ □ ————

Love does not delight in evil but rejoices with the truth.

1 CORINTHIANS 13:6

———— □ ☐ □ ————

332. Lo, He comes with clouds descending

HELMSLEY

With strength

18th century English melody

1. Lo, He comes with clouds descending, once for favour'd sinners slain; Alleluia! Alleluia! Alleluia! God appears on earth to reign.

thousand thousand saints attending swell the triumph of His train: Alleluia!

2. Every eye shall now behold Him
   Robed in glorious majesty;
   Those who set at naught and sold Him,
   Pierced and nailed Him to the tree,
   Deeply wailing,
   Deeply wailing,
   Deeply wailing,
   Shall their true Messiah see.

3. Those dear tokens of His passion
   Still His dazzling body bears;
   Cause of endless exultation
   To His ransomed worshippers:
   With what rapture,
   With what rapture,
   With what rapture,
   Gaze we on those glorious scars.

4. Yea, Amen, let all adore Thee,
   High on Thine eternal throne;
   Saviour, take the power and glory,
   Claim the kingdom for Thine own:
   Come, Lord Jesus!
   Come, Lord Jesus!
   Come, Lord Jesus!
   Everlasting God, come down!

Charles Wesley (1707-88)

Acts 1:9-11; 1 Thess 4:16-17; Rev 5:6-10; 22:17, 20

333. Look and see the glory of the King

———————— □ ☐ □ ————————

Listen, I tell you a mystery: We will not all sleep, but we will all be changed—in a flash, in the twinkling of an eye, at the last trumpet.

1 CORINTHIANS 15:51–52

———————— □ ☐ □ ————————

334. Look, ye saints, the sight is glorious

Capo 3(G)
TRIUMPH

(First tune)

Henry John Gauntlett (1805-76)

With strength

1. Look, ye saints, the sight is glo - rious; see the Man of Sor - rows now, from the fight re - turn'd vic - tor - ious, ev - 'ry knee to Him shall bow: Crown Him! Crown Him! Crown Him! Crown Him! Crowns be - come the Vic - tor's brow.

Alternative tune: CWM RHONDA (144)

2. Crown the Saviour, angels, crown Him;
Rich the trophies Jesus brings;
In the seat of power enthrone Him,
While the vault of heaven rings:
Crown Him! Crown Him!
Crown Him! Crown Him!
Crown the Saviour, King of kings!

3. Sinners in derision crowned Him,
Mocking thus the Saviour's claim;
Saints and angels throng around Him,
Own His title, praise His name:
Crown Him! Crown Him!
Crown Him! Crown Him!
Spread abroad the Victor's fame.

4. Hark, those bursts of acclamation!
   Hark, those loud triumphant chords!
   Jesus takes the highest station:
   O what joy the sight affords!
   Crown Him! Crown Him!
   Crown Him! Crown Him!
   King of kings, and Lord of lords!

Thomas Kelly (1769-1854)

Is 53:3; Mt 27:28-31; Heb 2:9; Rev 14:14

Look, ye saints, the sight is glorious
(Second tune)

Capo 3(G)

REGENT SQUARE

Henry Smart (1813-79)

1. Look, ye saints, the sight is glo-rious; see the Man of
Sor-rows now, from the fight re-turn'd vic-to-rious,
ev-'ry knee to Him shall bow: Crown Him! Crown Him!
Crown Him! Crown Him! Crowns be-come the Vic-tor's brow.

335. Lord and Father, King for ever

Noel Richards

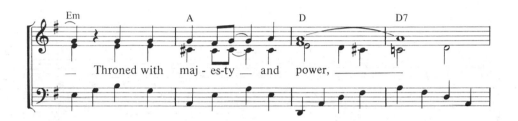

Lord and Fath - er, _____ King for ev - er, _____ Throned with maj - es - ty __ and power, _____ we a - dore You, _____ we ex - alt You. Wor - ship we bring, our off - er - ing, wor - ship we bring to You _ our __ King. _____

─── □ ▢ □ ───

Now the Lord is the Spirit, and where the Spirit of the Lord is, there is freedom.

2 CORINTHIANS 3:17

─── □ ▢ □ ───

336. Lord, enthroned in heavenly splendour

Capo 3(G)
ST HELEN

George C. Martin (1844-1916)

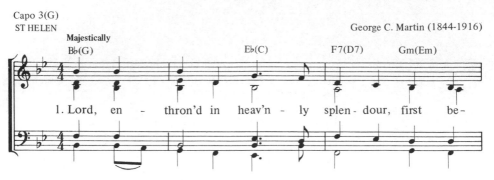

1. Lord, en - thron'd in heav'n - ly splen - dour, first be -

got - ten from the dead, Thou a - lone, our strong de -

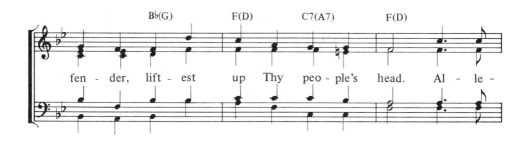

fen - der, lift - est up Thy peo - ple's head. Al - le -

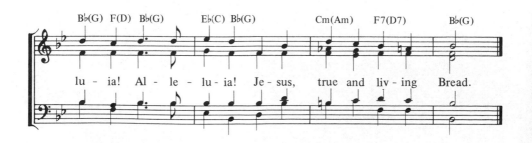

lu - ia! Al - le - lu - ia! Je - sus, true and liv - ing Bread.

2. Here our humblest homage pay we,
   Here in loving reverence bow;
   Here for faith's discernment pray we,
   Lest we fail to know Thee now.
   Alleluia! Alleluia!
   Thou art here, we ask not how.

3. Though the lowliest form doth veil Thee
   As of old in Bethlehem,
   Here as there Thine angels hail Thee
   Branch and Flower of Jesse's stem.
   Alleluia! Alleluia!
   We in worship join with them.

4. Paschal Lamb, Thine offering, finished
   Once for all when Thou wast slain,
   In its fullness undiminished
   Shall for evermore remain,
   Alleluia! Alleluia!
   Cleansing souls from every stain.

5. Life-imparting, heavenly Manna,
   Stricken Rock with streaming side,
   Heaven and earth with loud hosanna
   Worship Thee, the Lamb who died,
   Alleluia! Alleluia!
   Risen, ascended, glorified!

G.H. Bourne (1840-1925)

Ex 17:5-6; Ps 3:3; Is 11:1, 10; Rev 5:9

337. Lord, give me also

Iain Anderson
Josh 15:19; Jn 4:14

With pace and swing
Chorus

Lord, give me al-so springs of wa-ter, Lord, give me al-so springs of wa-ter,

Lord, give me al - so springs of wa-ter that I may ov - er - flow, ____

that I may ov - er - flow. 1. Lord, let the des-ert blos-som as a rose,

Lord, let the wilderness re - joice. Lord, let the world know that You are a-live,

Lord, let me ov - er - flow, ____ Lord, let me ov - er - flow.

2. O Lord, together let us overflow,
    Lord, let Your people be glad;
    We see the harvest field shining in the sun.
    Lord, let the river overflow,
    Lord, let the river overflow.

3. Hallelujah! Hallelujah!
    Hallelujah! Hallelujah!
    Hallelujah! Hallelujah!
    Lord, let me overflow,
    Lord, let me overflow.

338. Lord God, heavenly King

Capo 4 (C)

Sue Hutchinson

Worshipfully

Lord God,_____ hea-ven-ly King, You are our God,_____ To You we sing;_____ Re-ceive the wor-ship of our hearts,_____ the a-dor-a-tion of our lips; How we love____ You, Lord God, hea-ven-ly King.

339.

Lord, I feel

Dave Bolton
Heb 13:5-6

Lord, _____ I feel _____ Your sweet pre-sence wher-ev-er I go. _____ Lord, _____ I _____ feel _____ Your sweet pre-sence wher-ev-er I go. _____ go.

Verse

1. Lord, _____ in ___ You _____ is my se-cu-ri-ty, _____ I _____ can trust You _____ to keep me ___ safe-ly. _____

2. If I should fail and feel despair,
   You lift me up above all my care.

3. Lord, I love You and I know that You love me,
   I feel Your love embracing me.

340.

Lord, I want to be
(Closer to Thee)

Capo 2(C)

Eddie Espinosa

3. Lord, I want to be
   Closer and closer to Thee,
   I can feel You drawing me
   Closer and closer to Thee.

4. Lord, I want to be
   Closer and closer to Thee,
   I can hear You calling me
   Closer and closer to Thee.

341. Lord, I want to know
(More of You)

Mick Ray
Ps 42:1

Lord, I want to know more of You.

Lord, I want to know so much more of You; As a

hart longs for the flow-ing stream so my heart longs for You. Re-

veal Your-self, Lead me on in-to know-ing more of You.

———————— □ ☐ □ ————————

And we, who with unveiled faces all reflect the Lord's glory, are being transformed into his likeness with ever-increasing glory, which comes from the Lord, who is the Spirit.

2 CORINTHIANS 3:18

———————— □ ☐ □ ————————

Lord Jesus Christ

LIVING LORD

With breadth

Patrick Appleford (1925-)

1. Lord Je - sus Christ, You have come to us, You are one with us, Mar - y's Son. Cleans - ing our souls from all their sin. pour-ing Your love and good-ness in; Je-sus, our love for You we sing, Liv - ing Lord. Lord.

1st - 3rd time

4th time

(Optional communion verse:)

2. Lord Jesus Christ,
   Now and every day,
   Teach us how to pray,
   Son of God.
   You have commanded us to do
   This in remembrance, Lord of You:
   Into our lives Your power breaks through,
   Living Lord.

3. Lord Jesus Christ,
   You have come to us,
   Born as one of us,
   Mary's son.
   Led out to die on Calvary,
   Risen from death to set us free,
   Living Lord Jesus, help us see
   You are Lord.

4. Lord Jesus Christ,
   We would come to You,
   Live our lives for You,
   Son of God.
   All Your commands we know are true,
   Your many gifts will make us new,
   Into our lives Your power breaks through,
   Living Lord.

   Patrick Appleford (1925-)

   Is 7:14; Lk 11:1-4; Rom 12:1; 1 Cor 15:3-4

343. Lord Jesus, we enthrone You

Paul Kyle
Ps 22:3

Lord Je-sus,— we en-throne— You,———

Je - sus——— we en -

we pro - claim You our King,———

Stand - ing here——— in the midst of us———

——— we raise You up — with our

344. Lord make me an instrument

Capo 3 (D)

Author unknown
Arr. Margaret Evans

2. I'll sing You a love song,
   A love song of worship,
   I'll lift up my hands in Your name.
   I'll sing You a love song,
   A love song to Jesus,
   I'll lift up my hands in Your name.

3. For we are a symphony,
   A symphony of worship.
   We lift up our hands in Your name.
   For we are a symphony,
   A symphony of worship.
   We lift up our hands in Your name.

4. We'll sing You a love song,
   A love song of worship,
   We'll lift up our hands in Your name.
   We'll sing You a love song,
   A love song to Jesus,
   We'll lift up our hands in Your name.

345.   Lord, please make Your people one

Alan Woodroffe & Chris Head
Jn 17:21

2. All around the kingdoms fall,
    But we hear our Father call —
    You are safe, My children, with Me.
    Show My love, for I want the world to see.

3. Lord, You're making Your people one,
    And answering the prayer of Your dear Son,
    That the world may see that we are one,
    And give the glory unto You.

I have been crucified with Christ and I no longer live, but Christ lives in me. The life I live in the body, I live by faith in the Son of God, who loved me and gave himself for me.

GALATIANS 2:20

346.

Lord, teach us today

Joan Parsons
1 Jn 2: 27

Lord, teach us to-day, — show us the way — You'd have us be. — Lord, lead us in love, — op-en our eyes, — help us to see — all You have to give, — put Your Ho-ly Spi-rit with-in — and

347. Lord, we want to thank You

Capo 3 (D)

Unhurried

Dougie Brown

Lord, we want to thank You for Your love for us,____ That sweet love that watch-es ov-er us each day.____ Lord, re-lease our spi-rits so our praise can flow to You, Now we lift our hands to wor-ship You.____

348.
Lord, we worship You

Dave Bilbrough

Lord, we wor-ship You, __ Lord, we wor - ship You, Lord, we wor-ship You, __ Lord, we wor - ship You. In hum - ble ad-or - a - tion we lift our voi - ces to You, and sing in acc - la - ma - tion our song of praise __ to You. You.

To repeat

Last time only

349. Lord, You are more precious

Lynn DeShazo

Prayerfully

Lord, You are more precious than sil-ver,

Lord, You are more cost-ly than gold.

Lord, You are more beau-ti-ful — than diamonds, and

no-thing I de-sire com-pares with You.

―――――――――― □ □ □ ――――――――――

Praise be to the God and Father of our Lord Jesus Christ, who has blessed us in the heavenly realms with every spiritual blessing in Christ.

EPHESIANS 1:3

―――――――――― □ □ □ ――――――――――

350. Lord, You put a tongue in my mouth

Ian Smale

With pace

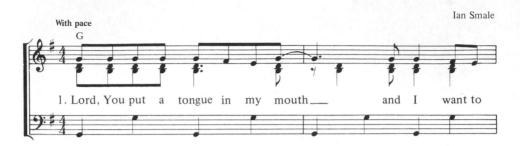

1. Lord, You put a tongue in my mouth ___ and I want to

sing to You, Lord, You put a tongue in my mouth

___ and I want to sing to You,

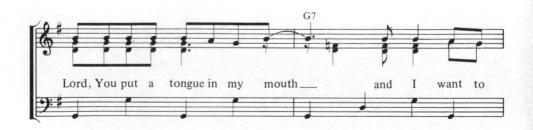

Lord, You put a tongue in my mouth ___ and I want to

sing on - ly to You. Lord Je - sus, free us in our praise; Lord Je - sus, free us in our praise.

1st and 2nd times

Last time only

2. Lord, You put some hands on my arms
   Which I want to raise to You. . . *(etc)*.

3. Lord, You put some feet on my legs
   And I want to dance to You. . . *(etc)*.

351. Lord Your ways are true and just

Wayne Drain

Ps 19: 9

Lord Your ways are true and just and I will praise Your name, and to You I give my trust and I will praise Your name.

352. Love beyond measure

Dave Bilbrough
Eph 3: 18-19

Love be-yond mea-sure, _____ mer-cy so free.

Your end-less re-sour-ces _____ giv-en to me.

Strength to the wea-ry, _____ heal-ing our lives,

Your love be-yond mea-sure _____ has op-en'd my eyes,

op-en'd my eyes.

—— □ □ □ ——

In him we have redemption through his blood, the forgiveness of sins, in accordance with the riches of God's grace that he lavished on us with all wisdom and understanding.

EPHESIANS 1:7–8

—— □ □ □ ——

353.

Love divine
(First tune)

BLAENWERN

With strength

William Penfro Rowlands (1860-1937)

1. Love di - vine, all loves__ ex - cell - ing,
joy of heav'n to earth__ come down!
Fix in us Thy hum - ble dwell - ing,
all Thy faith - ful mer - cies crown.
Je - sus, Thou__ art all__ com - pas - sion,

pure un - boun - ded love Thou art;
vis - it us with Thy sal - va - tion,
en - ter ev - 'ry tremb - ling heart.

Alternative tune: HYFRYDOL (266)

2. Breathe, O breathe, Thy loving Spirit
Into every troubled breast!
Let us all in Thee inherit,
Let us find Thy promised rest;
Take away the love of sinning;
Alpha and Omega be;
End of faith, as its beginning,
Set our hearts at liberty.

3. Come, Almighty to deliver,
Let us all Thy grace receive;
Suddenly return, and never,
Never more Thy temples leave.
Thee we would be always blessing,
Serve Thee as Thy hosts above,
Pray and praise Thee without ceasing,
Glory in Thy perfect love.

4. Finish then Thy new creation,
Pure and spotless let us be;
Let us see Thy great salvation,
Perfectly restored in Thee!
Changed from glory into glory,
Till in heaven we take our place;
Till we cast our crowns before Thee,
Lost in wonder, love and praise.

Charles Wesley (1707-88)

Ez 37: 9; 2 Cor 3: 18; 5: 17; Heb 4: 9-11; 1 Jn 4: 7-18; Rev 1: 8

Love divine
(Second tune)

LOVE DIVINE
Flowing

John Stainer (1840-1901)

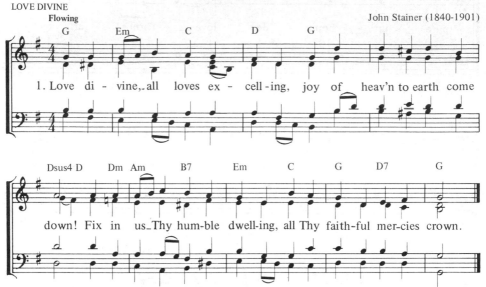

1. Love di - vine, all loves ex - cell-ing, joy of heav'n to earth come down! Fix in us Thy hum-ble dwell-ing, all Thy faith-ful mer-cies crown.

2. Jesus, Thou art all compassion,
   Pure, unbounded love Thou art;
   Visit us with Thy salvation,
   Enter every trembling heart.

3. Breathe, O breathe, Thy loving Spirit
   Into every troubled breast!
   Let us all in Thee inherit,
   Let us find Thy promised rest.

4. Take away the love of sinning;
   Alpha and Omega be;
   End of faith, as its beginning,
   Set our hearts at liberty.

5. Come, Almighty to deliver,
   Let us all Thy grace receive;
   Suddenly return, and never,
   Never more Thy temples leave.

6. Thee we would be always blessing,
   Serve Thee as Thy hosts above,
   Pray and praise Thee without ceasing,
   Glory in Thy perfect love.

7. Finish then Thy new creation,
   Pure and spotless let us be;
   Let us see Thy great salvation,
   Perfectly restored in Thee!

8. Changed from glory into glory,
   Till in heaven we take our place;
   Till we cast our crowns before Thee,
   Lost in wonder, love and praise.

Charles Wesley (1707-88)
Ez 37: 9; 2 Cor 3: 18; 5: 17; Heb 4: 9-11; 1 Jn 4: 7-18; Rev 1: 8

I pray also that the eyes of your heart may be enlightened in order that you may know the hope to which he has called you, the riches of his glorious inheritance in the saints, and his incomparably great power for us who believe.

EPHESIANS 1:18–19

354.

Love Him in the mornin'
(All day song)

John Fischer

prom - is - es to stay. When you think you got to

wor - ry _____ cos it seems the thing to do,

re - member He ain't in a hur - ry, _____

He's al - ways got time for you.

355.

Love one another

Nettie Rose
Jn 15:12

Love one an-oth-er as I have loved you,____ Be right-eous, be
ho - ly, in all that you do. Just seek Me, lis-ten to__Me, with
all your heart fol-low Me, and I pro-mise you shall __ not __ fall. _____
____ And I pro-mise you shall __ not __ fall. _____ So

356. Low in the grave He lay

Capo 3(G)
CHRIST AROSE!

Robert Lowry (1826-99)

1. Low in the grave He lay, Je - sus, my

Sa - viour, wait - ing the com - ing day,

Je - sus, my Lord: Up from the grave He a -

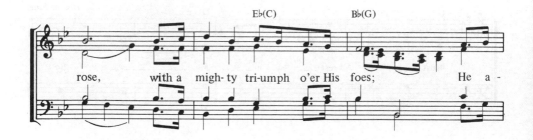

rose, with a migh-ty tri-umph o'er His foes; He a -

rose a Vic - tor from the dark do - main, and He lives for ev - er with His saints to reign: He a - rose! He a - rose! Al - le - lu - ia! Christ a - rose!

2. Vainly they watch His bed,
   Jesus, my Saviour;
   Vainly they seal the dead,
   Jesus, my Lord:

3. Death cannot keep his prey,
   Jesus, my Saviour;
   He tore the bars away,
   Jesus, my Lord:

Robert Lowry (1826-99)
Jn 20:1-18; 1 Cor 15:20-28

357.
Magnificent Warrior

Graham Kendrick

Josh 5:13-15;
Ps 93:1; 45:3-5; 149:6-9

1. Mag-ni-fi-cent War-ri-or ar-ray'd for bat - tle, we see You rea - dy to slay Your en - e - mies. O Migh-ty Cap - tain of heav-en's arm - ies, we bow be- fore You, we wor-ship You. So take Your sword up-on Your side, O Migh-ty One, clothe Your-self with splen-dour

and with maj-es-ty, and in Your maj-es-ty ride forth. Ride forth vic-

-tor-ious-ly for truth, hum-il-i-ty and right-eous-ness. Let Your

strong right hand dis-play Your awe-some deeds.

To repeat

To end

2. Mag-ni-fi-cent deeds.

2.   Magnificent Warrior,
      We hear Your strong command
      To join the ranks of light
      And march into the fight;
      By faith to overthrow
      Ten thousand Jerichos,
      To make Your judgements known
      In all the **earth**.

358.

Majesty

Capo 3 (G)

Jack W. Hayford
Rev 1:6

Ma - jes-ty, _____ wor-ship His ma - jes-ty, _____ un - to

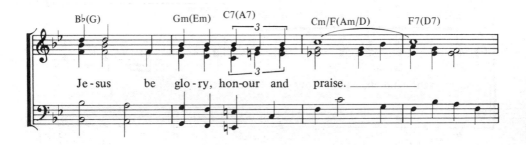

Je - sus be glo - ry, hon-our and praise. _____

Ma - jes-ty, _____ king-dom au - thor - i-ty, _____ flow from His

throne un - to His own, His an-them raise! _____ So ex -

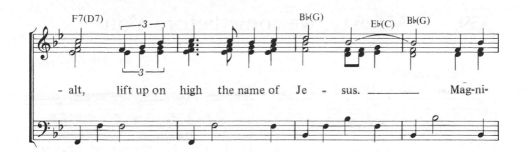

-alt, lift up on high the name of Je - sus. _____ Mag-ni-

-fy, come glo-ri - fy Christ Je-sus the King. _____

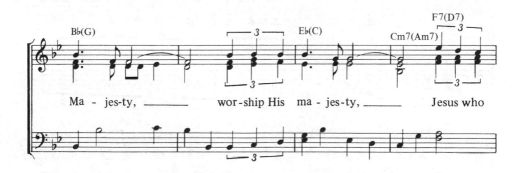

Ma - jes-ty, _____ wor-ship His ma-jes-ty, _____ Jesus who

died, now glor-i - fied, King of all kings. _____

359.   Majesty, we come before You

Wayne Drain & Dale Cox

Maj - est-y, ___ we come before _ You to know more of _ You.

Fan - ta-sy ___ can ne-ver be _ as thril - ling as Your rea-

- li-ty, ___ to feel Your touch_and to know Your pre - sence.

Lord we on - ly want to serve_You, Lord we on - ly want to know_Your_

love.

1st time · *Last time only*

360.

Make a joyful noise

Chris Head
Ps 100:1-2

Cheerfully

1. Make a joy-ful noise un-to the Lord, all ye lands, all ye lands.

Make a joy-ful noise un-to the Lord, all ye lands, all ye lands.

Come be-fore Him with sing-ing,— Come be-fore Him with joy.———

Make a joy-ful noise un-to the Lord, all ye lands, all ye lands.

2. Open your hearts before Him now.
Give Him your praise, give Him your praise.
Open your hearts before Him now.
Give Him your praise, give Him your praise.
Come before Him with singing,
Come before Him with joy.
Make a joyful noise unto the Lord,
All ye lands, all ye lands.

361.

Man of Sorrows

Capo 3(G)
GETHSEMANE

Philipp Bliss (1838-76)

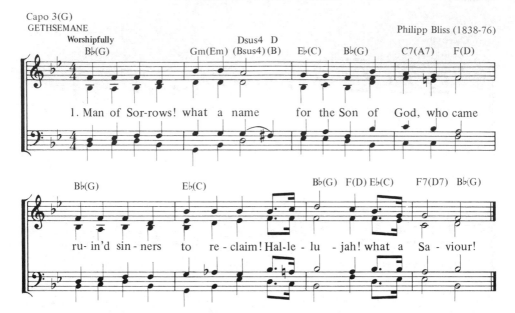

1. Man of Sor-rows! what a name for the Son of God, who came
ru-in'd sin-ners to re-claim! Hal-le-lu-jah! what a Sa-viour!

2. Bearing shame and scoffing rude,
   In my place condemned He stood;
   Sealed my pardon with His blood:
   Hallelujah! what a Saviour!

3. Guilty, vile, and helpless, we;
   Spotless Lamb of God was He:
   Full atonement — can it be?
   Hallelujah! what a Saviour!

4. Lifted up was He to die,
   'It is finished!' was His cry:
   Now in heaven exalted high:
   Hallelujah! what a Saviour!

5. When He comes, our glorious King,
   All His ransomed home to bring,
   Then anew this song we'll sing:
   'Hallelujah! what a Saviour!'

Philipp Bliss (1838-76)
Is 53:3-9; Jn 19:30; 1 Thess 4:16-17

362. Master, speak! Thy servant heareth

Capo 3(D)
OTTAWA

Lowell Mason (1792-1872)

1. Mas - ter, speak! Thy ser - vant hear - eth, long - ing for Thy
   long - ing for Thy voice that cheer - eth, Mas - ter let it
   gra - cious word,
   now be heard.
   I am list - 'ning,
   Lord, for Thee; what hast Thou to say to me?

2. Speak to me by name, O Master,
   Let me know it is to me;
   Speak, that I may follow faster,
   With a step more firm and free,
   Where the Shepherd leads the flock
   In the shadow of the rock.

3. Master, speak! though least and lowest,
   Let me not unheard depart;
   Master, speak! for O Thou knowest
   All the yearning of my heart,
   Knowest all its truest need;
   Speak, and make me blessed indeed.

4. Master, speak! and make me ready,
   When Thy voice is truly heard,
   With obedience glad and steady
   Still to follow every word.
   I am listening, Lord, for Thee;
   Master, speak! O speak to me!

Frances Ridley Havergal (1836-79)

Is 32:2; Mt 8:19

363.

Marvellous in our eyes

Leonard E. Smith Jnr.

Mk 12:10-11

Marvellous in our eyes, — marvellous in our eyes, —

this is the Lord's doing, and it's marvellous in our eyes, —

— marvellous in our eyes. — The —

stone that the builders re - jected, — the stone that the builders re-

jec-ted, __ has be-come the cor - ner-stone, and it's

marvellous in our eyes, marvellous in our eyes. __

This is the day that the Lord made, __ this is the day that the

Lord made, __ re-joice and be glad in it, for it's

D.C. al Fine

marvellous in our eyes, marvellous in our eyes. __

364.
May the Lord answer you

Phil Lawson Johnston
Ps 20

1. May the Lord answer you when you are in dis-tress, may the name of
God pro - tect you, may He send you help from the
sanc - tu - 'ry and grant you sup-port from Zi -
on. 2. May He give to you the de-sire of your heart and
make all your plans suc - ceed. We will shout for

365. May the Lord bless you

Capo 5(C)

Susie Hare
Num 6: 24-26

Gently

May the ___ Lord bless you and keep you, make His face to shine up-on you and be gra-cious un - to you. May the Lord lift up the light of His count - e-nance up - on ___ you and give you peace.

366.

May Your love

Capo 3 (C)

Dave Bilbrough
Jn 17:23

May Your love in me shine for all to see, that the world may know Your re-al-i-ty. Let us tru-ly live as we were meant to be, we are one in Your Son, we are fam-i-ly.

― □ ▢ □ ―

God raised us up with Christ and seated us with him in the heavenly realms in Christ Jesus, in order that in the coming ages he might show the incomparable riches of his grace expressed in his kindness to us in Christ Jesus.

EPHESIANS 2:6–7

― □ ▢ □ ―

367. Mighty God and gentle Saviour

Sally Karselis

Might-y God ___ and gen - tle Sav - iour, Spi - rit of love ___ and ___ pur - i - ty, here ___ we bow ___ in awe and won - der to ___ Your Maj - es - ty. ___

And we thank You Lord that You died for us ____ on the cross ____ of Cal - var - y, ____ and we thank You Lord that You rose a - gain ____ to set ____ Your chil - dren free. ____

368. Mine eyes have seen the glory

Capo 2(G)
BATTLE HYMN
Victory march

Melody attributed to William Steffe

1. Mine eyes have seen the glo-ry of the com-ing of the Lord; He is
tramp-ling out the vin-tage where the grapes of wrath are stor'd; He has
loos'd the fate-ful light-ning of His ter-ri-ble swift sword: His
truth is march-ing on.
Glo - ry, glo-ry, Al-le-lu - ia!

Glo - ry, glo - ry, Al - le - lu - ia!

Glo - ry, glo - ry, Al - le - lu - ia! His

truth is march - ing on.

2. He has sounded forth the trumpet that shall never call retreat;
   He is sifting out the hearts of men before His judgement-seat:
   O be swift, my soul, to answer Him; be jubilant, my feet!
   Our God is marching on.
   Glory, glory, Alleluia!
   Glory, glory, Alleluia!
   Glory, glory, Alleluia!
   Our God is marching on.

3. In the beauty of the lilies Christ was born across the sea,
   With a glory in His bosom that transfigures you and me;
   As He died to make men holy, let us live to make men free,
   While God is marching on.
   Glory, glory, Alleluia!
   Glory, glory, Alleluia!
   Glory, glory, Alleluia!
   While God is marching on.

Julia Ward Howe (1819-1910)
Josh 5:13-15; Dan 10:4-20; Rev 1:12-18

369.

Move Holy Spirit

Patricia Morgan
Eph 5: 18

Move Holy Spirit, we ask You to fill us afresh. We receive You.

370. My God, how wonderful Thou art

WESTMINSTER
Joyfully

James Turle (1802-82)

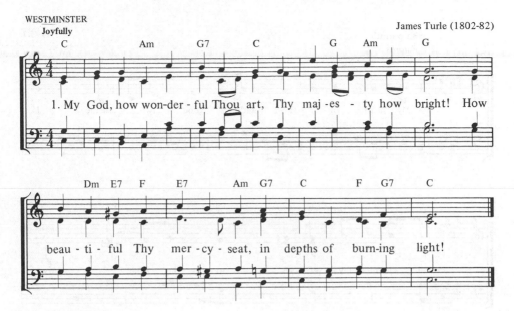

1. My God, how won-der-ful Thou art, Thy maj-es-ty how bright! How beau-ti-ful Thy mer-cy-seat, in depths of burn-ing light!

2. How dread are Thine eternal years,
   O everlasting Lord,
   By prostrate spirits day and night
   Incessantly adored!

3. How beautiful, how beautiful
   The sight of Thee must be,
   Thine endless wisdom, boundless power
   And awesome purity!

4. O how I fear Thee, Living God,
   With deepest, tenderest fears,
   And worship Thee with trembling hope
   And penitential tears!

5. Yet I may love Thee too, O Lord,
   Almighty as Thou art,
   For Thou hast stooped to ask of me
   The love of my poor heart.

6. No earthly father loves like Thee;
   No mother e'er so mild,
   Bears and forbears as Thou hast done
   With me, Thy sinful child.

7. Father of Jesus, love's reward,
   What rapture will it be
   Prostrate before Thy throne to lie,
   And gaze, and gaze on Thee.

Frederick William Faber (1814-63)
Lev 16:2; Is 28:29; Lk 12:30-32; Rev 22:4

371.

My heart overflows

Carolyn Govier
Ps 45:1

With warmth
Chorus

My heart ov - er - flows with a good - ly____ theme, I will add - ress my ver - ses to the King;____ My heart ov - er - flows with____ praise to my God, I'll give Him the love of my heart.

last time
Fine

Verse

1. For He is Lord of all the earth, He's ri-sen a-bove, He's seat-ed at God's right hand, and from Him and through Him and to Him are all things, that His glo-ry might fill the land.

D.C. al Fine

2. For He has chosen Mount Zion as His resting place,
   He says, 'Here will I dwell,
   I will abundantly bless and satisfy,
   And her saints will shout for joy.

3. 'Lift up your eyes round about and see,
   Your heart shall thrill and rejoice,
   For the abundance of the nations is coming to you,
   I am glorifying My house.'

372. My heart's desire is to worship the Lord

Roger Marlow

Ps 84:1-2

My heart's — de-sire is to wor-ship the Lord, to sing my prais-es to Him. _____ To stand be-fore the throne of my God, to hon-our and wor-ship Him, _____ to hon-our and wor-ship Him. _____

———— □ ☐ □ ————

Now to him who is able to do
immeasurably more than all we ask or
imagine, according to his power that
is at work within us, to him be glory
in the church and in Christ Jesus
throughout all generations, for ever
and ever! Amen.

EPHESIANS 3:20–21

———— □ ☐ □ ————

373.

My life is really blessed

Alison Huntley

Verse

1. Some-times I won-der if I'll e - ver get through,

And I see my life's in need of chang-ing, _____

But though He dis - ci - plines, it's al - ways in love, _____

And so with con - fid-ence I say _____

D.C. al Fine

2. So I'm really happy to be walking with God
   Knowing His care from day to day,
   He is the answer to my every desire,
   And so with confidence I say. . .

374.   My Lord and Master

Gill Paterson

Songs 2: 16

My Lord and Mas-ter, how I love You; for You are ho-ly, Your word is true. My voice I lift in praise, my hands to You I raise, for You are my be-lov'd and I am Yours.

375. My Lord, He is the fairest of the fair

Joan Parsons
Jn 4:14

My Lord ___ He is the fair-est of the fair, ___ He is the li - ly of the

val - ley, ___ the bright and mor-ning star, ___ His

love ___ is writ-ten deep within my heart, ___ He is the ne-ver end-ing

foun - tain ___ of ev-er-last - ing life. ___ And He

lives ___ He ___ lives ___ He ___ lives ___

1st time ___ He ___ lives in me. *Last time* me.

376. My Lord, You are so good to me

Capo 3 (G)

Pete & Dai Roe

Lyrics:
My Lord, You are so good to me and I'll love You as long as I live. And I'll try each day that I live to bless You and bring joy to Your heart. My

377.

My peace

Keith Routledge
Jn 14:27

Gently ♪= 120

1. My peace ___ I give ___ un-to you, ___ It's a
peace ___ that the world ___ can-not give, ___ It's a peace ___ that the
world ___ can-not un - der - stand. Peace to know,
peace to live. ___ My peace ___ I give ___ un - to you. ___

2. My joy I give unto you,
It's a joy that the world cannot give,
It's a joy that the world cannot understand.
Joy to know, joy to live.
My joy I give unto you.

3. My love I give unto you,
It's a love that the world cannot give,
It's a love that the world cannot understand.
Love to know, love to live.
My love I give unto you.

Speak to one another with psalms, hymns and spiritual songs. Sing and make music in your heart to the Lord, always giving thanks to God the Father for everything, in the name of our Lord Jesus Christ.

EPHESIANS 5:19–20

378. My song is love unknown

Capo 2(C)
LOVE UNKNOWN
With feeling

John Ireland (1879-1962)

1. My song is love un - known, my Sa - viour's love to me: love to the love - less shown, that they might love - ly be. O who am I, that for my sake my Lord should take frail flesh, and die?

2. He came from His blessed throne
   Salvation to bestow;
   But men made strange, and none
   The longed-for Christ would know:
   But O! my Friend, my Friend indeed,
   Who at my need His life did spend.

3. Sometimes they strew His way,
   And His sweet praises sing;
   Resounding all the day
   Hosannas to their King:
   Then 'Crucify!' is all their breath,
   And for His death they thirst and cry.

4. They rise and needs will have
   My dear Lord made away;
   A murderer they save,
   The Prince of Life they slay,
   Yet cheerful He to suffering goes,
   That He His foes from thence might free.

5. In life no house, no home
   My Lord on earth might have;
   In death, no friendly tomb,
   But what a stranger gave.
   What may I say? Heaven was His home;
   And mine the tomb wherein He lay.

6. Here might I stay and sing,
   No story so divine,
   Never was love, dear King!
   Never was grief like Thine.
   This is my Friend, in whose sweet praise
   I all my days could gladly spend.

   Samuel Crossman (c. 1624-83)
   Is 53; Lk 23:1-24:8

379.

My soul doth magnify

Susie Hare
Lk 1: 46-49

My soul doth magnify the Lord

Author unknown
Arr. Margaret Evans
Lk 1:46-49

381. Not by might but by My Spirit

Bill Tizzard
Zech 4:6

Not by might _____ but by my Spi-rit, says the Lord. Not by

pow'r _____ but in my strength you shall go forth.

Vic - t'ry is yours be-fore the bat - tle be - gins. Not by

might, not by pow'r but by My Spi-rit, says the Lord. _____ 1. All

D.C. al Fine

2. For whom shall we fear
    With the Lord on our side?
    For His word is mightier than the sword.
    What can man do? for the Lord will see us through.
    Not by might, not by power
    But by My Spirit, says the Lord.

382.

Not unto us, O Lord

Everett Perry
Ps 115:1; Mt 6:13

Capo 2(G)

Not un-to us, O Lord, not un-to us, but un-to

Thy name, give glory. Not un-to us, O Lord, not un-to

us, but un-to Thy name, Thine own name, give glory. For

Thine is the kingdom and the power and the glory, for

ev-er and ev-er, A-men and A-men.

383. Nothing can separate us

David Maguire

Rom 8:39

Slowly with feeling

No - thing can se - par-ate us from the love of _ God, _____ no - thing can se - par-ate us from the love of _ God, which is ours through Je - sus our Lord. No - thing can se - par-ate us from the love of God. _____

384.

Not without a cause

Bill Anderson
Josh 5: 13-15; Ps 149: 6-9;
2 Cor 10: 4; 1 Tim 1: 18

Capo 2(C)

Triumphantly

1. Not with-out a cause — do we go march -ing forth to war, — not with-out a cause — that we'll see right - eous-ness re - stor'd. — Clean your weap - ons, stir your hearts, — shed all fears be - fore — we start, when we stand to do our part —

we shall say:

'Not without a right do we unsheath our silent swords,
Not without a fight but we will crown Him Lord of lords.
Lift your banner, lift it high, Jesus is our battle cry.
As we've lived, so we shall die, by His side.'

2. Not without a foe do we prepare ourselves to fight,
    Not without a shout will we scale hell's unconquered height.
    Let the hosts of Satan pray, when we rise as one that day,
    Let them run in disarray, when we say:

3. Not without a cheer will we hear bells and trumpets ring,
    Not without a tear we'll set Him on the throne of kings.
    Eyes on fire and faces grim, we will free Jerusalem,
    Through the gates we'll follow Him, as we say:

385. No weapon formed

*Being confident of this, that he who
began a good work in you will carry
it on to completion until the day of
Christ Jesus.*

PHILIPPIANS 1:6

386. Now thank we all our God

Capo 3(C)
NUN DANKET

Johann Crüger(1598-1662)

1. Now thank we all our God, with hearts and hands and voi - ces; who won - drous things has done, in whom His world re - joi - ces; who from our moth - er's arms has bless'd us on our way with count-less gifts of love, and still is ours to - day.

2. O may this bounteous God
   Through all our life be near us,
   With ever joyful hearts
   And blessèd peace to cheer us;
   And keep us in His grace,
   And guide us when perplexed,
   And free us from all ills
   In this world and the next.

3. All praise and thanks to God
   The Father now be given,
   The Son, and Him who reigns
   With them in highest heaven,
   The one eternal God,
   Whom earth and heaven adore;
   For thus it was, is now
   And shall be evermore.

Martin Rinkart (1586-1649)
Tr. Catherine Winkworth (1829-78)

Ps 134; Jer 1:5; 2 Cor 9:8; Rev 1:8
(Based on Ecclesiasticus 50:22-24)

387.

O accept these words
(Song of offering)

Capo 3 (G)

Brent Chambers

Heb 13:15

Flowing with feeling

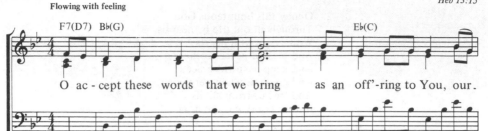

O ac-cept these words that we bring as an off'-ring to You, our.

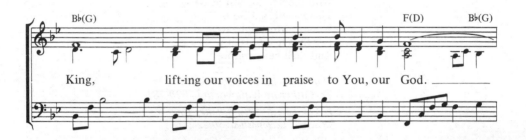

King, lift-ing our voices in praise to You, our God. _____

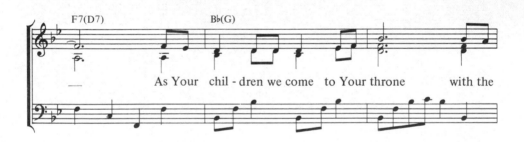

___ As Your chil-dren we come to Your throne with the

wor-ship that is Yours a-lone, giv-ing our-selves with our

praise to You, our God. _____ Al - le - lu - ia, _____

Al - le - lu - ia, _____ Fruit of our lips we

off-er to Your name. _____ O ac-cept these words that we

bring as an off' - ring to You, our _ King,

lift - ing our voi - ces in praise to You, our God. _____

388. O Breath of Life, come sweeping through us

Capo 2(C)
SPIRITUS VITAE

Mary J. Hammond (1878-1964)

2. O Wind of God, come, bend us, break us,
Till humbly we confess our need;
Then in Thy tenderness remake us,
Revive, restore; for this we plead.

3. O Breath of Love, come, breathe within us,
Renewing thought and will and heart:
Come, love of Christ, afresh to win us,
Revive Thy church in every part.

4. Revive us, Lord! is zeal abating
While harvest fields are vast and white?
Revive us, Lord, the world is waiting,
Equip Thy church to spread the light.

Elizabeth Porter Head (1850-1936)

Gen 2:7; Job 33:4; Ez 37:6; Jn 3:8; 4:35

389.

O come let us adore Him

18th Century melody,
'ADESTE FIDELES'

1. O come let us a - dore Him, O come let us a - dore Him, O come let. us a - dore Him, — Christ the Lord.

2. For He alone is worthy... (etc).

3. We'll give Him all the glory... (etc).

390.

O come let us worship

Iain Anderson
Ps 95:6

391.

O Father, I do love You

Dave Bolton

2. O Jesus, I adore You, *(three times)*
   Hallelujah, Hallelujah.

3. O Spirit, I do bless You, *(three times)*
   Hallelujah, Hallelujah.

392. O for a closer walk with God

MARTYRDOM
Joyfully

Hugh Wilson (1766-1824)

1. O for a clo-ser walk with God, a calm and heav'n-ly frame, a light to shine up-on the road that leads me to the Lamb!

2. Where is the blessèdness I knew
   When first I saw the Lord?
   Where is the soul-refreshing view
   Of Jesus and His word?

3. What peaceful hours I once enjoyed!
   How sweet their memory still!
   But they have left an aching void
   The world can never fill.

4. The dearest idol I have known,
   Whate'er that idol be,
   Help me to tear it from Thy throne,
   And worship only Thee.

5. So shall my walk be close with God,
   Calm and serene my frame:
   So purer light shall mark the road
   That leads me to the Lamb.

William Cowper (1731-1800)
Ex 20: 4-6; Mic 6: 8; Mal 2: 5-6

393. O for a heart to praise my God
(First tune)

Capo 3 (C)
STOCKTON (First tune)

Thomas Wright (1763-1829)

Prayerfully

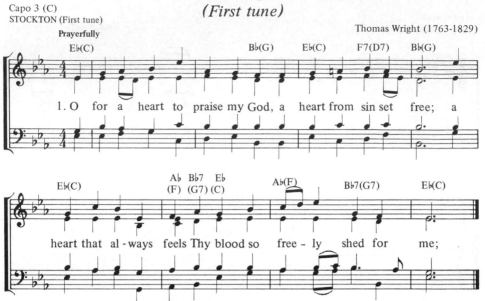

1. O for a heart to praise my God, a heart from sin set free; a heart that al - ways feels Thy blood so free - ly shed for me;

2. A heart resigned, submissive, meek,
   My great Redeemer's throne,
   Where only Christ is heard to speak,
   Where Jesus reigns alone;

3. A humble, lowly, contrite heart,
   Believing true, and clean;
   Which neither life nor death can part
   From Him who dwells within;

4. A heart in every thought renewed,
   And full of love divine;
   Perfect and right, and pure, and good:
   A copy, Lord, of Thine.

5. Thy nature, gracious Lord, impart;
   Come quickly from above;
   Write Thy new name upon my heart,
   Thy new best name of love.

Charles Wesley (1707-88)

Rom 8: 1-2, 39; 12: 1-2; 2 Cor 3: 3; Eph 3: 17

O for a heart to praise my God
(Second tune)

Capo 3(G)

SAWLEY

James Walch (1837-1901)

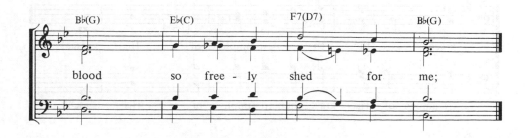

394.   O for a thousand tongues

LYNGHAM

Thomas Jarman (1782-1862)

1. O for a thou - sand tongues to sing my great Re-deem-er's praise, my great Re - deem - er's praise! The glo - ries of my God and King, the the tri - umphs of His grace, the tri - umphs of His grace, the tri - umphs of His grace!

2. Jesus! the name that charms our fears,
   That bids our sorrows cease,
   That bids our sorrows cease;
   'Tis music in the sinner's ears,
   'Tis life, and health, and peace.

3. See all your sins on Jesus laid;
   The Lamb of God was slain,
   The Lamb of God was slain;
   His soul was once an offering made
   For every soul of man.

4. He breaks the power of cancelled sin,
   He sets the prisoner free,
   He sets the prisoner free;
   His blood can make the foulest clean,
   His blood availed for me.

5. He speaks and, listening to His voice,
   New life the dead receive,
   New life the dead receive;
   The mournful, broken hearts rejoice,
   The humble poor believe.

6. Hear Him, ye deaf; His praise, ye dumb,
   Your loosened tongues employ,
   Your loosened tongues employ;
   Ye blind, behold your Saviour come;
   And leap, ye lame, for joy!

7. My gracious Master and my God,
   Assist me to proclaim,
   Assist me to proclaim;
   To spread through all the earth abroad
   The honours of Thy name.

Charles Wesley (1707-88)
Is 42: 7; Phil 2:9-11; Rev 5:9

395.

O give thanks

Joanne Pond
Ps 136:1

O give thanks to the Lord, all you His peo-ple, O give thanks to the Lord for He is good. ___ Let us praise, let us thank, let us ce - le - brate and dance, O give thanks to the Lord for He is good. ___

396. O give thanks to the Lord

Brent Chambers
1 Chron 16: 34

397.

O God my Creator

Graham Kendrick
Rev 22:1

Worshipfully

1. O God my Cre - a - tor, cre - ate in

me that ri - ver of wa - ter that

flows full and free. Let it bring life to the

dead and stag-nant sea; spring up O

well and flow on out of me. We

come — to the throne where flows the liv-ing stream, and

drink from the wa - ter, and drink from the wa-ter, and

drink — from the wa - ter that flows from Thee.

2. O God my Creator, create in me
That new way of living that flows full and free.
Let it bring life to the wilderness of man;
Spring up O well and flood this thirsty land.

398.

O how I love

Joan Parsons
Lam 3: 22-23

Unhurried (Round)

O how I love, — Lord, to ex-tol You, wor-ship Your name,

bless You al-ways. You gave me life, — Fa-ther, I thank You, thank You Lord

all my days. ____ You're the light in my life, new ev'ry mor-ning

is Your love, Lord, un-to me. You're the song in my heart

and I will praise You through all e - ter - ni - ty. ____

— □ ▯ □ —

God exalted him to the highest place
and gave him the name that is
above every name,
that at the name of Jesus every knee
should bow,
in heaven and on earth and under
the earth,
and every tongue confess that Jesus
Christ is Lord,
to the glory of God the Father.

PHILIPPIANS 2:9–11

— □ ▯ □ —

399.

O I will sing unto You with joy
(Rock of my salvation)

Shona Sauni
Ps 89: 26

Capo 5(C)

O I will sing un-to You with joy, O Lord, for You're the rock of my sal-va-tion, come be-fore You with thanks-giv-ing and ex-tol You with a song. For You're the great-est King a-bove all else, You hold the depths of the earth in Your hand.

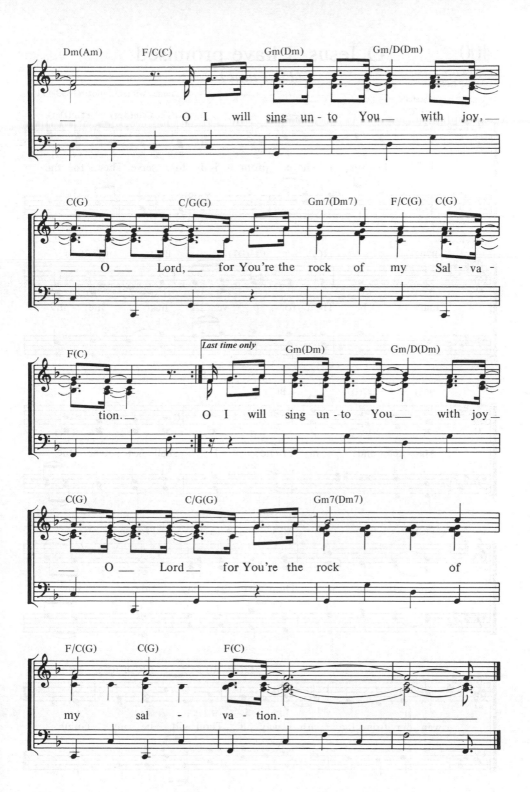

400.

O Jesus, I have promised
(First tune)

Capo 4 (C)
DAY OF REST

James William Elliott (1833-1915)

1. O Jesus, I have prom - is'd to serve Thee — to the end; be Thou for e - ver — near me, my Mas - ter and my Friend; I shall not fear the bat - tle if Thou art by my side, nor — wan - der from the path - way if Thou wilt — be my Guide.

Alternative tune: PENLAN (213)

2. O let me feel Thee near me;
   The world is ever near;
   I see the sights that dazzle,
   The tempting sounds I hear;
   My foes are ever near me,
   Around me and within;
   But Jesus, draw Thou nearer,
   And shield my soul from sin.

3. O let me hear Thee speaking
   In accents clear and still,
   Above the storms of passion,
   The murmurs of self-will;
   O speak to reassure me,
   To hasten, or control;
   O speak, and make me listen,
   Thou Guardian of my soul.

4. O Jesus, Thou hast promised
   To all who follow Thee
   That where Thou art in glory
   There shall Thy servants be;
   And, Jesus, I have promised
   To serve Thee to the end;
   O give me grace to follow
   My Master and my Friend.

5. O let me see Thy footmarks,
   And in them plant mine own;
   My hope to follow duly
   Is in Thy strength alone.
   O guide me, call me, draw me,
   Uphold me to the end;
   And then in heaven receive me,
   My Saviour and my Friend.

John Ernest Bode (1816-74)

1 Kings 19: 12; Ps 31: 3; 91; Is 30: 21; Jn 14: 1-4; 15:

O Jesus, I have promised
(Second tune)

Capo 2 (C)
THORNBURY

Basil Harwood (1859-1949)

2. O let me feel Thee near me;
    The world is ever near;
    I see the sights that dazzle,
    The tempting sounds I hear;
    My foes are ever near me,
    Around me and within;
    But Jesus, draw Thou nearer,
    And shield my soul from sin.

3. O let me hear Thee speaking
    In accents clear and still,
    Above the storms of passion,
    The murmurs of self-will;
    O speak to reassure me,
    To hasten, or control;
    O speak, and make me listen,
    Thou Guardian of my soul.

4. O Jesus, Thou hast promised
    To all who follow Thee
    That where Thou art in glory
    There shall Thy servants be;
    And, Jesus, I have promised
    To serve Thee to the end;
    O give me grace to follow
    My Master and my Friend.

5. O let me see Thy footmarks,
    And in them plant mine own;
    My hope to follow duly
    Is in Thy strength alone.
    O guide me, call me, draw me,
    Uphold me to the end;
    And then in heaven receive me,
    My Saviour and my Friend.

John Ernest Bode (1816-74)

1 Kings 19: 12; Ps 31: 3; 91; Is 30: 21; Jn 14: 1-4; 15: 14-15

401.

O Jesus my King
(Life-giving blood)

Bob Brogan
Phil 2: 6-8; Heb 9: 14; Rev 5: 12

Tenderly

1. O Je-sus my King, how can it be so, that
You who cre-at-ed the won-ders I know, would
live as a man and yet suf-fer no loss, then
pour out Your life on a sin - stain'd cross?

Chorus Life - giv - ing blood, pour'd on the

earth, e - ter - nal blood, e - ter - nal
worth. Call - ing the dust to e - ter - nal
birth; life - giv-ing blood, life - giv - ing
blood of God.

2. My sweet holy Lamb, how worthy You are
   Of all adoration, how worthy You are.
   You've purchased our souls with a marvellous price,
   You've given us life who were once dead twice.

3. O life-giving blood, I always will praise
   The virtue within You that cleanses my ways
   From evil destructions that call me to hell,
   To Jesus within me — Emmanuel.

402.

O Lamb of God

Dave Fellingham
Rev 12:11

O Lamb of God, You take a - way our sin,
You clothe us now in robes of right - eous-ness.
You set us free and pro-tect us from all harm,
in ho-li - ness we wor-ship You. And

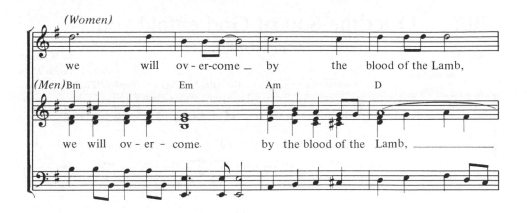

(Women)

we will ov-er-come _ by the blood of the Lamb,

(Men) Bm   Em   Am   D

we will ov - er - come. by the blood of the Lamb, _____

as we de-clare _ the test-i-mo-ny of the word,

B7   Em   A   D

_____ as we de - clare the test-i-mo-ny of the word,

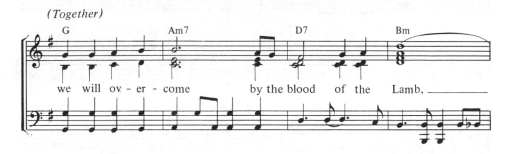

(Together)

G   Am7   D7   Bm

we will ov - er - come by the blood of the Lamb, _____

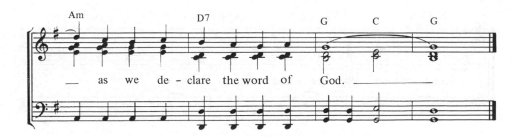

Am   D7   G   C   G

_____ as we de - clare the word of God. _____

403. O let the Son of God enfold you
(Spirit song)

Capo 2(C)

John Wimber

Jn 10:10-16; Rev 19:4

1. O let the Son of God en-fold you with His Spi-rit and His love, let Him fill your heart and sat-is-fy your soul. O let Him have the things that hold you, and His Spi-rit like a dove will de-scend up-on your life and make you whole.

2. O come and sing this song with gladness
   As your hearts are filled with joy,
   Lift your hands in sweet surrender to His name.
   O give Him all your tears and sadness,
   Give Him all your years of pain,
   And you'll enter into life in Jesus' name.

404.

O Lord, I will praise You

Arthur & Rita Simmonds

Ps 9:1-2

O Lord, _____ I will praise You with all my heart, O Lord, _____ I will praise You with all my heart and tell ev'-ry-one a-bout the things You do, and tell ev'-ry-one a-bout the things that You do. _ I will be glad, _____ I will be glad, _____ I will be glad be-cause of You. _____

405. O Lord most Holy God

Wendy Churchill
Mt 6:10; 1 Pet 2:5

Worshipfully

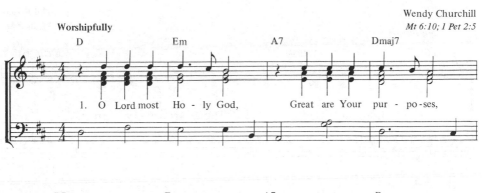

1. O Lord most Ho-ly God, Great are Your pur-po-ses,

Great is Your will for us, Great is Your love.

And we re-joice in You, And we will sing to You,

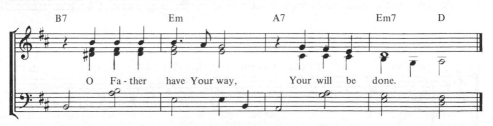

O Fa-ther have Your way, Your will be done.

2.   For You are building
A temple without hands,
A city without walls
Enclosed by fire.
A place for You to dwell,
Built out of living stones,
Shaped by a Father's hand
And joined in love.

406. O Lord my God, Thou art very great

Capo 5 (C)

Phil Rogers
Ps 104:1, 24, 33-35

O Lord my God, Thou art ve-ry great, _____ Thou art clothed in splen-dour and maj-est-y. O Lord my God, how ma-ny are Thy works, _____ in wis-dom Thou hast made __ them __ all. _____

407.

O Lord my God!

HOW GREAT THOU ART

Thee, how great Thou art! How great Thou art!

Alternative ending

Thee, how great Thou art! How great Thou art!

2. When through the woods and forest glades I wander
   And hear the birds sing sweetly in the trees;
   When I look down from lofty mountain grandeur,
   And hear the brook, and feel the gentle breeze;

3. And when I think that God His Son not sparing,
   Sent Him to die — I scarce can take it in.
   That on the cross my burden gladly bearing,
   He bled and died to take away my sin:

4. When Christ shall come with shout of acclamation
   And take me home — what joy shall fill my heart!
   Then shall I bow in humble adoration
   And there proclaim, my God, how great Thou art!

Russian hymn
Tr. Stuart K. Hine

Ps 8; Rom 5: 9-11; 1 Thess 4: 16-17

408.

O Lord, my Lord

Capo 2 (C)

Diane Fung

—— □ ▢ □ ——

Rejoice in the Lord always. I will say it again: Rejoice!

PHILIPPIANS 4:4

—— □ ▢ □ ——

409.

O Lord our God
(We will magnify)

Phil Lawson Johnston
Ps 8:1-9

Flowing

Verse

1. O Lord our God, — how ma-jest - ic is Your — name, ————— the earth — is filled with Your glo - ry.— — O Lord our God, — You are robed in ma-jes - ty, ————— You've set Your glo-ry a-bove-the hea - vens.

Chorus

We will mag - ni-fy, ———— we will mag - ni-fy ————

the Lord en - throned in Zi - on. We will

mag - ni - fy, _____ we will mag - ni - fy _____ the Lord en -

throned in Zi - on.

2. O Lord our God, You have established a throne,
   You reign in righteousness and splendour.
   O Lord our God, the skies are ringing with Your praise,
   Soon those on earth will come to worship.

3. O Lord our God, the world was made at Your command,
   In You all things now hold together.
   Now to Him who sits on the throne and to the Lamb,
   Be praise and glory and power for ever.

410. O Lord our God, You are a great God

Mike Kerry
Ex 15:11

O Lord our God, You are a great God, ___ Your maj - est - y be-yond com-pare. ___ Who is a God like un - to You, and who like me could know Your care? ___ It's good, dear Lord, to know Your great - ness, ___ it's good, dear Lord, to know Your care. ___ It's good just to be in Your presence, it's good just to know that You are there. ___

411. O Lord, You are my God

Capo 2 (C)

David J. Hadden

Is 25:1

412.

O Lord, You are my light

Dave Fellingham
Col 3:3

Joyfully with pace

O Lord, You are my light, O Lord, You are my sal-va-tion. You have deliver'd me from all my fear, for You are the defence of my life. For my life is hid-den with Christ in God. You have concealed me in Your love, You've lift-ed me up, placed my feet on a rock. I will shout for joy in the house of God. O

——————— □ ▢ □ ———————

Do not be anxious about anything, but in everything, by prayer and petition, with thanksgiving, present your requests to God. And the peace of God, which transcends all understanding, will guard your hearts and your minds in Christ Jesus.

PHILIPPIANS 4:6–7

——————— □ ▢ □ ———————

413.   O Lord, You're beautiful

Keith Green

Capo 5(C)

Ps 27: 4, 8; 2 Cor 9: 8; Rev 2: 4-5

2. O Lord, please light the fire
   That once burned bright and clear,
   Replace the lamp of my first love
   That burns with holy fear!

3. O Lord, You're beautiful,
   Your face is all I seek,
   For when Your eyes are on this child,
   Your grace abounds to me.

414. O Lord, You've done great things

Joyfully with pace

Carolyn Govier

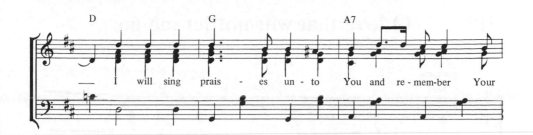

I will sing prais - es un - to You and re-mem-ber Your

good - ness, _____ my past Is for - giv - en _____

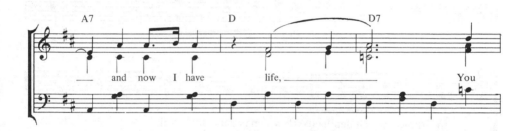

_____ and now I have life, _____ You

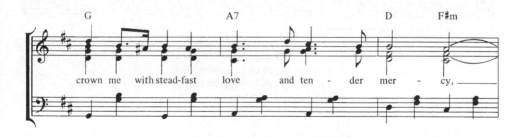

crown me with stead-fast love and ten - der mer - cy, _____

_____ I'll do Your will _____ and bless You, O Lord.

415. O love that wilt not let me go

ST MARGARET

Albert Lister Peace (1844-1912)

With feeling

1. O love that wilt not let me go, ___ I rest my wea-ry soul in thee: ___ I give thee back the life I owe, ___ that in thine o-cean depths its flow may rich-er, full - er be.

2. O light that followest all my way,
   I yield my flickering torch to thee:
   My heart restores its borrowed ray,
   That in thy sunshine's blaze its day
   May brighter, fairer be.

3. O joy that seekest me through pain,
   I cannot close my heart to thee:
   I trace the rainbow through the rain,
   And feel the promise is not vain,
   That morn shall tearless be.

4. O cross that liftest up my head,
   I dare not ask to fly from thee:
   I lay in dust life's glory dead,
   And from the ground there blossoms red
   Life that shall endless be.

George Matheson (1842-1906)

Gen 9: 13; Neh 8: 10; Jn 8: 12; Rom 8: 38-39; Col 1: 19-20

416.   O magnify the Lord with me

David Garratt
Ps 34: 3

2. I'll magnify the Lord with you,
I'll magnify the Lord with you,
I'll magnify the Lord with you,
And we'll exalt His name together.

417.

One shall tell another
(The wine of the kingdom)

Graham Kendrick
Ps 145:11-12; Acts 2:42-47

Lightly with increasing pace

1. One shall tell a - noth - er, and he shall tell his friend, hus - bands, wives and chil - dren shall come fol - low - ing on. From house to house in fam - i - lies shall more be gath - ered in, and lights will shine in ev' - ry street, so warm and welcom - ing.

Chorus

Come on in ___ and taste the new wine, the wine of the

kingdom, the wine of the kingdom of God. __

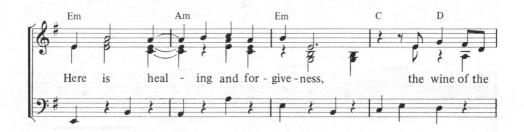

Here is heal - ing and for - give - ness, the wine of the

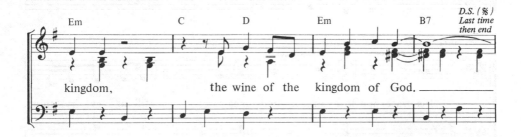

kingdom, the wine of the kingdom of God. ____

D.S. (%)
Last time
then end

Last time only
Em

2. Compassion of the Father
   Is ready now to flow,
   Through acts of love and mercy
   We must let it show.
   He turns now from His anger
   To show a smiling face
   And longs that men should stand beneath
   The fountain of His grace.

3. He longs to do much more than
   Our faith has yet allowed,
   To thrill us and surprise us
   With His sovereign power.
   Where darkness has been darkest
   The brightest light will shine,
   His invitation comes to us,
   It's yours and it is mine.

418.

One with God

Dave Bryant
1 Cor 6: 17; 2 Cor 3: 18; 4: 6-7; Col 2: 9-10

Capo 3(D)
With strength

One with God, now and for ev - er, cho - sen of the King ___ we stand ___ se - cure ___ and free. ___ His grace and love, ours be-yond mea-sure, fill-ing ev - 'ry - thing, ___ we share ___ in His vic - to - ry. ___ See the life ___ of Je - sus shi - ning ___ through, ___ re-vealed ___

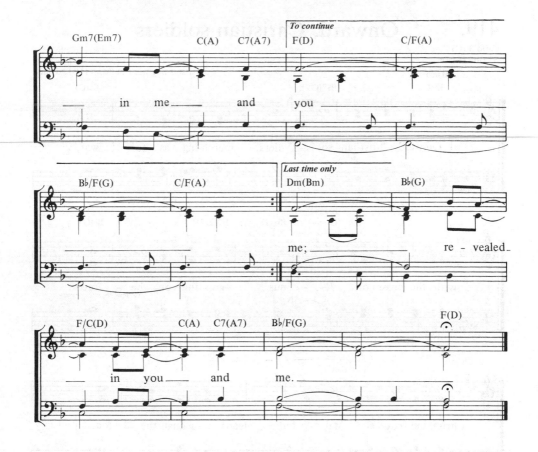

2. Perfect peace, total surrender,
   That's the gift He brings
   To all who love His name.
   Emptied hearts filled with a treasure
   Glowing from within,
   Like an ever burning flame.
   A love light shining out for all men to see
   Revealed in you and me.

   (Last time)
   Revealed in you and me.

419.

Onward, Christian soldiers

Capo 3 (C)
ST GERTRUDE

March

Arthur Seymour Sullivan (1842-1900)

1. On-ward, Christ-ian sol - diers, march-ing as to war,

with the cross of Je - sus go-ing on be - fore!

Christ, the roy - al Mas - ter, leads a - gainst the foe;

for-ward in - to bat - tle,___ see, His ban-ners go!

Chorus

On-ward, Christ-ian sol - diers, march-ing as to___ war,

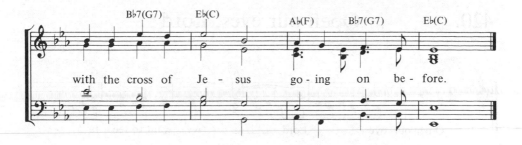

with the cross of Je - sus go - ing on be - fore.

2. At the name of Jesus
   Satan's host doth flee;
   On then, Christian soldiers,
   On to victory!
   Hell's foundations quiver
   At the shout of praise;
   Brothers, lift your voices;
   Loud your anthems raise:

3. Like a mighty army
   Moves the church of God:
   Brothers we are treading
   Where the saints have trod.
   We are not divided
   All one body we,
   One in hope and doctrine,
   One in charity.

4. Crowns and thrones may perish,
   Kingdoms rise and wane,
   But the church of Jesus
   Constant will remain;
   Gates of hell can never
   'Gainst that church prevail;
   We have Christ's own promise,
   And that cannot fail:

5. Onward, then, ye people!
   Join our happy throng;
   Blend with ours your voices
   In the triumph-song:
   Glory, laud, and honour
   Unto Christ the King!
   This through countless ages
   Men and angels sing:

Sabine Baring-Gould (1834-1924)

Mt 16: 18; Eph 4: 4-6; Col 2: 15; 2 Tim 2: 3-4

420.

Open our eyes, Lord

Bob Cull

— ◻ ◻ ◻ —

He is the image of the invisible God,
the firstborn over all creation. For
by him all things were created: things
in heaven and on earth, visible and
invisible, whether thrones or powers
or rulers or authorities; all things
were created by him and for him.

COLOSSIANS 1:15–16

— ◻ ◻ ◻ —

421.

O praise ye the Lord

Capo 3 (D)
LAUDATE DOMINUM (GAUNTLETT)
With strength

Henry John Gauntlett (1805-76)

1. O praise ye the Lord! Praise Him in the height; re - joice in His word, ye an - gels of light; ye hea - vens a - dore Him by whom ye were made, and wor - ship be - fore Him in bright - ness ar - ray'd.

Alternative tune: LAUDATE DOMINUM (PARRY) (628i)

2. O praise ye the Lord!
    Praise Him upon earth,
    In tuneful accord,
    Ye sons of new birth;
    Praise Him who hath brought you
    His grace from above,
    Praise Him who hath taught you
    To sing of His love.

3. O praise ye the Lord,
    All things that give sound;
    Each jubilant chord,
    Re-echo around;
    Loud organs, His glory
    Forthtell in deep tone,
    And sweet harp, the story
    Of what He hath done.

4. O praise ye the Lord!
    Thanksgiving and song
    To Him be outpoured
    All ages along;
    For love in creation,
    For heaven restored,
    For grace of salvation,
    O praise ye the Lord!

Henry Williams Baker (1821-77)

Ps 100; 148

422.

O taste and see

Phil Rogers

Ps 34:4,8

Capo 5 (C)

O taste and see _____ that the Lord is

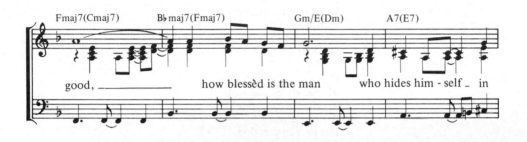

good, _____ how blessèd is the man who hides him - self _ in

Him. _____ I sought the Lord _____

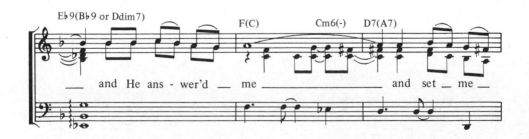

_ and He ans - wer'd _ me _____ and set _ me _

423.
O the valleys shall ring

Capo 3 (D)

Dave Bilbrough

Is 9:7

O the val - leys shall ring with the sound of praise, and the li - on shall lie with the lamb. Of His gov - ern - ment there shall be no end, and His glo - ry shall fill the earth. May Your will be done, may Your king - dom come! Let it rule, let it reign in our lives. There's a shout in the camp as we ans - wer the call, Hail the King! Hail the Lord of lords!

— □ ▢ □ —

He is the head of the body, the church; he is the beginning and the firstborn from among the dead, so that in everything he might have the supremacy.

COLOSSIANS 1:18

— □ ▢ □ —

424. O Thou who camest from above
(First tune)

Capo 3 (C)
HEREFORD

Samuel Sebastian Wesley (1810-76)

1. O Thou who cam-est from a-bove the pure ce-

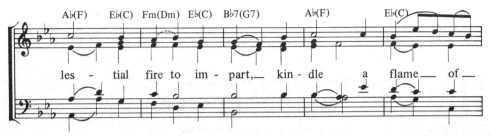

les-tial fire to im-part, kin-dle a flame of

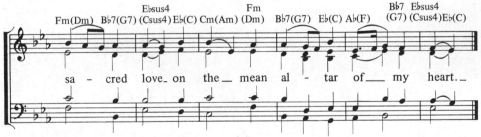

sa-cred love on the mean al-tar of my heart.

2. There let it for Thy glory burn
   With inextinguishable blaze,
   And trembling to its source return,
   In humble prayer and fervent praise.

3. Jesus, confirm my heart's desire
   To work, and speak, and think for Thee;
   Still let me guard the holy fire,
   And still stir up Thy gift in me;

4. Ready for all Thy perfect will,
   My acts of faith and love repeat,
   Till death Thy endless mercies seal,
   And make the sacrifice complete.

Charles Wesley (1707-88)
Mt 3: 11-12; 2 Tim 1: 6-7; Heb 12: 28-29

O Thou who camest from above
(Second tune)

WILTON

With life

Samuel Stanley (1767-1822)

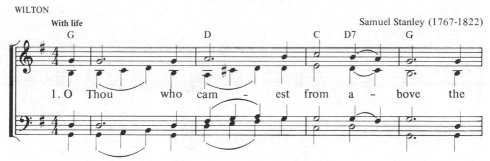

1. O Thou who cam - est from a - bove the

pure ce - les - tial fire to im - part, kin -

dle _ a _ flame _ of _ sa - cred _ love _____ on

the mean al - tar of my ___ heart.

425.   Our eyes have seen the King

Carolyn Govier
Ps 99:2; Is 9:7

1. Our eyes have seen the King seat-ed on Da-vid's throne, and of His king-dom there shall be no end, for the zeal of the Lord of hosts has es-tab-lished it for e-ver-more.

2. The Lord is great in Zi-on, the ci-ty of our God, He has found-ed it to be His dwell-ing that His will may be known on earth and His ways known a-mong all na-tions, for none is great like our God.

□ ▢ □

God was pleased to have all his
fulness dwell in him, and through him
to reconcile to himself all things,
whether things on earth or things in
heaven, by making peace through his
blood, shed on the cross.

COLOSSIANS 1:19–20

□ ▢ □

426. Our God is a God of war

Capo 3 (Em)

Brightly with strength

Dave Fellingham

Is 42:13; Eph 6:11-13

1. Our God is a God of war and He is high-ly ex-alt-ed. Our God is our strength and song, the Lord is a migh-ty war-rior. We're sing-ing and danc-ing and shout-ing and marching as we ex-e-cute the just-ice and rule of our God. We'll take the

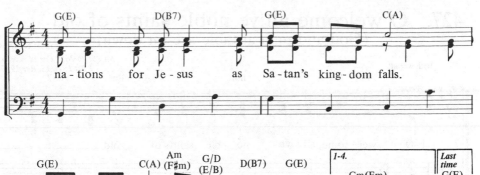

na - tions   for Je - sus   as   Sa - tan's king - dom falls.

Right-eous-ness and truth will pre-vail through our God.   2. Our —

2. Our God has a sword on His thigh,
   And He has girded it for battle.
   In majesty and splendour
   He will ride on victoriously.

3. His own arm has brought salvation,
   He's put on righteousness as a breastplate.
   He's put on garments of vengeance
   And wrapped Himself with zeal as a mantle.

4. We are the army of God,
   As a church we stand in God's armour,
   The powers of darkness are trembling
   As Jesus our Captain goes before us.

5. By His power we can run through a troop,
   By His strength we will leap over walls.
   The standard of God we are raising,
   The Spirit is moving us forward.

427. O welcome all ye noble saints of old
(God and man at table are sat down)

Robert Stamps

Mt 26: 26-28; 1 Cor 11: 23-26;
1 Pet 1: 10-12; Rev 19: 7

1. O wel-come, all ye no-ble saints of old, as now be-fore your ve-ry eyes un-fold the won-ders all so long a-go fore-told; God and man at ta-ble are sat down, God and man at ta-ble are sat down,

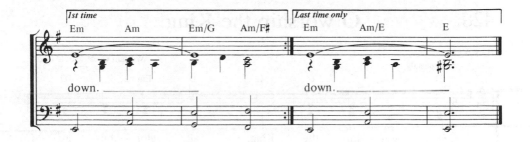

2. Elders, martyrs, all are falling down
   And prophets, patriarchs are gathering round.
   What angels longed to see, now man has found;

3. Beggars, lame, and harlots also here,
   Repentant publicans are drawing near,
   Wayward sons come home without a fear;

4. Who is this who spreads the victory feast?
   Who is this who makes our warring cease?
   Jesus, risen Saviour, Prince of Peace.

5. Here He gives Himself to us as bread,
   Here, as wine, we drink the blood He shed.
   Born to die, we eat and live instead;

6. Worship in the presence of the Lord,
   With joyful songs and hearts in one accord,
   And let our Host of table be adored;

7. When at last this earth shall pass away,
   When Jesus and His bride are one to stay,
   The feast of love is just begun that day;

428.

O worship the King

HANOVER

William Croft (1678-1727)

Alternative tune: PADERBORN (628ii)

2. O tell of His might,
   O sing of His grace,
   Whose robe is the light,
   Whose canopy space;
   His chariots of wrath
   The deep thunder-clouds form,
   And dark is His path
   On the wings of the storm.

3. The earth, with its store
   Of wonders untold,
   Almighty, Thy power
   Hath founded of old;
   Hath 'stablished it fast,
   By a changeless decree,
   And round it hath cast,
   Like a mantle, the sea.

4. Thy bountiful care
   What tongue can recite?
   It breathes in the air,
   It shines in the light;
   It streams from the hills,
   It descends to the plain,
   And sweetly distils
   In the dew and the rain.

5. Frail children of dust,
   And feeble as frail,
   In Thee do we trust,
   Nor find Thee to fail;
   Thy mercies how tender,
   How firm to the end,
   Our Maker, Defender,
   Redeemer, and Friend!

Robert Grant (1779-1838)

Ps 144: 2; Dan 7: 9

429.

O worship the Lord

WAS LEBET, WAS SCHWEBET

With strength

Rheinhardt manuscript, Üttingen (1754)

1. O wor-ship the Lord in the beau-ty of hol-i-ness, bow down be-fore Him, His glo-ry pro-claim; with gold of o-be-dience and in-cense of low-li-ness, kneel and a-dore Him: the Lord is His name.

2. Low at His foot lay thy burden of carefulness,
   High on His heart He will bear it for thee,
   Comfort thy sorrows, and answer thy prayerfulness,
   Guiding thy steps as may best for thee be.

3. Fear not to enter His courts in the slenderness
   Of the poor wealth that wouldst reckon as thine;
   Truth in its beauty, and love in its tenderness,
   These are the offerings to lay on His shrine.

4. These, though we bring them in trembling and fearfulness,
   He will accept for the name that is dear;
   Mornings of joy give for evenings of tearfulness,
   Trust for our trembling, and hope for our fear.

5. O worship the Lord in the beauty of holiness,
   Bow down before Him, His glory proclaim;
   With gold of obedience and incense of lowliness,
   Kneel and adore Him: the Lord is His name.

   John Samuel Bewley Monsell (1811-75)
   1 Chron 16: 29; Hos 6: 6; 2 Pet 5: 7

430.

Pass through

Pete Lawry
Is 62: 6-7, 10, 12

Capo 5(C)

Pass through, pass through the gates! Prepare the way for the peo-ple. Build up, build
up the road! Re-move the stones, raise a ban-ner for the na-
tions.

1. I have post-ed watch-men on your
walls, O Je-ru-sa-lem, they will nev-er be si-lent.

2. I declare you will be called the Holy People,
   The Redeemed of the Lord;
   You will be called the Loved One, Sought After,
   The City No Longer Laid Waste,
   When He establishes Jerusalem,
   And makes her the praise of the earth!

431.　Peace is flowing like a river

Author unknown
Arr. Margaret Evans
Is 43: 18-21

Capo 3(C)

Flowing

1. Peace is flow-ing like a riv - er, flow - ing out through you and me, spread - ing out in - to the des - ert, set - ting all the cap-tives free. Let it flow through me, let it flow through me, let the

migh - ty peace of God flow — out through me. Let it

flow through me, let it flow through me, let the

migh - ty peace of God flow — out through me.

2. Love is flowing. . . *(etc)*.

3. Joy is flowing. . . *(etc)*.

4. Faith is flowing. . . *(etc)*.

5. Hope is flowing. . . *(etc)*.

432.

Perfect love

Phil Lawson Johnston

1 Jn 4:18

Unhurried

1. Per-fect love, Per-fect love means that Je-sus is near.

Per-fect love, Per-fect love means no room for my fear.

With-out warn-ing a song seems to — rise in my heart, as love

finds a home, seek-ing to — set me a-part for Je

sus a - lone, ———— for Je - sus a - lone. ————

2. Perfect love, perfect love means that Jesus is here.
   Perfect love, perfect love is the cross I must bear.
   As a seed is sown I must fall to the ground
   And I must learn to die,
   Surrender myself to the sound
   Of Jesus first not I,
   Of Jesus first not I.

433.

Pierce my ear

Steven Croft

Deut 15:17

1. Pierce my ear, O Lord my God,
take me to Your throne this day.
I will serve no oth - er god;
Lord, I'm here to stay. (For)

2. For You have paid the price for me,
With Your blood You ransomed me,
I will serve You eternally,
A free man I'll never be.

434. Praise and adoration

Lance Lincoln

435. Praise God for the body

Anne Ortlund

Lk 9: 1-3; Eph 4: 16

Capo 3(Em)

Unhurried

1. Praise God for the bo-dy,— praise God for the Son;—
praise God for the life that binds our hearts in one.

Chorus

Joy is the food we share; love is our home, bro-thers.

Praise God for the bo-dy; Sha-lom, Sha - lom.

2. Guard your circle, brothers,
Clasp your hand in hand;
Satan cannot break
The bond in which we stand.

3. Shed your extra clothing,
Keep your baggage light;
Rough will be the battle,
Long will be the fight, but

4. Praise God for the body,
Praise God for the Son;
Praise God for the life
That binds our hearts in one.

436. Praise God from whom all blessings flow
(Doxology)

Jimmy Owens
Traditional words by
Thomas Ken

Capo 3(C)

— □ ◻ □ —

God has chosen to make known among the Gentiles the glorious riches of this mystery, which is Christ in you, the hope of glory.

COLOSSIANS 1:27

— □ ◻ □ —

437. Praise Him in His sanctuary

Author unknown
Arr. Margaret Evans

Ps 150

1. Praise Him in His sanc-tu - a - ry, praise Him in the skies a-bove, praise Him

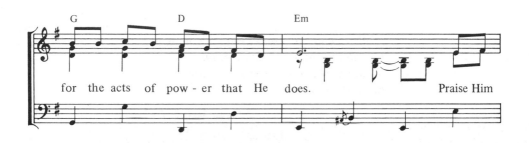

for the acts of pow - er that He does. Praise Him

for sur - pass - ing great-ness, with the trum-pet, harp and lyre, with the

tam - bour-ine and danc - ing, praise Him now.

Come and praise ____ Him, for the Lord is good, and His

mer - cy's ev - er last - ing. ____

2. Praise Him with the clashing cymbals,
   Let them hear it far and near.
   With the strings and flute we'll praise the Lord our God,
   Who with majesty is reigning,
   He has power over all.
   Give Him glory, and be thankful for His love.

438. Praise Him on the trumpet

John Kennett
Ps 150:3-6

With pace and swing

Praise Him on the trumpet, the psaltery and harp, — praise Him on the timbrel —

and the dance, — praise Him — with stringed in - struments too.

Praise Him on the loud

cym - bals, — praise Him on the loud cym - bals, — let

439. **Praise Him, praise Him!**
Jesus our blessèd Redeemer

PRAISE HIM! PRAISE HIM!
Triumphantly

Chester G. Allen (1838-78)

Praise Him, praise Him! Je-sus, our bless-èd Re-deem - er;

sing, O earth, His won-der-ful love pro-claim! __

Hail Him, hail Him! high-est arch-an-gels in glo - ry,

strength and hon-our give to His ho-ly name. __

Like a shep - herd, Je-sus will guard His child - ren,

in His arms He car-ries them all day long; ___

O ye saints that dwell in the moun-tains of Zi - on,

praise Him, praise Him! ev - er in joy - ful song. ___

2. Praise Him, praise Him! Jesus, our blessèd Redeemer;
   For our sins He suffered and bled and died.
   He, our Rock, our hope of eternal salvation,
   Hail Him, hail Him! Jesus the Crucified.
   Loving Saviour, meekly enduring sorrow,
   Crowned with thorns that cruelly pierced His brow;
   Once for us rejected, despised, and forsaken,
   Prince of glory, ever triumphant now.

3. Praise Him, praise Him! Jesus, our blessèd Redeemer;
   Heavenly portals loud with hosannas ring!
   Jesus, Saviour, reigneth for ever and ever,
   Crown Him, crown Him! Prophet and Priest and King!
   Death is vanquished, tell it with joy, ye faithful!
   Where is now thy victory, boasting grave?
   Jesus lives, no longer thy portals are cheerless;
   Jesus lives, the mighty and strong to save.

   Fanny J. Crosby (1820-1915)
   Is 12: 6; Mt 27: 28-31; Jn 10: 14-15; 1 Cor 15: 54-57; 1 Pet 3: 18

440.   Praise Him, praise Him

Mike Herron

With energy

Praise ____ Him,   praise ____ Him,   with our voic - es

raise Him on high. ___   He   is   the

Lord of glo - ry,   He   is   the King of   kings,

in   the great   re - demp - tion sto - ry,

through our hearts let Him   sing.   sing.

— □ ▢ □ —

*Let the word of Christ dwell in you
richly as you teach and admonish one
another with all wisdom, and as you
sing psalms, hymns and spiritual songs
with gratitude in your hearts to God.*

COLOSSIANS 3:16

— □ ▢ □ —

441. Praise, my soul, the King of heaven

Capo 2 (C)
PRAISE, MY SOUL

John Goss (1800-80)

2. Praise Him for His grace and favour
   To our fathers in distress;
   Praise Him, still the same for ever,
   Slow to chide, and swift to bless.
   Praise Him! Praise Him!
   Praise Him! Praise Him!
   Glorious in His faithfulness.

3. Father-like, He tends and spares us;
   Well our feeble frame He knows;
   In His hands He gently bears us,
   Rescues us from all our foes.
   Praise Him! Praise Him!
   Praise Him! Praise Him!
   Widely as His mercy flows.

4. Angels in the height, adore Him;
   Ye behold Him face to face;
   Sun and moon, bow down before Him,
   Dwellers all in time and space.
   Praise Him! Praise Him!
   Praise Him! Praise Him!
   Praise with us the God of grace!

Henry Francis Lyte (1793-1847)

Ps 103

442.

Praise the Lamb

Bruce Clewett
Is 45: 23-24; Rev 5: 12

Praise— the Lamb,— praise— the Lamb who for our sins was slain,— He rose up from the dead— now Ev-er-lasting is His name, Hal-le-lu - jah.— Praise— the Lamb,— praise— the Lamb whose name a-lone we bless,— ev-'ry knee shall bow— be-fore Him,

443.

Praise the Lord

Daniel Markoya
Ps 100: 1-2, 5

1. Serve the Lord ____ with glad - ness, bless His ho - ly name. Praise Him all ye peo - ple, for He's great - ly to be prais - èd. O_ 2. joy - ful noise ____ un - to the Lord, make a joy - ful noise un - to our God, for our God is worthy of _ our praise, God is wor-thy of _ our praise. O _

444.   Praise the Lord, for it is good

Joyfully
Chorus

Howard Bardsley
Ps 147:1-5

Praise the Lord, _____ for it is good to sing prai-ses to God, _ for it is plea-sant and prai-ses are come-ly _ to our God, _ our God.

1. The Lord is building Jer-us-a-lem, _ He is gath'ring _ the outcasts of Is-ra-el. _____ He heals the brok-en in heart, He binds their wounds. _____

2. He knows the number of stars He made,
He calls each one of them by their name.
Great is His power and might,
Great is His love.

445. Praise the Lord in the beauty of holiness

Author unknown
Arr. Margaret Evans
2 Chron 20:21

Praise the Lord in the beau-ty of ho-li-ness

for He is our God,

and His mer-cy en-dur-eth for ev-er

for He is our God.

446.

Praise the Lord
(Praise God in His sanctuary)

Brightly with pace

David J. Hadden
Ps 150:1-6

Praise the Lord, ___ praise God in His sanc-tu-a - ry, praise Him in His migh-ty heav'ns. ___ Praise Him for His great-ness and praise Him for His power. Praise the Lord, _ power. 1. Praise Him with the sound of trum - pets, ___ praise Him with the harp and lyre, ___

praise Him with the tambourine _ and with danc-ing. _____ Let ev'ry-thing _ that has breath _ praise _ the Lord.

D.C. al Fine

2. Praise Him with the clash of cymbals,
Praise Him with the strings and flute,
Praise Him with the tambourine and with dancing.
Let everything that has breath praise the Lord.

447.　　　　　Praise the Lord together

author unknown
arranged Margaret Evans

Round

2nd voice
enters here

Praise the Lord to-ge-ther sing-ing A - lle-lu-ia A - lle-lu-ia A - lle-lu-ia.

448. Praise the Lord with all your heart

Capo 5(G)

Carl Tuttle

Deut 6: 5; Jn 4: 23-24

Joyfully

1. Praise the Lord with all your heart, praise the Lord with all your strength.
2. Praise the Lord in spirit and truth, praise the Lord with in all that you do.

He's worthy to be prais'd, so glorify His name. Praise the Lord, praise the

449.   Praise the name of Jesus

Capo 3 (C)

Roy Hicks

Ps 18:2

Worshipfully

Praise the name of Je - sus, praise the name of

Je - sus, He's my rock,

He's my fort-ress, He's my de-liv-er-er, in Him will I trust.

Praise the name of Je - sus.

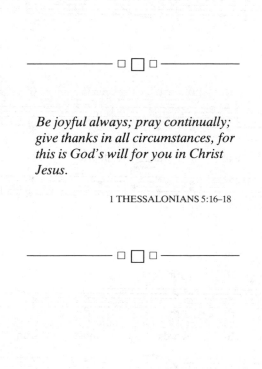

Be joyful always; pray continually; give thanks in all circumstances, for this is God's will for you in Christ Jesus.

1 THESSALONIANS 5:16–18

450.   Praise to the Holiest in the height

GERONTIUS

John Bacchus Dykes (1823-76)

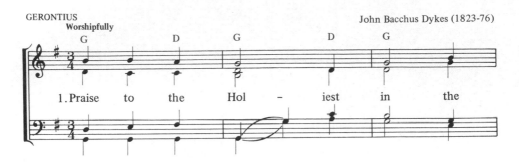

1. Praise to the Hol - iest in the

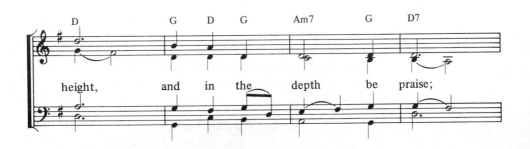

height, and in the depth be praise;

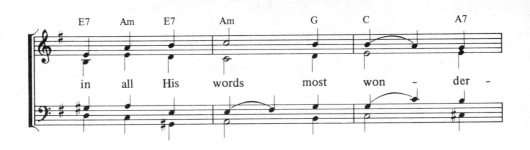

in all His words most won - der -

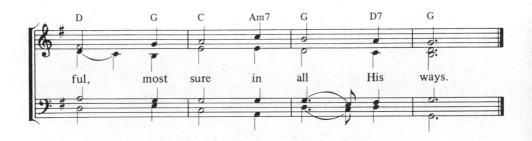

ful, most sure in all His ways.

2. O loving wisdom of our God!
    When all was sin and shame,
    A second Adam to the fight
    And to the rescue came.

3. O wisest love! that flesh and blood,
    Which did in Adam fail,
    Should strive afresh against the foe,
    Should strive and should prevail;

4. And that a higher gift than grace
    Should flesh and blood refine,
    God's presence and His very self,
    And essence all-divine.

5. O generous love! that He, who smote
    In Man for man the foe,
    The double agony in Man
    For man should undergo;

6. And in the garden secretly,
    And on the cross on high,
    Should teach His brethren, and inspire
    To suffer and to die.

7. Praise to the Holiest in the height,
    And in the depth be praise;
    In all His words most wonderful,
    Most sure in all His ways.

John Henry Newman (1801-90)

Ps 148: 1, 7; Jn 15: 13; Rom 5: 12-17; 1 Cor 15: 22, 47

451.

Praise to the Lord

Capo 3(D)

Graham Kendrick
Lam 3:22-23; Ps 148; 34:8

1. Praise to the Lord! Sing Al - le - lu - ias
Praise to His name! Let ev - 'ry crea - ture

to the ___ King of all the ___ earth.
join in the joy - ful

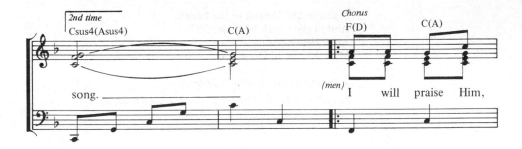

song. ___

(men) I will praise Him,

(women) *(men)* *(women)*
(I will praise Him,) I will ex - alt Him (I will ex - alt Him)

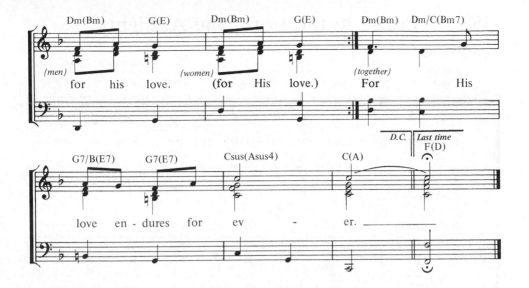

2. Praise to the Lord!
   The wind and the waves,
   The thunder and rain,
   Display His power.
   Raise now the shout!
   Come lift up your voice
   And join with all nature's song.

3. Praise to the Lord!
   O taste and see
   His goodness and mercy
   Never fail.
   Praise to His name!
   Who gives to His children
   Gifts from His generous hand.

452. Praise to the Lord, the Almighty

Capo 5 (C)
LOBE DEN HERREN

Stralsund Gesangbuch (1665)

With life

1. Praise to the Lord, the Al - migh - ty, the King of cre - a - tion! O my soul, praise Him, for He is thy health and sal - va - tion! All ye who hear, bro- thers and sis - ters, draw near, praise Him in glad ad - or - a - tion.

2. Praise to the Lord, who doth prosper thy work and defend thee;
   Surely His goodness and mercy here daily attend thee:
   Ponder anew
   What the Almighty can do,
   Who with His love doth befriend thee.

3. Praise to the Lord, who doth nourish thy life and restore thee,
   Fitting thee well for the tasks that are ever before thee,
   Then to thy need
   He like a mother doth speed,
   Spreading the wings of grace o'er thee.

4. Praise to the Lord, who when tempests their warfare are waging,
   Who, when the elements madly around thee are raging,
   Biddeth them cease,
   Turneth their fury to peace,
   Whirlwinds and waters assuaging.

5. Praise to the Lord, who, when darkness of sin is abounding,
   Who, when the godless do triumph, all virtue confounding,
   Sheddeth His light,
   Chaseth the horrors of night,
   Saints with His mercy surrounding.

6. Praise to the Lord! O let all that is in me adore Him!
   All that hath life and breath, come now with praises before Him!
   Let the Amen
   Sound from His people again:
   Gladly for aye we adore Him.

Joachim Neander (1650-80)
Tr. Catherine Winkworth (1829-78) & Percy Dearmer (1867-1936)

Ps 47: 6-9; 91; 150: 6; Phil 4: 19

453.

Praise ye the Lord

Chris A. Bowater
Ps 126:3

Praise ye the Lord, praise
ye the Lord, for He has done
mar-vel-lous things where-of we are glad, we are
glad. Praise ye the Lord,
praise ye the Lord.

454.
Praise You, Lord

Capo 3 (C)

With majesty

Nettie Rose

Is 61:1

1. Praise You,— Lord, for the won-der of Your heal-ing.

Praise You,— Lord, for Your love so free-ly given,

out-pour-ing a-noint-ing, flow-ing in to— heal our wounds.

Praise You,— Lord, for Your love for——— me.

2. Praise You, Lord, for Your gift of liberation.
Praise You, Lord, You have set the captives free;
The chains that bind are broken by the sharpness of Your sword,
Praise You, Lord, You gave Your life for me.

3. Praise You, Lord, You have born the depths of sorrow.
Praise You, Lord, for Your anguish on the tree;
The nails that tore Your body and the pain that tore Your soul.
Praise You, Lord, Your tears, they fell for me.

4. Praise You, Lord, You have turned our thorns to roses.
Glory, Lord, as they bloom upon Your brow.
The path of pain is hallowed, for Your love has made it sweet,
Praise You, Lord, and may I love You now.

455. Praise Your name, Lord Jesus

Tony Humphries
Rom 10:9

─── □ □ □ ───

Now to the King eternal, immortal,
invisible, the only God, be honour and
glory for ever and ever. Amen.

1 TIMOTHY 1:17

─── □ □ □ ───

456.

Precious Father

Capo 2 (C)

Susie Hare
Ps 51: 10-12

Unhurried

D(C)   Em(Dm)   A(G)   F♯(E)

1. Pre - cious Fa - ther, how I love ___ You

Bm(Am)   G(F)   A(G)   D(C)

as I lift ___ my hands ___ a - bove.

B7(A7)   Em(Dm)   A(G)   F♯(E)

Bless me, cleanse ___ me, re - cre - ate ___ me,

Bm(Am)   G(F)   A(G)   D(C)

keep me ev - er in ___ Your love.

Bm(Am)   F♯m(Em)   D7(C7)

Come now Fa - ther and take me, for

I am Yours.

Pre - cious Fa - ther, how I love You,

and I want to love You more.

2. Precious Jesus, how I love You
As I look into Your face.
Bless me, cleanse me, recreate me,
Keep me ever in Your grace.
Come now Jesus and use me,
For I am Yours.
Precious Jesus, how I love You,
And I want to love You more.

3. Precious Spirit, how I love You,
May Your power live in me.
Bless me, cleanse me, recreate me,
By Your presence set me free.
Come now Spirit and fill me,
For I am Yours.
Precious Spirit, how I love You,
And I want to love You more.

457. Prepare the way for Jesus to return

Capo 2(C)

Pip & Alison Roseblade
Is 40: 3-5

1. Pre - pare the way for Je- sus to re - turn, in the des-ert make a high - way, through the wil-der-ness make straight the way for Him, where streams of liv-ing wa - ter may flow.

Chorus
We'll make a high-way for the Lord, we'll make a

2. Every valley shall be raised up,
   Every mountain, hill brought low,
   And all the rough ground shall be made smooth
   And the rugged places a plain.

3. And the glory of the Lord shall be revealed
   As He purifies our lives:
   And the whole wide world shall see the bride prepared
   As the darkness comes to the light.

458.

Prepare the way

Mary Smail
Lk 3:4; Mt 21:9

1. Pre - pare the way of the Lord, — make His paths straight, — o - pen the gates — that He may en - ter free - ly in - to our life, — Ho - sa - nna we cry — to the Lord. _____ And we will fill the earth with the

sound of His praise, — Jesus is Lord! — Let

Him be a - dored! — Yes we will have this Man to

reign ov-er us, — Ho - sa - nna! We fol - low the Lord!

2. And He will come to us as He came before,
Clothed in His grace,
To stand in our place,
And we behold Him now our Priest and King,
Hosanna we sing to the Lord.

3. His kingdom shall increase
To fill all the earth
And show forth His worth,
Then every knee shall bow and every tongue confess
That Jesus Christ is Lord.

459.
Reigning in all splendour

Capo 5 (Am)

Dave Bilbrough
Phil 2:9-11

Majestically

Reign-ing in all splen - dour, vic - tor - i - ous love,

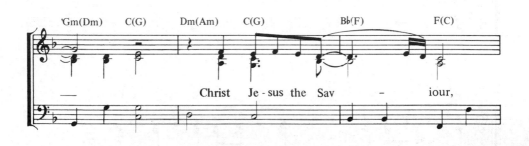

Christ Je - sus the Sav - iour,

tran - scen-dent a- bove.___ All earth-ly dom-in-

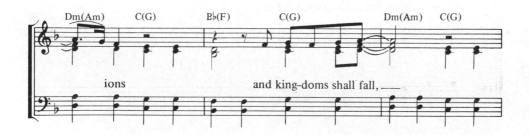

ions and king-doms shall fall,___

460. Reign, King Jesus, reign

Jimmy Rosano

Brightly

Reign, King Je-sus, reign ov-er all the na-tions of the earth. Reign, King Je-sus, reign ov-er all the na-tions of the earth. Let the whole earth be fill'd with the glo-ry of the Lord, let the peo-ples come, let them bow before Thee, for Thou a-lone art wor-thy to reign, reign, reign!

Fight the good fight of the faith.
Take hold of the eternal life to which
you were called when you made your
good confession in the presence of
many witnesses.

1 TIMOTHY 6:12

461.

Rejoice!

Graham Kendrick

1 Cor 4:20; 2 Cor 4:7; 12:10; Col 1:27

Triumphantly

Chorus

Re-joice! Re-joice! Christ is in you, the hope of glo-ry in our hearts. He lives! He lives! His breath is in you, a-rise a migh-ty ar - my, we a - rise.

Verse

1. Now is the time for us to march u-pon the land, into our

hands He will give the ground _ we claim. _____

He rides in ma-jes-ty _ to lead us in-to vic-to-ry, _

the world shall see that Christ is Lord! _____ Re -

2. God is at work in us
   His purpose to perform,
   Building a kingdom
   Of power not of words,
   Where things impossible
   By faith shall be made possible;
   Let's give the glory
   To Him now.

3. Though we are weak, His grace
   Is everything we need;
   We're made of clay
   But this treasure is within.
   He turns our weaknesses
   Into His opportunities,
   So that the glory
   Goes to Him.

462.   Rejoice in the Lord always

Two-part round

Capo 3(C)

Brightly

Evelyn Tarner

Phil 4:4

463. Rejoice, the Lord is King!

GOPSAL

George Frederick Handel (1685-1759)

Majestically

1. Re - joice, the Lord is King! Your Lord and King a - dore; mor - tals, give thanks and sing, and tri - umph ev - er - more: lift up your heart, lift up your voice; re-joice! A - gain I say: re - joice!

2. Jesus the Saviour reigns,
   The God of truth and love;
   When He had purged our stains,
   He took His seat above:

3. His kingdom cannot fail,
   He rules o'er earth and heaven;
   The keys of death and hell
   Are to our Jesus given:

4. He sits at God's right hand
   Till all His foes submit,
   And bow to His command,
   And fall beneath His feet:

5. Rejoice in glorious hope;
   Jesus the Judge shall come,
   And take His servants up
   To their eternal home:

We soon shall hear the archangel's voice;
The trump of God shall sound: rejoice!

Charles Wesley (1707-88)

Ps 47: 7; 1 Cor 15: 24-28, 51-52; Eph 1: 18-23

464.

Restore, O Lord

Graham Kendrick/Chris Rolinson

Lk 11:2

1. Re - store, O Lord, the hon-our of Your name, in
   works of sov'reign pow - er come shake the earth a - gain, that
   men may see and come with rev'-rent fear to the liv - ing God
   whose king-dom shall _ out-last the years.

2. Restore, O Lord,
   In all the earth Your fame,
   And in our time revive
   The church that bears Your name.
   And in Your anger,
   Lord, remember mercy,
   O living God
   Whose mercy shall outlast the years.

3. Bend us, O Lord,
   Where we are hard and cold,
   In Your refiner's fire
   Come purify the gold.
   Though suffering comes
   And evil crouches near,
   Still our living God
   Is reigning, He is reigning here.

4. *As verse 1*

465.   Revive Thy work, O Lord!

TYTHERTON

With strength

L.R. West (1753-1826)

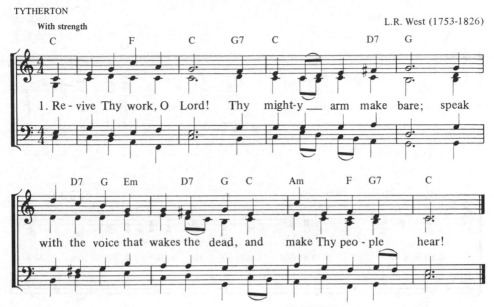

1. Re - vive Thy work, O Lord! Thy might-y arm make bare; speak with the voice that wakes the dead, and make Thy peo - ple hear!

Alternative tune: CARLISLE (487i)

2. Revive Thy work, O Lord!
   While here to Thee we bow;
   Descend, O gracious Lord, descend!
   O come, and bless us now!

3. Revive Thy work, O Lord!
   Disturb this sleep of death;
   Quicken the smouldering embers now
   By Thine almighty breath.

4. Revive Thy work, O Lord!
   Exalt Thy precious name!
   And may Thy love in every heart
   Be kindled to a flame!

5. Revive Thy work, O Lord!
   And bless to all Thy Word!
   And may its pure and sacred truth
   In living faith be heard!

6. Revive Thy work, O Lord!
   Give Pentecostal showers!
   Be Thine the glory, Thine alone!
   The blessing, Lord, be ours!

Albert Midlane (1825-1909)

Ps 85: 1-7; Is 57: 15-19; Hab 3: 2

466.
Rise up, my fair one

Slowly with feeling

Chorus

Mike Kerry

Is 40:31

Rise up, my fair one and come a-way, come a-way. 1. Do not fear the vall-ey be-low, do not cling on-to your ledge for safe-ty, for you know you shall rise up on eag-les' wings.

2.   Leave behind your darkness and your sorrow,
      There's a higher plane where I must lead you,
      To a land of happiness and light and laughter.

3.   Do you know a longing in your heart?
      Do you feel a stirring in your spirit?
      Do you hear the voice of your Beloved calling you?

467.
Rise up, O church

Capo 1 (G)

Christine & Stuart Dawling

Rise up, O church, be-gin to sing, be-gin to march as the ar-my of the King. For the prais-es of His peo-ple are a glo-ry un-to Him, so rise up, O church, and let the val-leys ring.

468.

River wash over me

Capo 3 (C)

Unhurried (with strength)

Dougie Brown

1. Riv - er___ wash ov - er me,___
Cleanse me and make me new.___
Bathe me, re - fresh me and fill me a - new,
Ri - ver___ wash o - ver me.

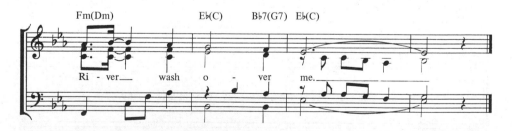

2. Spirit watch over me,
  Lead me to Jesus' feet.
  Cause me to worship and fill me anew,
  Spirit watch over me.

3. Jesus rule over me,
  Reign over all my heart.
  Teach me to praise you and fill me anew,
  Jesus rule over me.

469.

Capo 3 (C)
PETRA

Rock of Ages
(First tune)

Richard Redhead (1820-1901)

1. Rock of Ag - es, cleft for me, let me hide my - self in Thee;

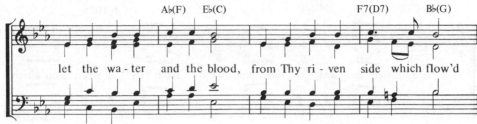

let the wa - ter and the blood, from Thy ri - ven side which flow'd

be of sin the doub - le cure, cleanse me from its guilt and pow'r.

2. Not the labour of my hands
   Can fulfil Thy law's demands;
   Could my zeal no respite know,
   Could my tears for ever flow,
   All for sin could not atone:
   Thou must save, and Thou alone.

3. Nothing in my hand I bring,
   Simply to Thy cross I cling;
   Naked, come to Thee for dress;
   Helpless, look to Thee for grace;
   Foul, I to the fountain fly:
   Wash me, Savoiur, or I die.

4. While I draw this fleeting breath,
   When mine eyes shall close in death,
   When I soar to worlds unknown,
   See Thee on Thy judgement throne,
   Rock of Ages, cleft for me,
   Let me hide myself in Thee.

Augustus Montague Toplady (1740-78)

Is 48:21; Zech 13:1; Jn 19:34; Rom 3:21-26

Rock of Ages
(Second tune)

Capo 3 (G)
TOPLADY

Augustus Montague Toplady (1740-78)

1. Rock of Ag - es, cleft for me, let me hide my - self in Thee; let the wat - er and the blood, from Thy ri - ven side which flow'd, be of sin the dou-ble cure, cleanse me from its guilt and pow'r.

2. Not the labour of my hands
   Can fulfil Thy law's demands;
   Could my zeal no respite know,
   Could my tears for ever flow,
   All for sin could not atone:
   Thou must save, and Thou alone.

3. Nothing in my hand I bring,
   Simply to Thy cross I cling;
   Naked, come to Thee for dress;
   Helpless, look to Thee for grace;
   Foul, I to the fountain fly:
   Wash me, Saviour, or I die.

4 While I draw this fleeting breath,
   When mine eyes shall close in death,
   When I soar to worlds unknown,
   See Thee on Thy judgement throne,
   Rock of Ages, cleft for me,
   Let me hide myself in Thee.

Augustus Montague Toplady (1740-78)
Is 48:21; Zech 13:1; Jn 19:34; Rom 3:21-26

470. Royal sons of a royal King

Capo 3 (C)

Brenda McArthur

Rev 5:10

Slowly with majesty

1. Roy - al sons of a roy - al King, made to wor - ship, made to praise. Kings and priests to the King of kings, made to wor - ship Him.

1st time

Last time only

Him.

2. Lord, we offer royal praise,
    Gold and frankincense and myrrh.
    Lord, we come in holiness,
    Lord, we worship You.

471.

Seek ye first

Capo 3 (C)

Karen Lafferty

Mt 6:33

Hal - le - lu - jah!

Hal - le - lu - jah!

Hal - le - lu, Hal - le - lu - jah!

2. Man shall not live by bread alone,
   But by every word
   That proceeds from the mouth of God,
   Hallelu, Hallelujah!

3. Ask and it shall be given unto you,
   Seek and ye shall find.
   Knock and it shall be opened unto you,
   Hallelu, Hallelujah!

4. If the Son shall set you free,
   Ye shall be free indeed.
   Ye shall know the truth and the truth shall set you free,
   Hallelu, Hallelujah!

5. Let your light so shine before men
   That they may see your good works
   And glorify your Father in heaven,
   Hallelu, Hallelujah!

6. Trust in the Lord with all thine heart,
   He shall direct thy paths,
   In all thy ways acknowledge Him,
   Hallelu, Hallelujah!

472.

Seek ye the Lord
(Peace like a river)

Joan Parsons
Is 55:1, 6-7, 12-13

1. Seek ye the Lord all ye people, Turn to Him while He is near. Let the wicked forsake his own way and call on Him while He may hear. Ho ev-'ry-one who is thirsty, Come to the waters of life, Come and drink of the milk and the wine, Come without money and price.

2. For you shall go out in joy
and be led forth in peace.
The mountains and hills before you shall sing
and the trees of the field clap their hands.
Instead of the thorns shall come cyprus,
and myrtle replace every brier.
And it shall be to remember the Lord
an everlasting sign.

473.

Set my spirit free

author unknown
arranged Margaret Evans

Set my spi-rit free that I might wor - ship Thee,

Set my spi-rit free that I might praise Thy Name.

Let all bond-age go and let de - li - v'rance flow,

Set my spi-rit free to wor - ship Thee.

— □ ▢ □ —

For God did not give us a spirit of timidity, but a spirit of power, of love and of self-discipline.

2 TIMOTHY 1:7

— □ ▢ □ —

474.
Shout for joy

Capo 2(C)

Dave Bilbrough
Col 1: 26-27,
Rev 19: 7-8, 21: 2, 10

1. Shout for joy and sing, — let your prais-es ring; — see that God is build-ing a king - dom for a King. — His dwell-ing place with men, the new Jer - u - sa-lem; where Je - sus is Lord ov - er all. —

And we will wor - ship, — wor - ship,

we will wor – ship Je-sus the

1st time
Lord.

2nd time
We will Lord._____ (2. A)

Verse 2
2. A work so long con-ceal'd, in time will be re-veal'd, as the sons of God shall rise and take their stand. *etc*

Verse 3
3. Sov -'reign ov – er all, hail Him ris - en Lord. He a - lone is wor -thy of our praise. *etc*

2. A work so long concealed,
    In time will be revealed,
    As the sons of God shall rise and take their stand.
    Clothed in His righteousness,
    The church made manifest,
    Where Jesus is Lord over all.

3. Sovereign over all,
    Hail Him risen Lord.
    He alone is worthy of our praise.
    Reigning in majesty,
    Ruling in victory,
    Jesus is Lord over all.

475.

Shout for joy to the Lord

Capo 3(G)

With energy

Pete Lawry

Ps 98: 4-8

Shout for joy to the Lord all the earth,___ burst in-to jub-i-lant song to-geth-er; make mu-sic to the Lord all the earth,___ let cre-a-tion res-pond with sing-ing.___ Let the sea re-sound, let the world re-joice,___ let the trum-pet blast with a migh-ty voice,___ let the peo-ple dance as they cel-e-brate and praise.___

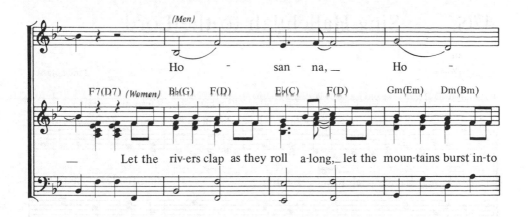

(Men)

Ho - san - na, __ Ho -

F7(D7) *(Women)* Bb(G) F(D) Eb(C) F(D) Gm(Em) Dm(Bm)

__ Let the riv-ers clap as they roll a-long,__ let the moun-tains burst in-to

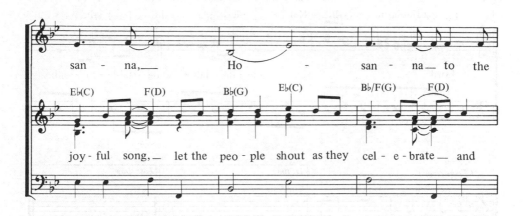

san - na,__ Ho - san - na__ to the

Eb(C) F(D) Bb(G) Eb(C) Bb/F(G) F(D)

joy - ful song, __ let the peo - ple shout as they cel - e - brate __ and

To repeat | *Last time only*

King. Shout for King.

Bb(G) Cm7/F(D) Bb(G)

praise Shout for praise.

476.   Sing Hallelujah to the Lord

Capo 3 (Am)

Linda Stassen

2.   Jesus is risen from the dead . . . *etc.*

3.   Jesus is Lord of heaven and earth . . . *etc.*

4.   Jesus is living in His church . . . *etc.*

5.   Jesus is coming for His own . . . *etc.*

477. Sing praises to the Lord

Joan Parsons
Ps 30:4-5; Jn 8:12

Flowing

Sing prai - ses to the Lord ___ O you His saints, And give thanks to His ho - ly name, ___ For His an - ger ___ is for a mo - ment, His fav - our for a life - time, Weep-ing may tar -ry for the night, ___ But joy comes with the morn - ing. A - lle - lu - ia, A - lle - lu - ia, A - lle - lu - ia, Praise_ the Lord. ___ He is the Light of all the world, the Sun that e - ver shines, Give Him the glo - ry, praise His name al - ways.

478.

Sing praises unto God

Capo 2 (G)

Melva Lea
Ps 47:1,6-7

With energy

Sing prai-ses un-to God, sing prai - ses, ____ sing

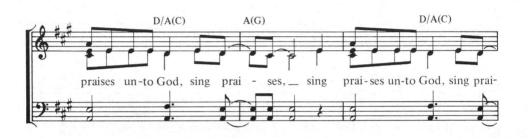

praises un-to God, sing prai - ses, _ sing prai-ses un-to God, sing prai-

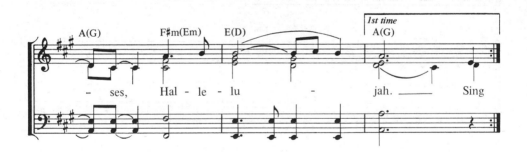

- ses, Hal - le - lu - jah. ____ Sing

jah. For God is the King ov - er

479.
Sing to the Lord

Capo 4(C)

Simon Fenner

Is 42: 10-13

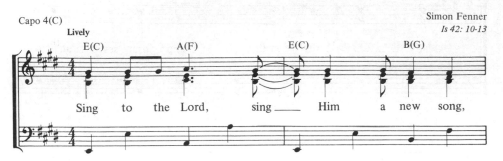

Sing to the Lord, sing ___ Him a new song,

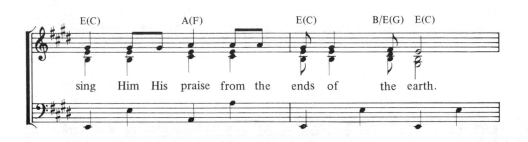

sing Him His praise from the ends of the earth.

Let the peo-ple sing for joy, let them shout from the

moun-tain tops. ___ Give glo - ry to the Lord, and pro-

480. Sing unto God

Dave Richards
Ex 15:1

Sing un-to God ____ for He is ex-alt-ed,

Sing un-to Him, Sing un-to Him.

Lift high His name ____ for He is vic-tor-ious,

Sing un-to Him, Sing un-to Him.

He saved us through the washing of rebirth and renewal by the Holy Spirit, whom he poured out on us generously through Jesus Christ our Saviour, so that, having been justified by his grace, we might become heirs having the hope of eternal life.

TITUS 3:5–7

481. Sing unto the Lord a new song

Mick Ray
Ps 96:1-2

With swing
Chorus

Sing un - to the Lord a new song, sing un - to the Lord, all the earth. Sing to the

Last time to Coda

Lord, bless His name, He is great - ly to be prais'd, sing un - to the Lord a new song.

Verse

1. Tell a - mong the na - tions the Lord reigns,

the world shall nev - er be moved. _____ Let the
hea - vens be glad and the earth re - joice,
sing un - to the Lord _ a new song. _____ [G Am G D]

✛ *CODA*

sing un - to the Lord _ a new song. _____

2. Then shall all the trees sing for joy
    Before the Lord, for He comes,
    He will judge the world
    With His righteousness,
    Sing unto the Lord a new song.

482.

So freely

Capo 2(G)

With a sense of mystery

Dave Bilbrough
1 Jn 4: 7-18

1. So free - ly, ___ flows the end - less love ___ You give ___ to me; ___ so free - ly, ___ not de - pen - dent on ___ my part. ___ As I am reach - ing out ___ re - veal the love with - in Your ___

heart, _____ as I am reach-ing out_ re-veal the love with-in Your_ heart. _____

To repeat / Last time only

2. Com - ___

2. Completely,
    That's the way You give Your love to me,
    Completely.
    Not dependent, on my part.
    As I am reaching out
    Reveal the love within Your heart,
    As I am reaching out
    Reveal the love within Your heart.

3. So easy,
    I receive the love You give to me.
    So easy,
    Not dependent on my part.
    Flowing out to me
    The love within Your heart,
    Flowing out to me
    The love within Your heart.

483.

Capo 5(C)
ST ETHELWALD

Soldiers of Christ, arise
(First tune)

William Henry Monk (1823-89)

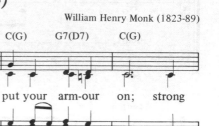

1. Sol - diers of Christ, a - rise, and put your arm-our on; strong in the strength which God sup - plies through His e - ter - nal Son;

2. Strong in the Lord of hosts,
   And in His mighty power;
   Who in the strength of Jesus trusts
   Is more than conqueror.

3. Stand, then, in His great might,
   With all His strength endued;
   And take, to arm you for the fight,
   The panoply of God.

4. Leave no unguarded place,
   No weakness of the soul;
   Take every virtue, every grace,
   And fortify the whole.

5. From strength to strength go on;
   Wrestle and fight and pray;
   Tread all the powers of darkness down,
   And win the well-fought day.

6. That having all things done,
   And all your conflicts past,
   Ye may o'ercome, through Christ alone,
   And stand complete at last.

Charles Wesley (1707-88)

Rom 8: 35-37; 16: 20; Eph 6: 10-18; 2 Tim 2: 3-4

Soldiers of Christ, arise
(Second tune)

FROM STRENGTH TO STRENGTH   Edward Woodall Naylor (1867-1934)

1. Sol-diers of Christ, a - rise, and put your ar - mour on; strong in the strength that God supp-lies, through His e - ter - nal Son; strong in the Lord of hosts and in His migh - ty pow'r; who in the strength of Je - sus trusts is more than con - quer - or.

2. Stand, then, in His great might,
With all His strength endued;
And take, to arm you for the fight,
The panoply of God.
Leave no unguarded place,
No weakness of the soul;
Take every virtue, every grace,
And fortify the whole.

3. From strength to strength go on;
Wrestle and fight and pray;
Tread all the powers of darkness down,
And win the well-fought day.
That having all things done,
And all your conflicts past,
Ye may o'ercome, through Christ alone,
And stand complete at last.

Charles Wesley (1707-88)

Rom 8: 35-37; 16: 20; Eph 6: 10-18; 2 Tim 2: 3-4

484. Some folks may ask me
(He is my everything)

Sally Ellis

Some folks may ask me, __ Some folks may say, __ Who is this Je - sus __ you talk a - bout ev - 'ry day? He is my Sav - iour, __ He set me free, __ now lis - ten while I tell you __ what He means to me. __ He is my ev - 'ry - thing, __ He is my all, __ He is my ev - 'ry - thing __ both great and small. __ He made my life com - plete, __ made ev - 'ry - thing new. __ He is my ev - 'ry - thing, __ now how a - bout you? __

485. Sovereign Lord

John McCree

Sov'-reign Lord, _____ sov'reign Lord, _____ in our wor-ship we en-throne You as our God. _____ All we want to do is bless You and mag-ni-fy Your name. Sov'reign Lord, _____ sov'reign Lord, _____ all we want to do is praise You and glo-ri-fy Your name, sov'reign Lord, _____ sov'reign Lord, _____ sov'reign Lord.

486. Spirit of God

Capo 2(D)

Prayerfully

Ian Smale
Eph 5: 18; 1 Jn 4: 13

Spi-rit of God, please fill me now to ov-er-flow-ing, Spi-rit of God, give me the words You want me to say. Spi-rit of God, re-lease my tongue to praise the Ho-ly Son, Spi-rit of God, fill this spi-rit of mine.

487.

Stand up, and bless the Lord

(First tune)

CARLISLE

Charles Lockhart (1745-1815)

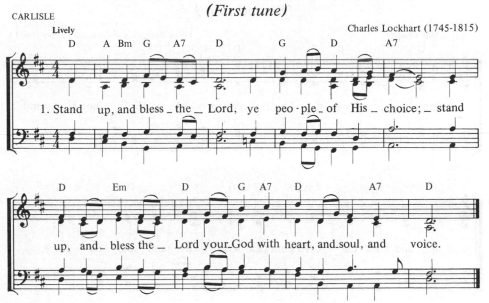

1. Stand up, and bless the Lord, ye peo-ple of His choice; stand
up, and bless the Lord your God with heart, and soul, and voice.

2. Though high above all praise,
   Above all blessing high,
   Who would not fear His holy name,
   And laud and magnify?

3. O for the living flame
   From His own altar brought,
   To touch our lips, our minds inspire,
   And wing to heaven our thought!

4. God is our strength and song,
   And His salvation ours;
   Then be His love in Christ proclaimed
   With all our ransomed powers.

5. Stand up, and bless the Lord,
   The Lord your God adore;
   Stand up, and bless His glorious name
   Henceforth for evermore.

James Montgomery (1771-1854)

Deut 10: 8; 29: 10-15; Neh 9: 5; Ps 118: 14; Is 6: 5-7

Stand up, and bless the Lord

(Second tune)

ST MICHAEL

Composed or adapted by
Louis Bourgeois in *Genevan Psalter* (1551)

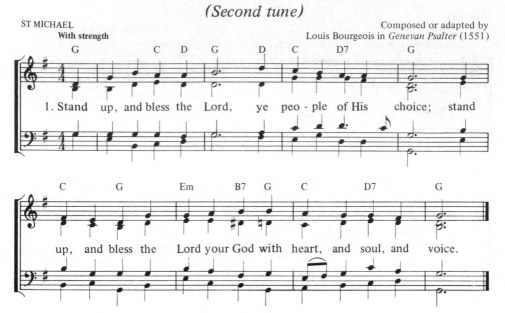

1. Stand up, and bless the Lord, ye peo - ple of His choice; stand
up, and bless the Lord your God with heart, and soul, and voice.

2. Though high above all praise,
   Above all blessing high,
   Who would not fear His holy name,
   And laud and magnify?

3. O for the living flame
   From His own altar brought,
   To touch our lips, our minds inspire,
   And wing to heaven our thought!

4. God is our strength and song,
   And His salvation ours;
   Then be His love in Christ proclaimed
   With all our ransomed powers.

5. Stand up, and bless the Lord,
   The Lord your God adore;
   Stand up, and bless His glorious name
   Henceforth for evermore.

James Montgomery (1771-1854)

Deut 10: 8; 29: 10-15; Neh 9: 5; Ps 118: 14; Is 6: 5-7

488. Stand up and bless the Lord your God

Capo 5(C)

With excitement

Author unknown
Arr. Steve Criddle

Ps 41:13

Stand up and bless the Lord your God from ev-er-last - ing to ev-er-

- last-ing. Stand up and bless the Lord your God from ev-er-last-ing to ev-er-

- last-ing - last-ing. And bless-èd be Your glor-i-ous name, O Lord, which is ex-

- al - ted a-bove all bless-ing and praise. And bless-èd be Your glo - ri-ous name,

O Lord, which is ex - al - ted, which is ex - al - ted. Stand

489. Stand up, stand up for Jesus

MORNING LIGHT

With enthusiasm

George James Webb (1803-87)

1. Stand up, stand up for Je - sus, ye sol - diers of the cross! Lift high His roy - al ban - ner; it must not suf - fer loss. From vic - t'ry un - to vic - t'ry His ar - my He shall lead, _____ till ev - 'ry foe is van - quish'd, and Christ is Lord in - deed.

2. Stand up, stand up for Jesus!
   The trumpet-call obey;
   Forth to the mighty conflict
   In this His glorious day!
   Ye that are His, now serve Him
   Against unnumbered foes;
   Let courage rise with danger,
   And strength to strength oppose.

3. Stand up, stand up for Jesus!
   Stand in His strength alone;
   The arm of flesh will fail you,
   Ye dare not trust your own.
   Put on the gospel armour,
   Each piece put on with prayer;
   Where duty calls, or danger,
   Be never wanting there.

4. Stand up, stand up for Jesus!
   The strife will not be long;
   This day the noise of battle,
   The next the victor's song.
   To him that overcometh
   A crown of life shall be;
   He with the King of glory
   Shall reign eternally.

George Duffield (1818-88)

Songs 6: 4; Eph 6: 10-18; 1 Thess 5: 8; 1 Pet 3: 15; Rev 3: 21

490.

Such love

Dave Bryant

Rom 8:39

Slowly with feeling

Such love! Such grace!

makes the pie - ces come fall - ing in - to place,

breaks through the dark-ness, turns on the light,

mak-ing blind - ness give way — to sight. —

Your love has con-quered, has set us free to be-

491. Summon Your power, O God
(Call to war)

Dale Garratt
Ps 68: 1, 17, 28

With strength

Sum-mon Your pow'r, O God, ___ show us Your strength as You have

done be - fore. ___ Sum-mon Your pow'r, O God, ___

show us Your strength ___ as You have done be - fore, ___

Women—stems up
Men—stems down

___ O God. ___ O

(Women)

Fine

God. ___ (The) ___

492.

Sweet fellowship

Ronnie Wilson

Mt 18:20

With pace

1. Sweet ___ fel-low-ship, Je-sus in ___ the midst. Life blos-soms in the Church, men by men are blessed When Je - sus ___ is in ___ the midst. ___ ___ I've ne-ver known a time like this, Feel the spi-rit with-in ___ me rise, Come and see what God is doing, Lord, we love ___ You. ___

Fine

D.C. al Fine

2. Peace and harmony — Jesus reigning here;
The Church moves at His command,
No room for doubt or fear
For Jesus is reigning here.

I've never known a time like this,
Feel the spirit within me rise.
Come and see what God is doing,
Lord, we love You . . .

3. Sweet fellowship, Jesus in the midst,
Life blossoms in the Church.
Men by men are blessed
When Jesus is in the midst.

I pray that you may be active in sharing your faith, so that you will have a full understanding of every good thing we have in Christ.

PHILEMON 6

493. Take, eat, this is My body

Paul Simmons
*Is 1: 18; Mt 26: 26-28;
Jn 3: 16; 6: 53-58; 8: 36*

2. Though your sins be as scarlet
   They shall be white as snow,
   Though they be red like crimson
   They shall be as wool,
   They shall be as wool.

3. For God so loved the world
   He gave His only Son,
   That whosoever believeth on Him
   Might have everlasting life,
   Might have everlasting life.

494. Take me deep

Robert Newey

Take me deep, deep, deep-er in - to You,

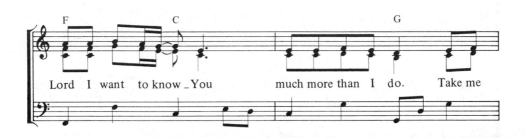

Lord I want to know _ You much more than I do. Take me

high – er un - til my spi-rit soars _____ near-er to

You, Lord, till I'm on - ly Yours.

495.

Take my life

Composer unknown
Words adapted from F.R. Havergal (1836-79)

Rom 12: 1

Capo 2(G)

Take my life, O Lord, — and let it, let it be
con - se - cra - ted Lord, to Thee. Take my life, O Lord, — my
mo - ments and my days, let them flow ___ in
cease - less praise. Take my life, O Lord, — and let it, let it be
some - thing pure ___ and beau - ti - ful, beau - ti - ful Lord for _ Thee.

496.
Take my life, and let it be

Capo 3 (D)
NOTTINGHAM

Attributed to
Wolfgang Amadeus Mozart (1756-91)

With feeling

1. Take my life, and let it be con - se - cra - ted, Lord, to Thee; take my mo - ments and my days, let them flow— in cease - less praise.

2. Take my hands, and let them move
   At the impulse of Thy love;
   Take my feet, and let them be
   Swift and beautiful for Thee.

3. Take my voice, and let me sing
   Always, only, for my King;
   Take my lips, and let them be
   Filled with messages from Thee.

4. Take my silver and my gold,
   Not a mite would I withhold;
   Take my intellect, and use
   Every power as Thou shalt choose.

5. Take my will, and make it Thine;
   It shall be no longer mine;
   Take my heart, it is Thine own;
   It shall be Thy royal throne.

6. Take my love; my Lord, I pour
   At Thy feet its treasure store:
   Take myself, and I will be
   Ever, only, all for Thee.

Frances Ridley Havergal (1836-79)
Ex 32: 29; Rom 12: 1-2

497. Take My yoke upon you

Fred Chedgey
Mt 11:29-30

With quiet feeling

Take My yoke u-pon you and learn from Me,_____ Take

My yoke u-pon you and learn from Me, For I am gen-tle and

low-ly in heart_____ and you will find rest for your souls._____ For My

yoke is ea-sy, for My yoke is ea-sy and My bur-den is

light, My bur-den is light._____

498.

Tell out, my soul

Capo 2 (G)
WOODLANDS

Walter Greatorex (1877-1949)

1. Tell out, my soul, the great-ness of the Lord! Un-num-ber'd bless-ings give my spi-rit voice; ten-der to me the pro-mise of His word; in God my Sav-iour shall my heart re - joice.

2. Tell out, my soul,
   The greatness of His name!
   Make known His might,
   The deeds His arm has done;
   His mercy sure,
   From age to age the same;
   His holy name:
   The Lord, the Mighty One.

3. Tell out, my soul,
   The greatness of His might!
   Powers and dominions
   Lay their glory by;
   Proud hearts and stubborn wills
   Are put to flight,
   The hungry fed,
   The humble lifted high.

4. Tell out, my soul,
   The glories of His word!
   Firm is His promise,
   And His mercy sure:
   Tell out, my soul,
   The greatness of the Lord
   To children's children
   And for evermore!

Timothy Dudley-Smith (1926-)

Lk 1: 46-55

499. Terrible as an army with banners

Dave Fellingham
Song 6:4; Eph 3:9-11

Capo 3(Em)

We raise _____ our song of
Ter-ri-ble as an ar-my with ban-ners we are the

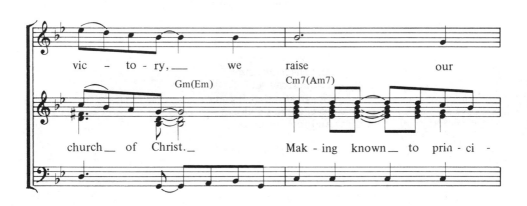

vic-to-ry,___ we raise our
church___ of Christ.___ Mak-ing known___ to prin-ci-

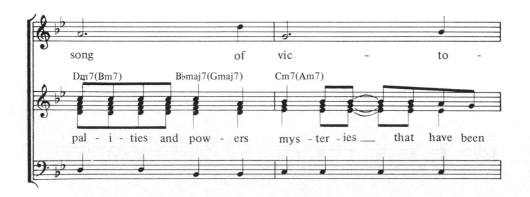

song of vic - to -
pal-i-ties and pow-ers mys-ter-ies ___ that have been

500.

Thank You Jesus

Author unknown
Arr. Margaret Evans

Verse

1. You went to Cal-va-ry, ____ and there you died for me, ____ thank You Lord ____ for lov-ing me. ____ You went to Cal-va-ry, ____ and there you died for me, thank You Lord ____ for lov-ing me. ____

2.   You rose up from the grave,
    To me new life You gave,
    Thank You Lord for loving me.
    You rose up from the grave,
    To me new life You gave,
    Thank You Lord for loving me.

501. Thank You, Jesus, for Your love to me

Alison Huntley

Thank You, Je - sus, _____ for Your love to me. _____

Thank You, Je - sus, _____ for Your grace so free. _____

_____ I'll lift my voice to praise Your name, Praise You a - gain and a-

gain. You are ev - 'ry - thing, _____ You are my Lord. _____

502. Thank You Jesus, praise You Jesus

Tom Hamilton

Thank You Je - sus, praise You Je - sus for Your con - stant love to me. I want to thank You, I want to praise You just for be - ing a friend to me. just for be - ing a friend to me.

503.   The Church of God is moving

Author unknown
Arr. Margaret Evans

———— □ ☐ □ ————

The Son is the radiance of God's glory and the exact representation of his being, sustaining all things by his powerful word.

HEBREWS 1:3

———— □ ☐ □ ————

504.

The Church of God

Mick Ray
Eph 2:22

The Church of God is not stee - ples, _____ house meet - ings or ca - the - drals. __ But the Church of God is peo - ple _____ whose hearts have be - come the dwell - ing place of God in the Spi - rit; __ Walk - ing in the light with God and one an - oth - er, be - ing built to - ge - ther _____

505. The Church's one foundation

Samuel Sebastian Wesley (1810-76)

Capo 2 (C)
AURELIA

1. The Church-'s one found - at - ion is Jes - us Christ, her
Lord; she is His new cre — at - ion by
wat - er and the word; from heav'n He came and
sought her to be His ho - ly bride, with
His own blood He bought her, and for her life He died.

2. Elect from every nation,
Yet one o'er all the earth,
Her charter of salvation
One Lord, one faith, one birth;
One holy name she blesses,
Partake one holy food,
And to one hope she presses
With every grace endued.

3. Though with a scornful wonder
Men see her sore oppressed,
By schisms rent asunder,
By heresies distressed,
Yet saints their watch are keeping,
Their cry goes up, 'How long?'
And soon the night of weeping
Shall be the morn of song.

4. 'Mid toil, and tribulation,
And tumult of her war,
She waits the consummation
Of peace for evermore;
Till with the vision glorious
Her longing eyes are blessed,
And the great church victorious
Shall be the church at rest.

5. Yet she on earth hath union
With God the Three in One,
And mystic sweet communion
With those whose rest is won:
O happy ones and holy!
Lord, give us grace that we,
Like them, the meek and lowly,
On high may dwell with Thee.

Samuel John Stone
Eph 4:1-6; 5:22-32; 1 Pet 2:4-10; Rev 21:1-5

506. The day Thou gavest, Lord, is ended

ST CLEMENT

Clement Cotterill Scholefield (1839-1904)

Peacefully

1. The day __ Thou ga - vest, Lord, __ is end - ed, the dark - ness falls __ at Thy be - hest; to Thee __ our morn - ing hymns __ as - cend - ed, Thy praise __ shall sanc - ti - fy __ our rest.

2. We thank Thee that Thy church unsleeping,
   While earth rolls onward into light,
   Through all the world her watch is keeping,
   And rests not now by day or night.

3. As o'er each continent and island
   The dawn leads on another day,
   The voice of prayer is never silent,
   Nor dies the strain of praise away.

4. The sun that bids us rest is waking
   Our brethren 'neath the western sky,
   And hour by hour fresh lips are making
   Thy wondrous doings heard on high.

5. So be it, Lord! Thy throne shall never,
   Like earth's proud empires, pass away;
   Thy kingdom stands, and grows for ever,
   Till all Thy creatures own Thy sway.

John Ellerton (1826-93)

Ps 113: 3; Dan 6: 26

507.　　The God of Abraham praise

LEONI

Adapted from Hebrew melody

With strength

1. The God of Ab - r'ham praise, who reigns en-thron'd a - bove. An - cient of ev - er - last - ing days and God of love. Je - ho - vah, Great I AM! By earth and heav'n con - fess'd; I bow and bless the sa - cred name for ev - er bless'd.

2. The God of Abraham praise,
At whose supreme command
From earth I rise, and seek the joys
At His right hand.
I all on earth forsake —
Its wisdom, fame, and power—
And Him my only portion make,
My shield and tower.

3. The God of Abraham praise,
Whose all-sufficient grace
Shall guide me all my happy days
In all my ways.
He calls a worm His friend,
He calls Himself my God;
And He shall save me to the end
Through Jesu's blood.

4. He by Himself hath sworn,
I on His oath depend:
I shall, on eagles' wings upborne,
To heaven ascend;
I shall behold His face,
I shall His power adore,
And sing the wonders of His grace
For evermore.

5. There dwells the Lord our King,
The Lord our Righteousness,
Triumphant o'er the world and sin,
The Prince of Peace;
On Zion's sacred height
His kingdom still maintains,
And glorious with His saints in light
For ever reigns.

6. The God who reigns on high
The great archangels sing;
And, holy, holy, holy, cry,
Almighty King.
Who was and is the same,
And evermore shall be;
Jehovah, Father, Great I AM,
We worship Thee.

7. Before the Saviour's face
The ransomed nations bow;
O'erwhelmed at His almighty grace,
For ever new:
He shows His prints of love,
They kindle to a flame,
And sound through all the worlds above
The slaughtered Lamb.

8. The whole triumphant host
Gives thanks to God on high;
Hail, Father, Son, and Holy Ghost!
They ever cry.
Hail, Abraham's God, and mine!
I join the heavenly lays;
All might and majesty are Thine,
And endless praise.

Thomas Olivers (1725-99)

Ex 3:6; Is 40:31; Dan 7:9-10; Rev 22:3-5

508. The head that once was crowned with thorns

ST MAGNUS

Probably by Jeremiah Clarke (c. 1670-1707)

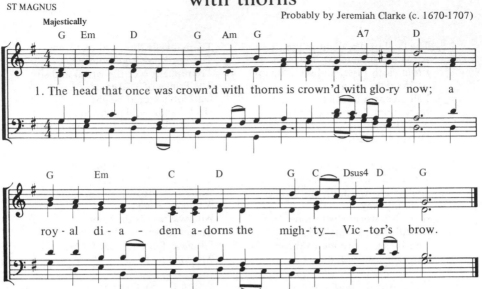

1. The head that once was crown'd with thorns is crown'd with glo-ry now; a roy-al di - a - dem a-dorns the migh-ty— Vic -tor's brow.

2. The highest place that heaven affords
   Is His by sovereign right,
   The King of kings, the Lord of lords,
   And heaven's eternal light.

3. The joy of all who dwell above,
   The joy of all below,
   To whom He manifests His love,
   And grants His name to know.

4. To them the cross, with all its shame,
   With all its grace, is given;
   Their name an everlasting name,
   Their joy the joy of heaven.

5. They suffer with their Lord below,
   They reign with Him above;
   Their profit and their joy to know
   The mystery of His love.

6. The cross He bore is life and health,
   Though shame and death to Him;
   His people's hope, His people's wealth,
   Their everlasting theme.

Thomas Kelly (1769-1854)

Mt 27:29; Heb 12:2-3; 1 Pet 2:24; Rev 19:12

But we see Jesus, who was made a
little lower than the angels, now
crowned with glory and honour because
he suffered death, so that by the
grace of God he might taste death for
everyone.

HEBREWS 2:9

509.

The joy of my salvation

Capo 3 (C)

Robin Hawkins

The joy of my sal-va - tion is the joy of know-ing
You, Your sweet pres-ence near to
me is the strength that holds me true.

1. When You're near I see Your hand in so man-y lit-tle things,
And each mo-ment that I share with You
helps my faith grow big - ger wings. The

2. That feeling when You're near, Lord,
   I want nothing to destroy,
   And I'll not flirt with any sin
   That would take away my joy.

3. When You're near I'm confident
   That I'm following Your Son,
   And the things I ask I know You'll grant
   Because our hearts are one.

4. When You're near I see so clear
   What things are right and wrong,
   And that makes me glad for I'd not do
   Anything to grieve Your Son.

510. The kingdom of this world

Capo 4 (C)

Peter Fung

Rev 11:15

Slow and easy

The king-dom of this world has be-come_ the
King-dom of our God and of His Christ_ And
He shall reign for e-ver and e-ver.

511.

The King is among us

Graham Kendrick
Mt 18:2; Eph 1:5-6; Acts 2:17;
Zeph 3:14-17

1. The King is a-mong us, His
Spi-rit is here, _____ let's draw near and
wor _____ ship, let songs fill the air. ___

2. He

2. He looks down upon us,
   Delight in His face,
   Enjoying His children's love,
   Enthralled by our praise.

3. For each child is special,
   Accepted and loved,
   A love gift from Jesus
   To His Father above.

4. And now He is giving
   His gifts to us all,
   For no one is worthless
   And each one is called.

5. The Spirit's anointing
   On all flesh comes down,
   And we shall be channels
   For works like His own.

6. We come now believing
   Your promise of power,
   For we are Your people
   And this is Your hour.

7. *As verse 1*

512.

The King of glory
(Reigning over all)

Dave Bilbrough
Is 9: 6; Rev 5: 5, 12

Light and easy

1. The King of Glo - ry, the Ev-er-last-ing Fa-ther, the Li-on of Ju-dah; He's reign-ing ov-er all.

Chorus

Hal - le-lu - jah, Hal - le-lu - jah, Hal-le-lu - jah, He's reign-ing ov-er all.

2. His name is exalted
   High above the heavens,
   The Lord of creation;
   He's reigning over all.

3. The Lamb is worthy,
   Worthy of honour,
   Honour and power;
   He's reigning over all.

513.

Capo 2 (F)
DOMINUS REGIT ME

The King of love
(First tune)

John Bacchus Dykes (1823-76)

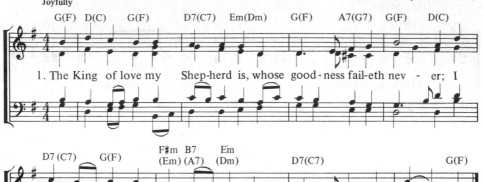

1. The King of love my Shep-herd is, whose good-ness fail-eth nev - er; I

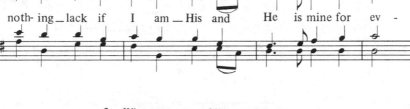

noth- ing lack if I am His and He is mine for ev - er.

2. Where streams of living water flow
   My ransomed soul He leadeth,
   And where the verdant pastures grow
   With food celestial feedeth.

3. Perverse and foolish oft I strayed,
   But yet in love He sought me,
   And on His shoulder gently laid,
   And home rejoicing brought me.

4. In death's dark vale I fear no ill
   With Thee, dear Lord, beside me;
   Thy rod and staff my comfort still,
   Thy cross before to guide me.

5. Thou spread'st a table in my sight;
   Thy unction grace bestoweth:
   And O what transport of delight
   From Thy pure chalice floweth!

6. And so through all the length of days
   Thy goodness faileth never;
   Good Shepherd, may I sing Thy praise
   Within Thy house for ever.

Henry Williams Baker (1821-77)

Ps 23

The King of love
(Second tune)

Capo 2 (C)
ST COLUMBA

Traditional Irish melody

1. The__ King of love my__ Shep - herd

is, whose good - ness fail - eth __ nev -

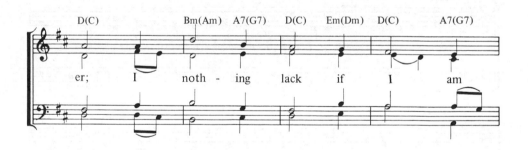

er; I noth - ing lack if I am

His and He is mine for ev - er.

514.

The law of the Lord

author unknown
arranged Margaret Evans
Ps 19:7-10

Capo 3 (C)

Brightly

2. The statutes of the Lord are right, rejoicing the heart,
   The commandment of the Lord is pure, enlightening the eyes.

3. The fear of the Lord is clean, enduring for ever,
   The judgements of the Lord are true and righteous altogether.

515.

The Lord bless thee

A song to share
men = tails down
women = tails up

Chuck Butler
Num 6:24-26

Lyrics:
The Lord bless thee, the Lord bless thee, and keep thee, and keep thee, The Lord make His face to shine upon thee, and be gracious unto thee, be gracious unto thee, The Lord lift up, the Lord lift up, His countenance, His countenance, upon thee and give thee peace.

516. The Lord has built up Zion

Capo 4 (C)

Wendy Churchill
Ps 102:15-16; Rev 7:9

The Lord has built up Zi - on to de-clare His praise, gi - ven her His glo - ry, gi - ven her His grace. We re-flect His love as stand-ing we a - dore, cho-sen to bring light that na-tions might fear His ho-ly name. ___ Fa - ther in hea - ven we lift our hearts to You, we dwell be - fore You in wor-ship ___ now clothed in white gar - ments, a - noin-ted with fresh oil we ov - er - flow with love to You.

Let us then approach the throne of grace with confidence, so that we may receive mercy and find grace to help us in our time of need.

HEBREWS 4:16

517.

The Lord has given

Capo 3(D)

Author unknown
Arr. Margaret Evans

Eph 6:11-13

With strength and pace

1. The Lord has gi - ven a land of good things, I will press in and make them mine. I'll know His pow - er, I'll know His glo - ry, and in His king - dom I will shine.

Chorus

With the high praises of God in our mouth and a

two - edged sword ___ in our hand, we'll

march right on to the vic - tor - y side, ___

right in - to Can - aan's land. _____

2. Gird up your armour, ye sons of Zion,
   Gird up your armour, let's go to war.
   We'll win the battle with great rejoicing
   And so we'll praise Him more and more.

3. We'll bind their kings in chains and fetters,
   We'll bind their nobles tight in iron,
   To execute God's written judgement.
   March on to glory, sons of Zion!

518.

The Lord has led forth

Chris A. Bowater
Ps 105: 43-45

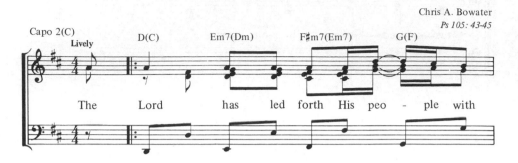

The Lord has led forth His peo - ple with

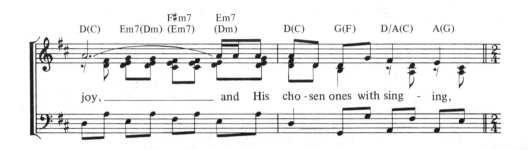

joy, _____ and His cho -sen ones with sing - ing,

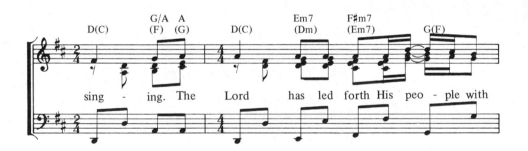

sing - ing. The Lord has led forth His peo - ple with

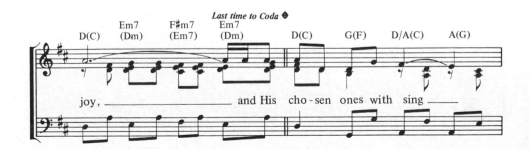

joy, _____ and His cho -sen ones with sing ____

ing.   He has giv'n to them the

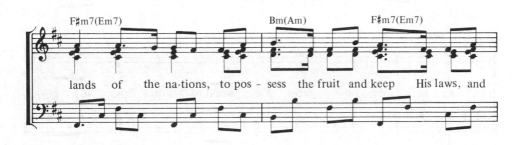

lands of the na-tions, to pos - sess the fruit and keep His laws, and

praise,   praise His name.   The

✦ CODA

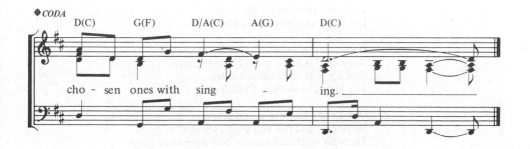

cho - sen ones with sing - ing.

519.
The Lord is King!
(First tune)

NIAGARA (First tune)

Robert Jackson (1842-1914)

Majestically

1. The Lord is King! lift up your voice, O earth, and all ye heav'ns, re - joice! From world to world the joy shall ring: 'The Lord om - ni - po - tent is King!'

2. The Lord is King! who then shall dare
Resist His will, distrust His care,
Or murmur at His wise decrees,
Or doubt His royal promises?

3. The Lord is King! child of the dust,
The Judge of all the earth is just;
Holy and true are all His ways;
Let every creature speak His praise.

4. He reigns! ye saints, exalt your strains;
Your God is King, your Father reigns;
And He is at the Father's side,
The Man of love, the Crucified.

5. One Lord, one empire, all secures;
He reigns, and life and death are yours;
Through earth and heaven one song shall ring:
'The Lord omnipotent is King!'

Josiah Conder (1789-1855)
Ps 47; 1 Tim 1: 17; Rev 19: 6, 16

The Lord is King!
(Second tune)

Capo 3 (G)
CHURCH TRIUMPHANT

James William Elliott (1833-1915)

1. The Lord is King! lift up your voice, O earth, and all ye heav'ns, rejoice! From world to world the joy shall ring: 'The Lord omnipotent is King!'

2. The Lord is King! who then shall dare
Resist His will, distrust His care,
Or murmur at His wise decrees,
Or doubt His royal promises?

3. The Lord is King! child of the dust,
The Judge of all the earth is just;
Holy and true are all His ways;
Let every creature speak His praise.

4. He reigns! ye saints, exalt your strains;
Your God is King, your Father reigns;
And He is at the Father's side,
The Man of love, the Crucified.

5. One Lord, one empire, all secures;
He reigns, and life and death are yours;
Through earth and heaven one song shall ring:
'The Lord omnipotent is King!'

Josiah Conder (1789-1855)
Ps 47; 1 Tim 1: 17; Rev 19: 6, 16

520.

The Lord is King

Capo 3(C)

Graham Kendrick
Ex 15: 2-3, 6-7

Triumphantly

The Lord is King, He is might-y in bat-tle,

work-ing won-ders, glor-ious in maj — es-

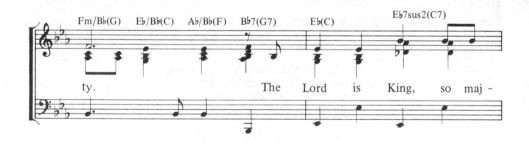

ty. The Lord is King, so maj-

est-ic in pow-er, His right hand has shat-ter'd the

521.

The Lord is my rock

David J. Evans
Ps 18:1-7; Rom 8:18,37

Capo 5(C)

Rocky

Chorus

The Lord is my rock,___ my fort-ress, my de - li - ver - er,___

my strength and my song;___ I'll trust Him all _ my days. __

He is my shield, __ my strong-hold, my sal - va - tion.___

I call to the Lord, _____ He's wor-thy to _ be prais'd. __

Fine

Verse

1. I shall not fear, for God is my sal - va - tion;_____

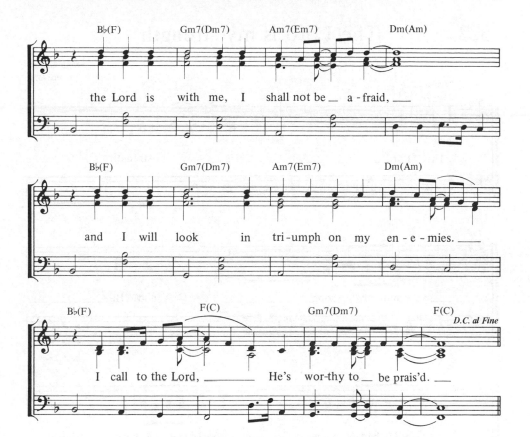

the Lord is with me, I shall not be __ a-fraid, __

and I will look in tri-umph on my en - e - mies. __

D.C. al Fine

I call to the Lord, _____ He's wor-thy to __ be prais'd. __

2. I stand secure, though dark times overwhelm me,
   The Lord surrounds me, I shall not be dismayed.
   I am unshaken through His steadfast love for me.
   I call to the Lord, He's worthy to be praised.

3. And I will raise a shout of joy and victory,
   In me God's power is mightily displayed;
   More than a conqueror through the life He lives in me.
   I call to the Lord, He's worthy to be praised.

522.

The Lord is my strength

Frank Gallian

Ex 15: 2

523.

The Lord reigns

Angela Pack
Ps 93:1-4

The Lord reigns, ___ the Lord reigns, ___ He is robed ___ in ma - je - sty, ___ the Lord is robed ___ in ma - jes - ty, ___ And He is gird - ed with strength. ___ 1. The ___

2. The floods have lifted up, O Lord,
   Lifted up their voice,
   Mightier than the thunder of the waves,
   The Lord on high is mighty.

524. The Lord reigns, let the earth rejoice

Capo 3 (D)

With strength and rhythm

Author unknown
Arr. Margaret Evans
Ps 99:1-5

The Lord reigns, let the earth re-joice, let the hills sing for
Lord reigns, let the na - tions know He's ex - alt - ed on cheru -

joy. ___ Let the for - ests lift their hands to Him, and the
bim. ___ Let the earth quake, for the Lord is great, He's ex -

Last time only

peo - ple hear His voice. The *Fine* them. ___
alt - ed ov - er them.

Call all the people to

praise His name, ___ to bow down at His foot-stool and pray. The

ho - ly God ___ and a mighty King we will hear Him and not turn a -

D.C. al Fine

way. The

──────── □ ▢ □ ────────

*Because Jesus lives for ever, he has a
permanent priesthood. Therefore he is
able to save completely those who come
to God through him, because he always
lives to intercede for them.*

HEBREWS 7:24–25

──────── □ ▢ □ ────────

525.

The Lord reigns

Phil Rogers
Ps 99:1-3

With drive

The Lord reigns, let the na - tions trem - ble; __ He sits en-thron'd __ be - tween the che - ru - bim, __ let the earth shake!

1st time
The

2nd time — *Last time to Coda ⊕*

Great is the Lord __ in Zi - on, __ ex - alt - ed a - bove all the na -

tions. _____ Let them praise His great and awe-some name. _____ The Ho-ly is He, Ho-ly is He, Ho-ly is the Lord. _____

Mighty is He. . . *(etc).*

Gracious is He. . . *(etc).*

Blessed is He. . . *(etc).*

Worthy is He. . . *(etc).*

526.
The Lord's my Shepherd

Capo 3 (D)
CRIMOND

Jessie Seymour Irvine (1836-87)

Broadly

1. The Lord's my Shepherd, I'll not want; He

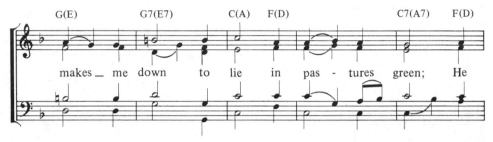

makes me down to lie in pastures green; He

lead - eth me the qui - et wa - ters by.

2. My soul He doth restore again;
   And me to walk doth make
   Within the paths of righteousness,
   E'en for His own name's sake.

3. Yea, though I walk in death's dark vale,
   Yet will I fear no ill;
   For Thou art with me; and Thy rod
   And staff me comfort still.

4. My table Thou hast furnishèd
   In presence of my foes;
   My head Thou dost with oil anoint,
   And my cup overflows.

5. Goodness and mercy all my life
   Shall surely follow me;
   And in God's house for evermore
   My dwelling place shall be.

Scottish Psalter (1650)

Ps 23

527. The nations shall see you justified

Paul Wakely
Is 62:2-3, 12

With steady strength

The na-tions shall see you jus-ti-fied, and all the kings your glo-ry, and you shall be called by a new name which the mouth of the Lord shall give. You shall be a crown of beau-ty in the hand of the Lord and a roy-al di-a-dem in the hand of God.

Fine

And you shall be called ho-ly ones, the re-deemed of the Lord, and you shall be called sought out, a ci-ty not for-sa-ken.

D.%. al Fine

528.

The price is paid

Graham Kendrick

Rom 8:1; Cor 7:23; Col 2:15;
Heb 9:14,28; 1 Pet 2:24-25; Rev 5:9-10

1. The price is paid, come let us en-ter in to all that Je-sus died to make our own. For ev-'ry sin more than e-nough He gave, and bought our free-dom from each guil-ty stain. The price is paid, A - lle - lu - ia, a - maz-ing grace, so strong and sure and so with all my heart, — my life in

ev - 'ry __ part, __ I live to thank You for __ the price You paid. __

paid.

2. The price is paid,
    See Satan flee away;
    For Jesus crucified
    Destroys his power.
    No more to pay,
    Let accusation cease,
    In Christ there is
    No condemnation now.

3. The price is paid,
    And by that scourging cruel
    He took our sicknesses
    As if His own.
    And by His wounds
    His body broken there,
    His healing touch may now
    By faith be known.

4. The price is paid,
    'Worthy the Lamb' we cry,
    Eternity shall never
    Cease His praise.
    The Church of Christ
    Shall rule upon the earth,
    In Jesus' name we have
    Authority.

529.

The promised land

Capo 3 (C)

With pace

P. Iszatt

Rev 22:1

1. The prom-ised land God gave us is right here at our feet
So let us build the ci-ty till hea-ven is complete. The ground on which we're stand-ing
on-ly we can mould, U-nique in ev-'ry touch
we make, yet blend-ing with the whole. *Chorus* Your

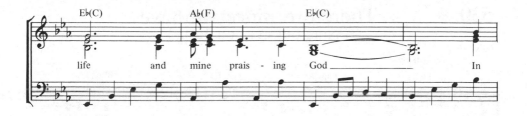

life and mine prais - ing God _____ In

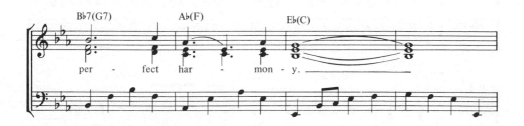

per - fect har - mon - y. _____

O come dear Fa - ther___ please live with us, ___ Re -

veal Your ma - jes - ty. _____

2. Behold the holy city,
   The new Jerusalem,
   Coming down from heaven,
   God's dwelling place with men.
   The bride and groom together,
   Eternity is sealed,
   And in the new creation
   God's heart and ours fulfilled.

3. See there is no temple
   To go and worship in:
   The Lamb and the Almighty
   Fill every living thing;
   And in the glory of their light,
   Flowing from the throne,
   A stream of living water,
   God's holiness, our home.

530.
Therefore, since we have
(Fixing our eyes on Jesus)

Capo 4(C)

Charlcie Phifer

Heb 12: 1-2

Thoughtfully

There-fore since we have so great a cloud of wit-nes-ses sur-round-ing us,

let us al - so lay a-side_ ev-'ry sin that so eas-i-ly en - tang - les us, _

_ and let us run with en-dur- ance, the race that is set be-

fore_ us. Fix-ing our eyes on Je

sus, the_ au-thor and per - fect-or of faith._

531.
Therefore the redeemed

Capo 3 (G)

With pace and swing

Ruth Lake

Is 51:11

There-fore the re-deemed of the Lord shall re-turn and come with sing-ing _ un-to Zi-on, _ and ev-er-last-ing _ joy shall be up-on their head. There-fore the re-head. They shall ob-tain

532.
There is a green hill far away

Capo 3 (C)
HORSLEY

William Horsley (1774-1858)

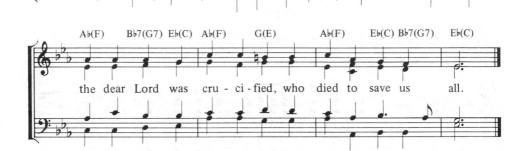

1. There is a green hill far a-way, out-side a cit-y wall, where
the dear Lord was cru-ci-fied, who died to save us all.

2. We may not know, we cannot tell,
   What pains He had to bear;
   But we believe it was for us
   He hung and suffered there.

3. He died that we might be forgiven,
   He died to make us good,
   That we might go at last to heaven,
   Saved by His precious blood.

4. There was no other good enough
   To pay the price of sin;
   He only could unlock the gate
   Of heaven, and let us in.

5. O dearly, dearly has He loved!
   And we must love Him too,
   And trust in His redeeming blood,
   And try His works to do.

Cecil Frances Alexander (1823-95)
Mk 15: 21-39; Heb 9: 28; 1 Jn 4: 7-12

Through Jesus, therefore, let us
continually offer to God a sacrifice
of praise—the fruit of lips that
confess his name.

HEBREWS 13:15

533. There is a name I love to hear

SAVIOUR'S NAME

With a lilt

W.H. Rudd

1. There is a name I love to hear, I love to speak its worth; it sounds like mu-sic in my ear, the sweet-est name on earth:

Chorus

O, how I love the Sav-iour's

name, O, how I love the Sav - iour's

name, O, how I love the Sav - iour's

name, the sweet - est name on earth.

2. It tells me of a Saviour's love,
   Who died to set me free;
   It tells me of His precious blood,
   The sinner's perfect plea.

3. It tells of One whose loving heart
   Can feel my deepest woe;
   Who in my sorrow bears a part
   That none can bear below.

4. It bids my trembling heart rejoice,
   It dries each rising tear;
   It tells me in a still, small voice
   To trust and never fear.

5. Jesus, the name I love so well,
   The name I love to hear!
   No saint on earth its worth can tell,
   No heart conceive how dear!

Frederick Whitfield (1829-1904)

1 Kings 19: 12; Ps 5: 11; Jn 14: 1; 1 Cor 6: 11; Eph 1: 20-21

534.

There is a Redeemer

Capo 2(D)

Melody Green

Is 47:4; Acts 1:8; Phil 2:9; Rev 22:3-4

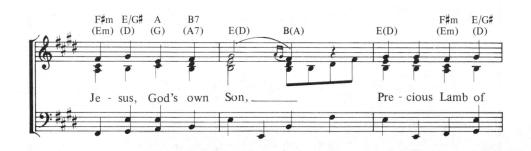

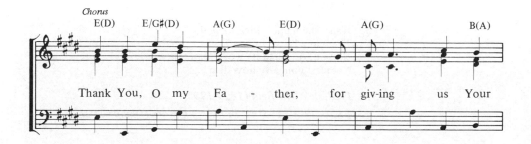

Son,_____ and leav - ing Your Spi - rit till the

To repeat | *Last time only*

work _ on _ earth is done. done.

2. Jesus my Redeemer,
   Name above all names,
   Precious Lamb of God, Messiah,
   O for sinners slain.

3. When I stand in glory
   I will see His face.
   And there I'll serve my King for ever,
   In that Holy Place.

535.

There is a river

Leonard E. Smith Jnr.

Capo 3 (G)

Ps 46:4-6

With feeling and some pace

There is a riv-er whose streams make glad the ci-ty, the ci-ty of God, the ho-ly dwell-ing pla-ces of the Most High God.

536.
There is no condemnation

Joan Parsons
Rom 8:1-2

1. There is no con-demna-tion for those who are in Christ

For the Spi-rit of life in Christ has set me free.

Chorus

O He's a-live, He's a-live, He's a-live. O He's a-

live, He's a-live, He's a-live. Praise the Lord.

2. If the Spirit of Him who raised Christ from the dead
   Be born in you, then He will give you life.

3. If God be for us, who can be against us?
   For He who sent His Son will freely give us all things.

537. There is none holy as the Lord

Gary Garrett
1 Sam 2:2

There is none ho - ly as the Lord, — there is none be - side Thee, — nei - ther is there an - y rock like our God. — There is none ho - ly as the Lord. —

538. There is no time for holding back

Ronnie Wilson
Rom 8: 31; 2 Cor 6: 2;
Heb 12: 12-13

1. There is no time— for hold-ing back—when you know you should go on,
_____ there is no time— for weak-ness when the Lord can make you strong.
_____ There is no time— like this time when Jesus walks—the earth; _____
_ this is the day for the peo - ple of _ the Lord._____

2. The Lord has poured His Spirit out
And you can drink your fill,
No matter what your problem is,
He can cure your ill.
There is no time for lying down,
His children will be known;
This is the day for the people of the Lord.

3. Hand in hand we'll walk the land,
We will not be afraid;
For with the Lord on our side
How can we be dismayed?
Together we will be as one,
And claim the victory;
This is the day for the people of the Lord.

539.

There's a city to build

Rita Pratt
Neh 2:17-18

Capo 2 (Am)

There's a ci-ty to build, there are walls to re-pair, where the peo-ple of God are to dwell. Let us streng-then our hands for the work of the Lord. Let us rise up, rise up and build. ___ Rise up and fight with the wea-pons our God has supplied, take up your tools He has taught you to use. ___ Rise up and serve in your place so we'll move as one man, that our God may be glori-fied.

540.   There's a sound on the wind
(Battle hymn)

Graham Kendrick
Rev 7:9-14

1. There's a sound on the wind like a vic-tor-y song, lis-ten now, let it rest on your soul. It's a song that I learn'd from a heav-en-ly King, it's the song of a bat-tle royal.

1st and 3rd time: royal.
2nd and 4th times: sing. / fly!

To refrain

fly! Come on, heav-en's chil-dren, the

ci-ty is in sight. There will be no

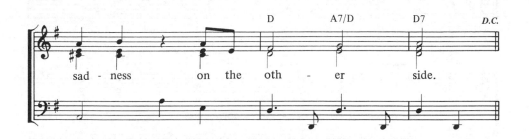

sad-ness on the oth-er side.

2. There's a loud shout of victory that leaps from our hearts
   As we wait for our conquering King.
   There's a triumph resounding from dark ages past
   To the victory song we now sing.

   Refrain

3. There'll be crowns for the conquerors and white robes to wear,
   There will be no more sorrow or pain.
   And the battles of earth shall be lost in the sight
   Of the glorious Lamb that was slain.

4. Now the King of the ages approaches the earth,
   He will burst through the gates of the sky.
   And all men shall bow down to His beautiful name;
   We shall rise with a shout, we shall fly!

   Refrain

5. *As verse 4.*

541. The steadfast love of the Lord

Edith McNeil
Lam 3:22-23

The stead-fast love of the Lord ne-ver ceas - es, His merc-ies ne-ver come to an end. They are new ev'-ry morn-ing, new ev'-ry morn-ing. Great is Thy faith-ful-ness, O Lord, great is Thy faith-ful-ness.

———— □ ▯ □ ————

May the God of peace, who through the blood of the eternal covenant brought back from the dead our Lord Jesus, that great Shepherd of the sheep, equip you with everything good for doing his will, and may he work in us what is pleasing to him, through Jesus Christ, to whom be glory for ever and ever. Amen.

HEBREWS 13:20–21

———— □ ▯ □ ————

542.
The time we have is precious
(God looks for a people)

Ronnie Wilson
Gen 19: 26; Prov 29: 18;
Mt 6: 10; Jn 4: 35; Heb 12: 1

1. The time we have is pre-cious, __ we have no time_ to waste_ in look-ing ov-er should-ers_ to see who'll take our place. __ We need to have_ a vis-ion_ and not a sense of lack; __ you ne-ver make_ de-ci-sions_ if you keep on look-ing back.

Chorus

God looks for a peo-ple,_ the faith-ful and the strong,

to speak to sit-u-a - tions and cause things to be born; cap-tives of a vis - ion, __ sing-ers of a song, __ who on-ly live __ to see __ His king-dom come, __ who on-ly live __ to see __ His king-dom come. __

2. The fields are white to harvest,
   The labourers are few,
   And word comes to the leaders:
   What now will you do?
   Will you sit in introspection
   Until the coming day,
   Or will you rise like young men,
   And will you lead the way?

3. We can't boast of tomorrow;
   We only have today.
   The past lies dead behind us,
   Forgotten along the way.
   Let faith rise up among us,
   To see His kingdom come,
   And let us run the race with joy;
   Let's see His will be done.

4. Will we be that people,
   Or will He pass us by?
   Is there no one among us
   Who'll even dare to try?
   Or will His zeal consume us,
   And will our lives be run
   Seeing kingdoms overthrown
   In the name of God's own Son?

543.
They rush on the city

Capo 3 (Am)

Craig Terndrup

Joel 2:9-11

With rhythm

They rush on the city, they run on the walls, — for great is the ar - my that carries out His word. They carries out His word. The Lord utters His voice __ be-fore His ar - my, __ the Lord utters His voice __ be-fore His ar - my. Blow a trumpet in Zi-on, Zi-on, sound an a-larm on My ho-ly mountain. Blow a trumpet in Zi-on, Zi-on, sound an a-larm. __

544.

They who wait for the Lord

Capo 2(C)

Susie Hare

Is 40: 30-31

545.

Capo 2(C)

MACCABAEUS

Triumphant

Thine be the glory

George Frederick Handel (1685-1759)

1. Thine be the glo-ry, ri-sen con-qu'ring Son,
Endless is the vic-t'ry Thou o'er death hast won.
Angels in bright rai-ment rolled the stone a-way,
kept the fold-ed grave-clothes where Thy bo-dy lay.

2. Lo, Jesus meets us, risen from the tomb!
Lovingly He greets us, scatters fear and gloom.
Let the Church with gladness hymns of triumph sing,
For Her Lord now liveth, death hath lost its sting.

3. No more we doubt Thee, glorious Prince of life;
Life is naught without Thee: aid us in our strife;
Make us more than conquerors, through Thy deathless love;
Lead us in Thy triumph to Thy home above.

Edmond Louis Burdy (1854-1932)
Tr. Richard Birch Hoyle (1875-1939)

Jn 20; Rom 8:37; 1 Cor 15:55-57; Rev 1:18

546.

This is His body
(Communion song)

Claire White
Mt 26:26; Rev 5:13

With feeling

This is His bo-dy —— which He gave —— for you, ——
I pray the Lord will keep you in — His — love. ——
This is His blood which He shed —— for you, —— I pray the
Lord will keep you in — His — love. —— We
praise You, Lord, — we bless You, Lord, —— Glo - ry
to the — Lamb. —— Lamb. ——

547.

This is the day

Les Garrett

Ps 118:24

Brightly with pace

This is the day, This is the day that the Lord has made, that the

Lord has made; We shall re - joice, We shall re - joice and be

glad in it, and be glad in it. This is the day that the

Lord has __ made, we shall re - joice and be glad in __ it;

This is the day, this is the day that the Lord has made.

548. Tho' the fig tree shall not blossom
(Hinds' feet)

Phil Lawson Johnston

Heb 3:17-19

Lyrics:

1. Tho' the fig tree shall not blos-som, nei-ther fruit be on the vine; And the pro-duce of the ol-ive tree shall fail.

Chorus

Yet I will re-joice in the Lord, I will re-joice in the Lord, I will re-joice in the Lord, I will joy in the God of my sal-

high,_____ up-on high_____ up-on high plac - es._____

_____ He will make me to high_____ up-on

high_____ up-on high plac - es._____

2. Though the fields shall yield no food,
   And the flock shall lose the fold,
   And there shall be no herd found in the stall.

549.

Thou art my God

Capo 3 (C)

Worshipfully

Tony Hopkins

Ps 118:28-29

Thou art my God and I will praise Thee, _____

Thou art my God, I will ex - alt ___ Thee. ___ O give

thanks un-to the Lord, for He is good, _____ for His

mer - cy en - dur - eth for ev - er.

550.

Thou art worthy

Capo 3 (G)

Pauline Michael Mills

Rev 4:11

Worshipfully

Thou art wor-thy, Thou art wor-thy, Thou art wor-thy, O Lord, ___

to re-ceive glo-ry, glo-ry and hon-our, glo-ry and hon-our and

power. ___ For Thou hast cre-a-ted, hast all things cre-a-ted,

Thou hast cre-a-ted all things. ___ And for Thy pleasure

they are cre-a-ted, Thou art wor-thy, O Lord. ___

551. Thou art worthy to take the book

Tony Pullen

Rev 5:9-10

Thou art wor-thy to take the book and to op-en its seals, for

Thou wast slain and by Thy blood didst ran-som men for

God, From ev-'ry tribe and tongue_ and peo-ple and

na-tion and hast made them a king-dom and priests to our God, and

they shall reign, shall ___ reign on earth.

——————— □ ☐ □ ———————

Is any one of you in trouble? He should pray. Is anyone happy? Let him sing songs of praise.

JAMES 5:13

——————— □ ☐ □ ———————

Thou didst leave Thy throne

Capo 2 (C)
MARGARET

Timothy Richard Matthews (1826-1910)

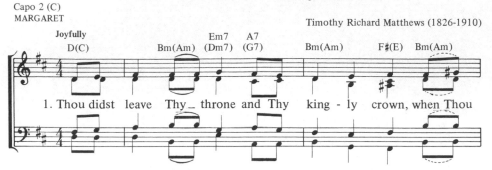

1. Thou didst leave Thy throne and Thy king-ly crown, when Thou

ca-mest to earth for __ me; but in Beth-le-hem's home there was

found no __ room for Thy ho-ly nat-i-vi-ty; O __

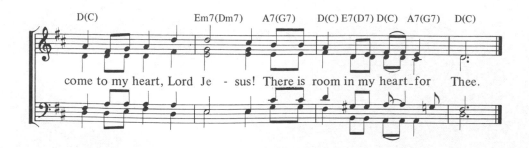

come to my heart, Lord Je-sus! There is room in my heart __ for Thee.

2. Heaven's arches rang when the angels sang,
   Proclaiming Thy royal degree;
   But of lowly birth cam'st Thou, Lord, on earth,
   And in great humility,
   O come to my heart, Lord Jesus!
   There is room in my heart for Thee.

3. The foxes found rest, and the birds had their nest,
   In the shade of the cedar tree;
   But Thy couch was the sod, O Thou Son of God,
   In the deserts of Galilee.
   O come to my heart, Lord Jesus!
   There is room in my heart for Thee.

4. Thou camest, O Lord, with the living word
   That should set Thy children free;
   But with mocking scorn, and with crown of thorn,
   They bore Thee to Calvary.
   O come to my heart, Lord Jesus!
   Thy cross is my only plea.

5. When heaven's arches shall ring, and her choirs shall sing,
   At Thy coming to victory,
   Let Thy voice call me home, saying, 'Yet there is room,
   There is room at My side for thee.'
   And my heart shall rejoice, Lord Jesus,
   When Thou comest and callest for me.

Emily Elizabeth Steele Elliott (1836-97)
Mt 27: 27-31; Lk 2: 6-15; 9: 58; Jn 14: 1-3; Phil 2: 5-8

553. Thou, O Lord, art a shield about me

Don Thomas and
Charles Williams

Ps 3: 3

Hal – le – lu – jah,

Hal – le – lu – jah,

Hal – le – lu – jah, You're the

lift – er of my head.

To repeat

Last time only

D.C.

head.

554. Thou, whose almighty word

MOSCOW

Joyfully

Felice de Giardini (1716-96)

1. Thou, whose al - migh - ty word cha - os and dark - ness heard, and took their flight; hear us, we hum - bly pray, and where the gos-pel day sheds not its glo-rious ray, let there be light!

2. Thou who didst come to bring,
On Thy redeeming wing,
Healing and sight,
Health to the sick in mind,
Sight to the inly blind,
O now to all mankind
Let there be light!

3. Spirit of truth and love,
Life-giving, holy Dove,
Speed forth Thy flight;
Move on the waters' face,
Bearing the lamp of grace,
And in earth's darkest place
Let there be light!

4. Blessèd and holy Three,
Glorious Trinity,
Wisdom, love, might;
Boundless as ocean's tide
Rolling in fullest pride,
Through the world far and wide
Let there be light!

John Marriott (1780-1825)

Gen 1: 3; Mt 5: 14-16; Jn 8: 12; 14: 16-17; 1 Jn 1: 5-7

555.
Through our God
(Victory song)

Capo 3 (Am)

Resolutely with steady pace

Dale Garratt

Ps 60:12; 108:13

Through our God we shall do val-iant-ly, it is He who will tread down our e-ne-mies. We'll sing and shout His vic-tor-y, Christ is King! For God has won the vic-tor-y and set His peo-ple free, His word has slain the en-e-my, the earth shall stand and see that through our

CODA

Christ is King! Christ is King! Christ is King!

556.

Thy loving kindness

Hugh Mitchell
Ps 63:3-4

Capo 3 (C)

Happily

1. Thy lov-ing kind - ness ___ is bet-ter than life, ___ Thy lov-ing

kind - ness ___ is bet-ter than life. ___ My lips shall praise Thee, ___ thus will I

bless Thee, ___ Thy lov-ing kind-ness is bet-ter than life. ___

2. I lift my hands up unto Thy name,
   I lift my hands up unto Thy name.
   My lips shall praise Thee, thus will I bless Thee,
   Thy loving kindness is better than life.

557.
Thy throne, O God

Capo 3 (C)

David Mansell
Heb 1:8-9

Majestically

Thy throne, O God, is for ev - er and ev - er, __ a scep-tre of right - eous - ness is the scep-tre of Thy King-dom, for Thou hast loved right-eous-ness _____ and hat - ed wick-ed-ness. There - fore God, there - fore __ God, there-fore Thy God has a - noin-ted Thee with the oil __ of glad - ness, with the oil __ of glad - ness, with the oil of glad - ness a - bove Thy fel - lows.

558. 'Tis the church triumphant singing

Capo 2 (G)
WORTHY THE LAMB

(First tune)

Triumphantly

James Mountain (1843-1933)

1.'Tis the church tri - um - phant sing - ing, wor - thy the Lamb! Heav'n through-out with prais - es ring - ing, wor - thy the Lamb! Thrones and pow'rs be - fore Him bend - ing, o - dours sweet with voice as - cend - ing, swell the chor - us nev - er end - ing, wor - thy the Lamb!

2. Every kindred, tongue and nation,
   Worthy the Lamb!
   Join to sing the great salvation;
   Worthy the Lamb!
   Loud as mighty thunders roaring,
   Floods of mighty waters pouring,
   Prostrate at His feet adoring,
   Worthy the Lamb!

3. Harps and songs for ever sounding,
   Worthy the Lamb!
   Mighty grace o'er sin abounding:
   Worthy the Lamb!
   By His blood He dearly bought us;
   Wandering from the fold He sought us;
   And to glory safely brought us:
   Worthy the Lamb!

4. Sing with blessed anticipation,
   Worthy the Lamb!
   Through the vale of tribulation,
   Worthy the Lamb!
   Sweetest notes, all notes excelling,
   On the theme for ever dwelling,
   Still untold, though ever telling,
   Worthy the Lamb!

John Kent (1766-1843)

Rev 5: 15

'Tis the church triumphant singing
(Second tune)

Capo 3 (D)
AR HYD Y NOS

Traditional Welsh melody

2. Every kindred, tongue and nation,
   Worthy the Lamb!
   Join to sing the great salvation;
   Worthy the Lamb!
   Loud as mighty thunders roaring,
   Floods of mighty waters pouring,
   Prostrate at His feet adoring,
   Worthy the Lamb!

3. Harps and songs for ever sounding,
   Worthy the Lamb!
   Mighty grace o'er sin abounding:
   Worthy the Lamb!
   By His blood He dearly bought us;
   Wandering from the fold He sought us;
   And to glory safely brought us:
   Worthy the Lamb!

4. Sing with blessed anticipation,
   Worthy the Lamb!
   Through the vale of tribulation,
   Worthy the Lamb!
   Sweetest notes, all notes excelling,
   On the theme for ever dwelling,
   Still untold, though ever telling,
   Worthy the Lamb!

John Kent (1766-1843)

Rev 5: 15

559.

To God be the glory!

TO GOD BE THE GLORY

William H. Doane (1832-1916)

Brightly
Verse

1. To God be the glo - ry! great things He hath done! So
lov'd He the world that He gave us His Son, who
yiel - ded His life an a - tone-ment for sin, and
op - en'd the life - gate that all may go in. Praise the

Chorus

Lord! Praise the Lord! Let the earth hear His voice! Praise the

Lord! Praise the Lord! Let the peo - ple re - joice! O
come to the Fa - ther through Je - sus the Son; and
give Him the glo - ry, great things He hath done!

2.   O perfect redemption, the purchase of blood!
       To every believer the promise of God;
       The vilest offender who truly believes,
       That moment from Jesus a pardon receives.

3.   Great things He hath taught us, great things He hath done,
       And great our rejoicing through Jesus the Son:
       But purer and higher and greater will be
       Our wonder, our worship, when Jesus we see!

Fanny J. Crosby (1820-1915)
Ps 126:3; Rom 10:9; Rev 1:4-7

560. Unto Thee do I lift my eyes

Paul Simmons
Ps 123:1

Peacefully

Un-to Thee do I lift my
1. eyes, _____
2. hands, _____
3. heart, _____
Un-to

Thee do I lift my
eyes,
hands,
heart,
O _____

Thou that dwel-lest in the hea - vens, Un-to

Thee do I lift my _____
eyes. _____
hands. _____
heart. _____

561.

Unto Thee, O Lord

Capo 5 (C)

Charles F. Munroe

Prayerfully

Ps 27:11

1. Un-to Thee, O Lord, — do I lift up my soul, —
un-to Thee, O Lord, — do I lift up my soul. —

Chorus — O my God, — I trust in Thee, —

Let me not be a - shamed, let not mine en - emies tri-umph ov-er me.

2. Yea let none that wait
On Thee be ashamed.
Yea let none that wait
On Thee be ashamed.

3. Show me Thy ways,
Thy ways, O Lord.
Teach me Thy paths,
Thy paths, O Lord.

4. Remember not
The sins of my youth.
Remember not
The sins of my youth.

5. The secret of the Lord
Is with them that fear Him,
The secret of the Lord
Is with them that fear Him.

6. *As verse 1.*

562.

Victory

Capo 3 (G)

Diane Fung
Col 1:13; 2:12

Victory is on our lips and in our lives, For Jesus has surely been raised from the dead, and never shall the powers of darkness doubt that Jesus is

563.
Wait on the Lord

Capo 3 (C)

Peacefully

Chuck Butler

Ps 27:14

Wait on the Lord and be of good cou-rage, and

He shall streng-then thine heart.

Wait, I say wait on the Lord, and

He shall streng-then thine heart.

564.

We acknowledge You

Sue Griffin
Jn 12:13

Easily

We ack - now - ledge You __ Je - sus as our King, __

To __ You we can sur - ren - der ev - 'ry - thing, __

__ For we know that in Your love You will bless us from a -

bove, and we wor - ship You Lord Je - sus as our King. __

565.

We are a chosen people

David J. Hadden
1 Pet 2:9

Triumphantly

Chorus

1. We are a cho - sen peo - ple, a roy - al priest-hood, a ho - ly na - tion be-long - ing to God. We are a God.

You have called us out of dark-ness to de-clare Your praise. We ex-alt You and en-throne You. Glo-ri-fy Your name.

1st time
2nd time Fine *Verse*

D.C. al Fine

2. You have placed us into Zion
   In the new Jerusalem.
   Thousand thousand are their voices,
   Singing to the Lamb.

566.

We are a kingdom

Tim Robinson
Rev 1:6

Thoughtfully

We _ are a king-dom, _____ priest-hood to God, _____

_ we _ are His chil – dren, _____ touched by His love.

Called forth in right-eous-ness, bringing in the rule of God,

we _ see His king-dom grow _ through you and me.

567. We are being built into a temple

Ian Traynar

Eph 2:21-22

We are be-ing built in-to a tem-ple,

Fit for God's own dwell-ing place;

In-to the house of God which is the Church, the pill-ar

568.   We are chosen, we are redeemed

Capo 3 (C)

Joan Parsons

Rom 8:29

1. We are cho - sen, ____ we are re - deemed. ____

____ We are cho - sen, ____ we are re - deemed. ____

____ Sons and daugh - ters ____ of our Lord, ____

____ We are cho - sen, ____ we are re - deemed. ____

2.   We are going to be like Him,
      We are going to be like Him,
      Pure and holy, crystal clear,
      We are going to be like Him.

3.   We are living to praise our King,
      We are living to praise our King,
      Feel His glory, fill the earth,
      We are living to praise our King.

We are gathering together

*You also, like living stones, are
being built into a spiritual house to
be a holy priesthood, offering
spiritual sacrifices acceptable to God
through Jesus Christ.*

1 PETER 2:5

569.   We are gathering together

Ian Traynar

Capo 3 (C)

Ps 100:1; 134:1; 150:6

With pace and swing

We are ga-ther - ing to-ge - ther Un-to the King of kings,

Come in the Spi - rit with joy___ and

peace, _____ Fill your heart with a song of glad-ness

for all He's done, _____ Come bless the Lord, come on and bless the Lord.

Let your spi - rit flow___

570. We are gathering together unto Him

Author unknown
Arr. Margaret Evans
Ps 102: 21-22

We are gath - er - ing to - ge - ther un - to Him, _____ we are gath - er - ing to - geth - er un - to Him; _____ un - to Him shall the gath - 'ring of the peo - ple _____ be, we are gath - er - ing to - geth - er un - to Him.

571.   We are God's own army

Capo 3 (C)

Joan Parsons

Rev 19:14

Steady pace

1. We are God's own ar - my, chil - dren of His Son,
Bro - thers in His King - dom, by His Spi - rit born. For our
God is King, yes our God is King, For our
God is King, _____ glo - ry to His name.

2. Moving as His body we shall claim that land
   He has set before us by His mighty hand.

3. Then shall God's own glory fill the earth abroad,
   Nations shall proclaim Him Christ and Lord of all.

572.
We are here to praise You

Graham Kendrick

Capo 2(D)

Ps 149:2-4; Rom 8:15-16; Heb 13:15

573.   We are more than conquerors

Capo 3 (D)

Bill & Janny Grine
Rom 8:37

574.

We are moving on

Ian Traynar

Eph 1:9-10

Capo 1 (D)

Flowing pace

1. We are mov-ing on in-to a deep ap-pre-ci-a-tion___ of the love which flows from Fa-ther out to ev-'ry child of God,___ Of the grace with which He hand-les ev-'ry mi-nute sit-u-a-tion, How He

wants the best for ev - 'ry - one who gives to Him his

Chorus

all. _____ Grace it seems is all He has, and

one big op - en heart; And it's so good _____ be-ing

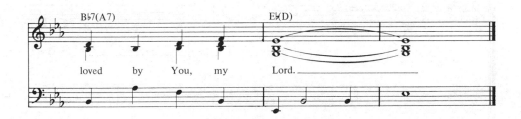

loved by You, my Lord. _____

2. We will know and understand
   His purposes more clearly,
   O, the mystery of the things He does
   In making us more whole.
   With His love He woos us,
   By His grace He sets us free;
   We can only trust Him
   And just hold on to His hand.

575.

We are never alone

Alan Woodroffe

Eph 4:32

Easily
Chorus

We are nev-er a - lone, God has giv - en us His fa - mi - ly. We are nev-er a - lone, In God's fa - mi - ly we have se-cu-ri-ty.

Verse

1. In the moun - tains _____ or in the val - leys, _____
_____ When things go right, _____ When things go wrong, _____
_____ It's good to know _____ We have God's fa - mi - ly, _____
_____ A fa - mi - ly where we know we be - long. _____

2. As we share and as we live,
    As we receive and as we give,
    We will build up
    Each other till we all attain
    The fulness of the stature of Christ.

576.

We are one, we are family

Ian Smale
Jn 17:21

We are one, we are fam-i-ly __ to-ge-ther,

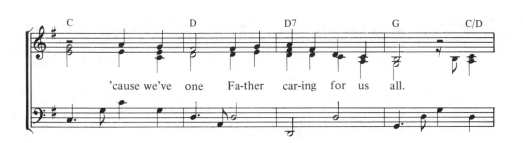

'cause we've one Fa-ther car-ing for us all.

We are one, we are re-lat-ed to each oth-er.

Lord help me to love my fam-i-ly much more. _____

577. We bring the sacrifice of praise

Capo 3(C)

Kirk Dearman
Ps 116: 17-19

Lyrics:

We bring the sac-ri-fice of praise ___ in-to the house of the Lord, we bring the sac-ri-fice of praise ___ in-to the house of the Lord. Lord. And we of-fer up to You ___ the sac-ri-fi - ces of thanks-giv-ing, and we of-fer up to You ___ the sac-ri-fi - ces of joy.

578.   We declare Your majesty

Malcolm du Plessis

Mic 5: 4

579.

We dwell in the courts
(He alone)

Claire White
Ps 91:1-2

With a swing

1. We dwell in the courts of the __ Most High; We shel-ter in the shade of His wings. __ He is our place of safe-ty; We __ are se-cure in His pro-mi-ses. He a-lone __ is my re-fuge, He's my God and I'm trust-ing Him. __ The des-truc-tion

Chorus

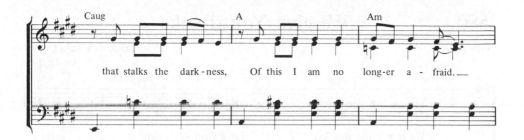

that stalks the dark-ness, Of this I am no long-er a-fraid. ___

He a-lone ___ is my re - fuge, I am no long-er a-fraid. ___

2. A thousand may fall at our right hand;
We stand alone amidst disaster.
Evil will not touch us;
From all we will be delivered.

3. We have made the Lord our refuge,
We have chosen Him for shelter.
His angels keep us from falling,
In His hands He bears us up.

4. Because you cleave to Me in love,
I will deliver you.
I will protect you
Because you know My name.

5. When you call, I will answer.
I will be with you in trouble;
You will know your joy fulfilled
And see My salvation.

580.

We give You thanks

Capo 3 (D)

Bill & Mary Anne Quigley

Rev 11:15-17

581.
We have come into this place
(We have come into His house)

Capo 3 (C)

Bruce Ballinger

Worshipfully

1. We have come into this place and gathered in His Name to worship Him, We have come into this place and gathered in His Name to worship Him, We have come into this place and gathered in His Name to worship Christ the Lord, Worship Him, Christ the Lord.

2. So forget about yourself and concentrate on Him and worship Him, (*repeat*)
    So forget about yourself and concentrate on Him and worship Christ the Lord,
    Worship Him, Christ the Lord.

3. He is all my righteousness, I stand complete in Him and worship Him, (*repeat*)
    He is all my righteousness, I stand complete in Him and worship Christ the Lord,
    Worship Him, Christ the Lord.

4. Let us lift up holy hands and magnify His Name and worship Him, (*repeat*)
    Let us lift up holy hands and magnify His Name and worship Christ the Lord,
    Worship Him, Christ the Lord.

582.

We'll sing a new song

Diane Fung
Heb 2:9; Rev 14:14

We'll sing a new song ___ of glor-ious tri - umph, ___ For we see the gov - ern - ment of God in our lives.

lives. He is crowned God of the whole world, crowned King of cre - a - tion, Crowned ru - ling the na - tions now. ___

___ Yes He is crowned God of the whole world, crowned ___ King of Cre - a - tion, crowned ru - ling the na - tions now. ___

583.
We love You Lord

Phil Lawson Johnston

584. We magnify Your name, Lord

Pam Hansford

Rom 12:1

Capo 1 (C)

Slow and with feeling

We mag-ni-fy Your name, Lord, _ We wor-ship and a - dore You, For who You are, For what You've done a - mong Your peo-ple here. We o-pen up our lives to You, Lay down our minds and wills, We want You Lord to have Your way, For we de-'light in You.

585. We place You on the highest place

Ramon Pink
Heb 8: 1

Capo 3(C)

Majestically

We place You ___ on the high-est place, ___ for ___

You ___ are the Great High Priest, ___ we place

You ___ high a - bove all ___

else; ___ and we come to You and

wor - ship at Your feet. ___

586. We raise a sound of joy to You
(Sound of joy)

Capo 5(C)

Joyfully

Dale Garratt

We raise a sound of joy to You, the
King of kings, our hearts en-throne You.
High on our praise we place You there, and
we de-clare that You a-lone are God, are
God, God.

587. We really want to thank You Lord

Capo 2(C)

Ed Baggett

Jn 1: 14; Rom 6: 18; Gal 5: 13

With pace

We real-ly want to thank You Lord,__

we real-ly want to bless Your name,__

Hal-le-lu-jah! Je-sus is__ our

King!

1. We thank You Lord,__ for Your

2. We thank You Lord for our life together,
   To live and move in the love of Christ,
   Tenderness which sets us free
   To serve You with our lives.

588.

Capo 5 (C)
FINLANDIA

We rest on Thee,
our Shield and our Defender!

Jean Sibelius (1865-1957)

Broadly

1. We rest on Thee, our Shield and our De-fend-er! _____ We go not forth a-lone a-gainst the foe; _____ strong in Thy strength, safe in Thy keep-ing ten-der, _____ we rest on Thee, and in Thy name we

(Alternative Words) His name, His name shall be called Won-der-ful; _____ His name, His name shall be called Coun-sell-or, _____ The Might-y God, the Ev-er-last-ing Fath-er, _____ The Prince of Peace through all e-tern-it-

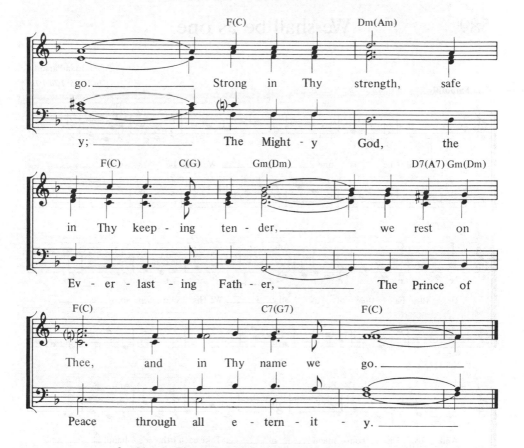

go. Strong in Thy strength, safe
y; The Might - y God, the
in Thy keep - ing ten - der, we rest on
Ev - er - last - ing Fath - er, The Prince of
Thee, and in Thy name we go.
Peace through all e - tern - it - y.

2. Yes, in Thy name, O Captain of salvation!
   In Thy dear name, all other names above,
   Jesus our Righteousness, our sure Foundation,
   Our Prince of glory and our King of love.
   Jesus our Righteousness, our sure Foundation,
   Our Prince of glory and our King of love.

3. We go in faith, our own great weakness feeling,
   And needing more each day Thy grace to know:
   Yet from our hearts a song of triumph pealing;
   We rest on Thee, and in Thy name we go.
   Yet from our hearts a song of triumph pealing;
   We rest on Thee, and in Thy name we go.

4. We rest on Thee, our Shield and our Defender!
   Thine is the battle, Thine shall be the praise;
   When passing through the gates of pearly splendour,
   Victors, we rest with Thee, through endless days.
   When passing through the gates of pearly splendour,
   Victors, we rest with Thee, through endless days.

Edith Gilling Cherry (d. 1897)

Josh 5: 13-15; 2 Chron 14: 11; Ps 28: 7; 115: 9-11; Mt 11: 28; 1 Cor 1: 30-31
Alternative words based on Is 9:6-7

589.

We shall be as one

Joan Parsons
Jn 13:35; 1 Jn 4:19

1. We shall be as one, ____ We shall be as one, ____
He the Fa - ther of us all, ____ We His cho - sen sons; ____
And by His com - mand ____ Take each oth - er's hand, ____
Live our lives in u - ni - ty, ____ We shall be as one. ____

2.   We shall be as one,
We shall be as one;
And by this shall all men know
Of the work He has done.
Love will take us on
Through His precious Son;
Love of Him who first loved us
We shall be as one.

But you are a chosen people, a royal priesthood, a holy nation, a people belonging to God, that you may declare the praises of him who called you out of darkness into his wonderful light.

1 PETER 2:9

590. We sing the praise of Him who died

Capo 2 (G)
FULDA

(First tune)

Gardiner's *Sacred Melodies* (1812)

1. We sing the praise of Him ____ who died, of Him ____ who died up - on ____ the cross; the sin - ner's hope ____ let men de - ride, ____ for this we count ____ the world ____ but loss.

Alternative tune: CHURCH TRIUMPHANT (519ii)

2. Inscribed upon the cross we see,
   In shining letters, 'God is love';
   He bears our sins upon the tree;
   He brings us mercy from above.

3. The Cross! it takes our guilt away;
   It holds the fainting spirit up;
   It cheers with hope the gloomy day,
   And sweetens every bitter cup.

4. It makes the coward spirit brave,
   And nerves the feeble arm for fight;
   It takes the terror from the grave,
   And gilds the bed of death with light;

5. The balm of life, the cure of woe,
   The measure and the pledge of love,
   The sinner's refuge here below,
   The angels' theme in heaven above.

Thomas Kelly (1769-1854)
1 Pet 2: 24; 1 Jn 4: 10; Rev 5: 9-10

We sing the praise of Him who died

Capo 3 (G)
WARRINGTON

(Second tune)

Majestically

Ralph Harrison (1748-1810)

1. We sing the praise of Him who died, of Him who died up - on the cross: the sin - ner's hope let men de - ride, for this we count the world but loss.

2. Inscribed upon the cross we see,
   In shining letters, 'God is love';
   He bears our sins upon the tree;
   He brings us mercy from above.

3. The Cross! it takes our guilt away;
   It holds the fainting spirit up;
   It cheers with hope the gloomy day,
   And sweetens every bitter cup.

4. It makes the coward spirit brave,
   And nerves the feeble arm for fight;
   It takes the terror from the grave,
   And gilds the bed of death with light;

5. The balm of life, the cure of woe,
   The measure and the pledge of love,
   The sinner's refuge here below,
   The angels' theme in heaven above.

   Thomas Kelly (1769-1854)
   1 Pet 2: 24; 1 Jn 4: 10; Rev 5: 9-10

591.

We stand redeemed

Patricia Morgan

With feeling

1 Cor 6:11

We stand re-deemed, washed, cleansed and jus-ti-fied.

You've clothed us, Lord, with the robes of right - eous-

- ness. ____ We cry to You, ____ O ____ Lord, to

move in our lives, ____ in our fam'lies and in our

592.
We will rejoice

Capo 4(C)

Dave Fellingham

Zeph 3:14-20

We ___ will re-joice ___ and sing our song of vic-t'ry,
God is res - tor - ing His peo - ple;
gath - er-ing in love, the op-press'd, the poor and lame, giv-ing them
praise ___ and re - nown in the earth. ___ We will re -
joice ___ with all our heart, ___
joice with all our heart, ___ a migh-ty King is in our midst,-

593.

We will sing praises

Capo 4 (C)

Paul Armstrong
Ps 47:6; 91:2

With pace and swing

We will sing prais - es to the Lord, ___ we will sing prais - es to the Lord, ___ we will praise and ex - tol the Name of our God. ___ We will shout glo - ry to the Lord, ___ We will shout glo - ry to the Lord, ___ we will mag - ni - fy the Name of the Lord our God. ___ God.

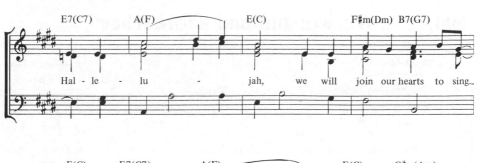

E7(C7) A(F) E(C) F#m(Dm) B7(G7)

Hal - le - lu - jah, we will join our hearts to sing..

E(C) E7(C7) A(F) E(C) C#m(Am)

_____ Hal - le - lu - jah, we'll give

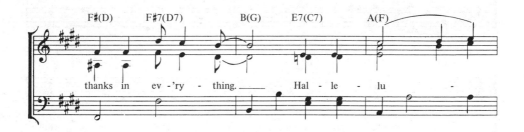

F#(D) F#7(D7) B(G) E7(C7) A(F)

thanks in ev -'ry - thing._____ Hal - le - lu -

E(C) F#m(Dm) B(G) E(C) C#m(Am)

jah, He's our re - fuge and our fort - ress, our

F#(D) F#7(D7) B7(G7) *D.C. al Fine*

God in whom we trust. _____

594.　We worship and adore Thee

Capo 3(G)

Thoughtfully

Author unknown
Arr. Margaret Evans

We wor-ship and a-dore Thee, bow-ing down be-fore Thee, songs of prais-es sing-ing,— Hal-le-lu-jahs ring-ing:— Hal-le-lu-jah, Hal-le-lu-jah, Hal-le-lu-jah, A-men.

595.

We worship and adore You

Deanne Trotter

Rev 17:14

1. We wor-ship and _____ a-dore You, ___ we bow ___ down be-fore _ You, _____ You are the Lord, _____ the King of kings, ___ You are ex-alt-ed ov-er all _ things. Hal-le-lu-jah, Hal-le-lu-jah, Hal-le-lu - jah! jah!___

2. We lift our hands, we lift our hearts,
   We lift our voices unto You, O Lord.
   All glory and honour
   And praise be Yours for evermore.

596. We worship and adore You

597. We worship Thee

Tony Humphries

Ex 25:22

With simplicity

We wor-ship Thee Lord, On bend-ed knee Lord, Lord God we fall at Thy feet. Thy glo-ry flames round Thee, Thy saints all sur-round Thee and look to Thy mer-cy seat. seat, And look to Thy mer-cy seat.

598. What a friend we have in Jesus

Capo 3 (D)
CONVERSE

Charles Crozat Converse (1832-1918)

Peacefully

1. What a friend we have in Je - sus, all our sins and griefs to bear!
What a priv · i-lege to car - ry ev - 'ry-thing to God in prayer!
O what peace we of-ten for - feit! O what need-less pain we bear!
All be-cause we do not car - ry ev - 'ry-thing to God in prayer.

Alternative tune: BLAENWERN (353i)

2. Have we trials and temptations?
Is there trouble anywhere?
We should never be discouraged;
Take it to the Lord in prayer.
Can we find a friend so faithful
Who will all our sorrows share?
Jesus knows our every weakness;
Take it to the Lord in prayer.

3. Are we weak and heavy-laden,
Cumbered with a load of care?
Precious Saviour, still our refuge,
Take it to the Lord in prayer.
Do thy friends despise, forsake thee?
Take it to the Lord in prayer;
In His arms He'll take and shield thee,
Thou wilt find a solace there.

Joseph Medlicott Scriven (1819-86)
Jn 15: 13-15; Eph 6: 18; Phil 4: 4-7; 1 Tim 2: 1-2

When He comes

Sue Read

2 Sam 7:12-17; Is 2:4; 9:6;
Mic 5:2; Rev 21:4

Gently

1. When He comes we'll see just a child, no war-rior Lord but a ba-by so mild. The Lord says: 'Beth-le-hem though you are but small, in you shall be born the King.' When He comes, when He comes.

2. When He comes His reign shall bring peace, when He

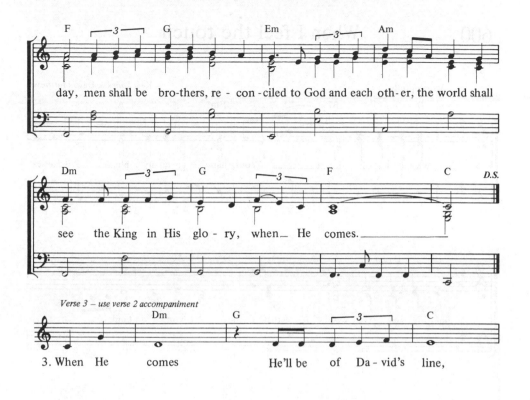

day, men shall be bro-thers, re - con -ciled to God and each oth- er, the world shall

see the King in His glo - ry, when— He comes.

Verse 3 – use verse 2 accompaniment

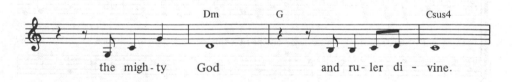

3. When He comes He'll be of Da - vid's line,

the migh - ty God and ru - ler di - vine.

They'll call Him Won-der-ful — and Coun-sell-or, and His kingdom shall never cease.

Back to the Chorus

— When He comes, when — He comes.

600.

When I feel the touch

Keri Jones & Dave Matthews

Worshipfully

When I feel the touch ____ of Your hand up-on my life, ____ it caus-es
me to sing a song that I love You, Lord.
So from deep with - in ____ my spi-rit sing - eth un - to Thee, ____ You are my
King, You are my God, and I love You, Lord.

*How great is the love the Father has
lavished on us, that we should be
called children of God! And that is
what we are!*

1 JOHN 3:1

601. When I look into Your holiness

Wayne & Cathy Perrin

Ps 29: 2

Worshipfully

When I look in-to Your ho - li-ness,— when I gaze in-to Your love - li -

ness, when all things that sur-round be-come sha-dows in the light of

You;_____ when I've found the joy of reach - ing Your

heart,__ when my will be-comes en-thrall'd in Your love, when all

things that sur-round be-come shad-ows in the light of You:_____

602. When I survey the wondrous cross

ROCKINGHAM

Peacefully

18th Century melody
Adapted by Edward Miller (1731-1807)

1. When I ___ sur - vey the won - drous cross on
which the Prince of glo - ry died, ___ my
rich - est gain I count ___ but loss, and
pour con - tempt on all ___ my pride.

2. Forbid it, Lord, that I should boast,
   Save in the death of Christ my God:
   All the vain things that charm me most,
   I sacrifice them to His blood.

3. See from His head, His hands, His feet,
   Sorrow and love flow mingled down:
   Did e'er such love and sorrow meet,
   Or thorns compose so rich a crown?

4. Were the whole realm of Nature mine,
   That were an offering far too small,
   Love so amazing, so divine,
   Demands my soul, my life, my all.

Isaac Watts (1674-1748)

Mk 15:22-39; 1 Cor 1:18-31; Gal 6:14

603.
When morning gilds the skies

Capo 3 (G)
LAUDES DOMINI

Joseph Barnby (1838-96)

1. When morn-ing gilds the skies ___ my heart a - wa - king cries: 'May Je - sus Christ be prais'd!' A - like at work and prayer to Je - sus I re - pair: 'May Je - sus Christ be prais'd!'

2. Does sadness fill my mind?
   A solace here I find:
   'May Jesus Christ be praised!'
   When evil thoughts molest,
   With this I shield my breast:
   'May Jesus Christ be praised!'

3. To God, the Word, on high
   The hosts of angels cry:
   'May Jesus Christ be praised!'
   Let mortals, too, upraise
   Their voice in hymns of praise:
   'May Jesus Christ be praised!'

4. Let earth's wide circle round
   In joyful notes resound:
   'May Jesus Christ be praised!'
   Let air, and sea, and sky,
   From depth to height, reply:
   'May Jesus Christ be praised!'

5. Be this while life is mine
   My canticle divine:
   'May Jesus Christ be praised!'
   Be this the eternal song,
   Through all the ages long:
   'May Jesus Christ be praised!'

Author unknown
Tr. Edward Caswall (1814-78)
Ps 5:3, 148; Heb 13:15

604.   When the Spirit of the Lord

Author unknown
Arr. Margaret Evans
2 Sam 6:14

With increasing pace

1. When the Spi-rit of the Lord is with-in my heart, I will sing as Dav-id sang.

When the Spi-rit of the Lord is with-in my heart, I will sing as Dav-id sang.

I will sing,____ I will sing,____ I will sing as Dav-id sang.

I will sing,__ I will sing,__ I will sing as Dav-id sang.

2.   When the Spirit of the Lord is within my heart,
      I will clap as David clapped . . . *etc.*

3. · When the Spirit of the Lord is within my heart,
      I will dance as David danced . . . *etc.*

4.   When the Spirit of the Lord is within my heart,
      I will praise as David praised . . . *etc.*

———————— □ ▢ □ ————————

To him who is able to keep you from falling and to present you before his glorious presence without fault and with great joy—to the only God our Saviour be glory, majesty, power and authority, through Jesus Christ our Lord, before all ages, now and evermore! Amen.

JUDE 24–25

———————— □ ▢ □ ————————

605.
When we walk with the Lord
(Trust and obey)

Capo 3 (D)
TRUST AND OBEY

Daniel Brink Towner (1850-1919)

1. When we walk with the Lord in the light of His Word, what a glo - ry He sheds on our way! While we do His good will He a - bides with us still, and with all who will trust and o - bey!

Chorus
Trust and o - bey! For there's no o - ther way to be

hap - py in Je - sus, but to trust and o - bey.

2. Not a shadow can rise,
   Not a cloud in the skies,
   But His smile quickly drives it away;
   Not a doubt nor a fear,
   Not a sigh nor a tear,
   Can abide while we trust and obey!

3. Not a burden we bear,
   Not a sorrow we share,
   But our toil He doth richly repay:
   Not a grief nor a loss,
   Not a frown nor a cross,
   But is blessed if we trust and obey!

4. But we never can prove
   The delights of His love
   Until all on the altar we lay;
   For the favour He shows,
   And the joy He bestows,
   Are for those who will trust and obey.

5. Then in fellowship sweet
   We will sit at His feet,
   Or we'll walk by His side in the way;
   What He says we will do,
   Where He sends we will go;
   Never fear, only trust and obey!

John Henry Sammis (1846-1919)

Ps 119: 105; Is 26: 3-4; Rom 12: 1; Eph 5: 2; 1 Tim 4: 9-10

606.   Where the Spirit of the Lord is

Graham Kendrick
2 Cor 3:17

1. Where the Spi-rit of the Lord is, ___ where the Spi-rit of the Lord is, ___ there is li - ber-ty, _____ there is li - ber-ty. _____ ___ And I will praise You, O Lord, ___ and I will praise You, O Lord, ___ and I will praise You, O Lord, ___ in the Spi - rit. _____ Spi - rit. _____

2. Where the presence of the Lord is,
    Where the presence of the Lord is,
    There is fullness of joy, there is fullness of joy. *(Repeat)*
    I will enjoy You, O Lord,
    I will enjoy You, O Lord,
    I will enjoy You, O Lord, in the Spirit. *(Repeat)*

3. Where the power of the Lord is,
    Where the power of the Lord is,
    There is victory, there is victory. *(Repeat)*
    And I will triumph, O Lord,
    And I will triumph, O Lord,
    And I will triumph, O Lord, in the Spirit. *(Repeat)*

607.
Where you go I will go

Capo 3 (C)

Author unknown
Arr. Margaret Evans

Ruth 1:16

Steadily

Eb(C)   Cm(Am)   Fm(Dm)   Bb7(G7)

Where you go   I will go,   where you lodge   I will lodge,

Eb(C)   Cm(Am)   Fm(Dm)   Bb7(G7)

do not ask me to turn a-way, for I will follow you. ___ We'll

Ab(F)   Gm(Em)   G(E)   Cm(Am)

serve the Lord to-ge-ther ___ and praise Him day to day,   for He

Eb(C)   Cm(Am)   Fm7(Dm7)   Bb7(G7)   Eb(C)

brought us to-ge-ther ___ to love Him and serve Him al - ways. ___

608.   Who is He in yonder stall?

WONDROUS STORY

Boldly

Benjamin Russell Hanby (1833-67)

1. Who is He in yon-der stall, at whose feet the shep-herds fall? 'Tis the Lord! O won-drous sto-ry! 'Tis the Lord, the King of glo-ry! At His feet we hum-bly fall. Crown Him! Crown Him, Lord of all!

2. Who is He to whom they bring
   All the sick and sorrowing?

3. Who is He that stands and weeps
   At the grave where Lazarus sleeps?

4. Who is He on yonder tree
   Dies in pain and agony?

'5. Who is He who from the grave
   Comes to rescue, help, and save?

6. Who is He who from His throne
   Sends the Spirit to His own?

7. Who is He who comes again,
   Judge of angels and of men?

Benjamin Russell Hanby (1833-67) Alt.

Lk 2: 15-18; 5:15; 23: 44-46; 24: 6-8; Jn 11: 32-38; 1 Cor 15: 24-25

609.

Who is like unto Thee?

Judy Horner-Montemayor

Ex 15:11

Who is like un-to Thee, ___ O ___ Lord a-mongst gods? ___ Who ___ is like un - to Thee, ___ glo-rious in ho - li - ness, ___ fear-ful in prais - es, ___ do - ing won - ders? ___ Who ___ is like un - to Thee? ___

610.
Who is on the Lord's side?

ARMAGEDDON

German melody
Adapted by John Goss (1800-80)

1. Who is on the Lord's side? Who will serve the King?
Who will be His help - ers oth - er lives to bring?
Who will leave the world's side? Who will face the foe?
Who is on the Lord's side? Who for Him will go?
By Thy call of mer - cy, by Thy grace di - vine,

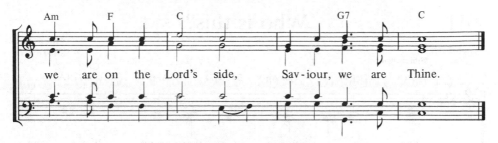

we are on the Lord's side, Sav-iour, we are Thine.

2. Jesus, Thou hast bought us
   Not with gold or gem,
   But with Thine own life-blood,
   For Thy diadem.
   With Thy blessing filling
   Each who comes to Thee
   Thou hast made us willing,
   Thou hast made us free.
   By Thy grand redemption,
   By Thy grace divine,
   We are on the Lord's side
   Saviour, we are Thine.

3. Fierce may be the conflict,
   Strong may be the foe,
   But the King's own army
   None can overthrow;
   Round His standard ranging
   Victory is secure;
   For His truth unchanging
   Makes the triumph sure.
   Joyfully enlisting,
   By Thy grace divine,
   We are on the Lord's side,
   Saviour, we are Thine.

4. Chosen to be soldiers
   In an alien land,
   Chosen, called, and faithful,
   For our Captain's band;
   In the service royal
   Let us not grow cold,
   Let us be right loyal
   Noble, true, and bold.
   Master, Thou wilt keep us,
   By Thy grace divine,
   Always on the Lord's side,
   Saviour, always Thine.

Frances Ridley Havergal (1836-79)

Ex 32: 26; Rom 6: 17-18; 8: 31; Eph 6: 10-18;
1 Tim 1: 18-19; Rev 3: 15, 21

611.
Who is this?

Phil Rogers
Songs 6:4, 10

Capo 3 (C)

With strength

1. Who is this that grows like the dawn, as bright as the sun, as fair as the moon? Who is this that grows like the dawn, as awe - some as an ar - my, as an ar - my with

612.
Who shall separate us

Author unknown
Arr. Margaret Evans
Rom 8: 35

Capo 3(C)

Stately

———— □ ▢ □ ————

*Do not be afraid. I am the First and
the Last. I am the Living One; I was
dead, and behold I am alive for ever
and ever!*

REVELATION 1:17–18

———— □ ▢ □ ————

613. Why should I lose my first love?

Ian Traynar

Rev 2:4

Capo 5 (C)

With warmth

1. Why should I lose my first love, When

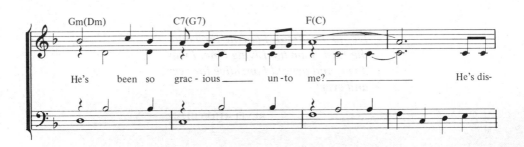

He's been so grac - ious _____ un-to me? _____ He's dis-

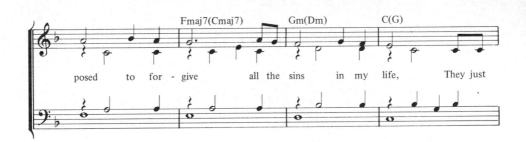

posed to for - give all the sins in my life, They just

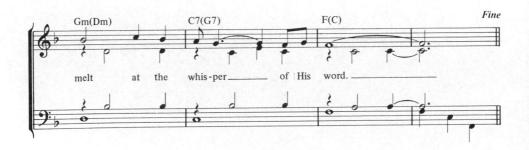

melt at the whis-per _____ of His word. _____

Fine

O the na-ture of that smile on His for-giv-ing

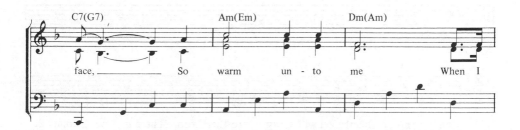

face, _____ So warm un-to me When I

need-ed so much grace. _____ 3. I

2. Why should I lose my first love
When I've seen Him so full of grace and truth?
Why run away from that blessed ground
Where I first met a love so warm and deep?

3. I love Him more now after I've sinned
For I've found out what He is really like.
He's a God of such love, He'll forgive and forget
So I can put my full trust in Him now.

614.
With all my heart

Steadily with feeling

Leonard E. Smith Jnr

615.

With honey from the rock

Leonard E. Smith Jnr

Capo 3 (C)

Ps 81:1-3, 16

616. Within the veil

Ruth Dryden
Heb 6:19

Gently

With - in the veil I now would come, in - to the Ho - ly Place to look up - on Thy face.

617.

With my whole heart

Graham Kendrick

Song 5:10

1. With my whole heart I will praise You, hold-ing no-thing back, Hal - le - lu - jah! You have made me glad and now I come with op - en arms to thank You, with my heart em - brace, Hal - le - lu - jah! I can see Your

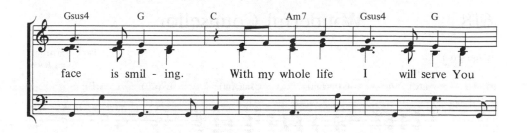

face is smil - ing. With my whole life I will serve You

cap-tur'd by Your love, Hal - le - lu - jah!

O a-maz-ing love, O a-maz-ing love!

2. Lord, Your heart is overflowing
   With a love divine, Hallelujah!
   And this love is mine for ever.
   Now Your joy has set You laughing
   As You join the song, Hallelujah!
   Heaven sings along, I hear the
   Voices swell to great crescendos,
   Praising Your great love, Hallelujah!
   O amazing love! O amazing love!

3. Come, O Bridegroom, clothed in splendour,
   My Beloved One, Hallelujah!
   How I long to run and meet You.
   You're the fairest of ten thousand,
   You're my life and breath, Hallelujah!
   Love as strong as death has won me.
   All the rivers, all the oceans
   Cannot quench this love, Hallelujah!
   O amazing love! O amazing love!

618.
Wonderful Counsellor

Capo 4 (C)

Paul Armstrong

Is 9:6

You are worthy, our Lord and God,
to receive glory and honour and
power,
for you created all things,
and by your will they were created
and have their being.

REVELATION 4:11

619.

Worship the King

Robert Newey
Heb 1: 3

Wor+ship the King, let us wor-ship the King,

for He de-sires our love and ad-or-

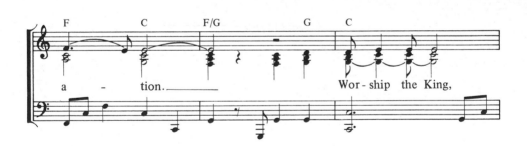

a - tion._____ Wor-ship the King,

come let us wor-ship the King, let us

620.

Worthy art Thou

Dave Richards
Rev 4:11

Thoughtfully

Wor-thy art Thou O Lord our God of ho-nour and power,

For You are reign - ing now on high, Ha-lle-lu-

jah. Je - sus is Lord of all the

earth, Ha-lle-lu - jah, Ha-lle-lu-

jah, Ha-lle-lu - jah.

621.   Worthy is the Lamb

Author unknown
Arr. Chris Smith
Rev 5:12

2. Holy is the Lamb . . . (*etc.*)

3. Precious is the Lamb . . . (*etc.*)

4. Praises to the Lamb . . . (*etc.*)

5. Glory to the Lamb . . . (*etc.*)

6. Jesus is our Lamb . . . (*etc.*)

622. Worthy is the Lamb seated on the throne

David J. Hadden
Rev 5:12-13

Wor - thy is the Lamb seat - ed on the throne, wor - thy is the Lamb who was slain, to re-ceive po-wer and rich - es, and wis - dom and strength, hon - our and glor-y, glor - y and praise, for ev - er and ev - er - more.

623. Worthy is the Lamb slain on Calvary

Nesta Mumford
Rom 5: 8; Rev 5: 12

Wor - thy is the Lamb ____

slain on Cal - va - ry.

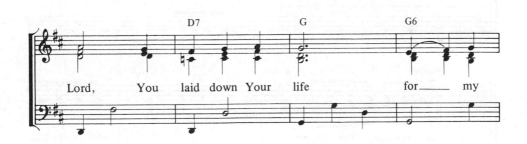

Lord, You laid down Your life for ____ my

sin that I might be free. ____

624. Worthy, O worthy are You Lord

Capo 3(C)

Mark S. Kinzer

Rev 4: 11

Flowing

Lyrics:
Wor-thy, O wor-thy are You Lord, wor-thy to be thank'd and prais'd and wor-shipp'd and a-dor'd. Wor-thy, O wor-thy are You Lord, wor-thy to be thank'd and prais'd and wor-shipp'd and a-dor'd.

625.

Yahweh is King

Leonard E. Smith Jnr.

Ps 97

Yah-weh is King, let the earth re-joice, let the ma-ny isles be glad.

Yah-weh is King, let the earth re-joice, let the ma-ny isles be glad.

1. Clouds and dark-ness sur-round Him,

just-ice sup-ports His throne. Clouds and dark-ness sur-round Him and

right-eous-ness sup-ports His throne.

Verse 2 – use verse 1 accompaniment

2. Moun-tains melt like wax at the com-ing of the Lord of the earth, the
heav-ens pro-claim His right-eous-ness, all na - tions see His
glo - ry! 3. Zi - on hears and re - joic - es, the
daugh-ters of Zi - on ex - ult at the ru-lings You ut-ter,___ O
Yah - weh, O Yah - weh.

Verse 4

4. You a - lone are Yah - weh, Most High ov - er the earth.
You a - lone are Yah - weh, tran - scend-ing all oth - er
gods. 5. Light dawns for the vir - tuous,
joy for up-right hearts, re - joice now in Yah- weh, re -
mem - ber His ho - li - ness.

626. Yahweh! Jehovah is the Lord our God

Majestic

Pete Lawry
Ex 15: 11

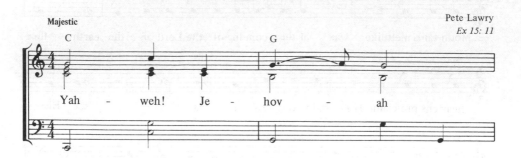

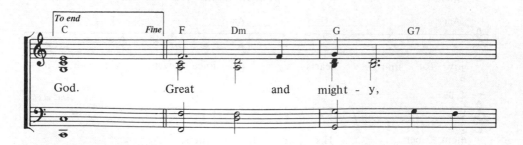

Yah - weh! Je - hov - ah is the Lord — our God. Yah - weh! Je - hov - ah is the Lord our God. God. Great and might - y,

627.

Ye holy angels bright

DARWALL'S 148th

Joyfully

John Darwall (1731-89)

1. Ye ho-ly an-gels bright, who wait at God's right hand, or through the realms of light fly at your Lord's com-mand, as-sist our song, or else the theme too high doth seem for mor-tal tongue.

2. Ye blessèd souls at rest,
   Who see your Saviour's face,
   Whose glory, e'en the least
   Is far above our grace,
   God's praises sound,
   As in His sight
   With sweet delight
   Ye do abound.

3. Ye saints who toil below,
   Adore your heavenly King,
   And onward as ye go,
   Some joyful anthem sing;
   Take what He gives,
   And praise Him still
   Through good and ill,
   Who ever lives.

4. My soul, bear thou thy part,
   Triumph in God above,
   And with a well-tuned heart
   Sing thou the songs of love.
   Let all thy days
   Till life shall end,
   Whate'er He send,
   Be filled with praise.

Richard Baxter (1615-91)
Altered by John H. Gurney (1802-62) &
Richard R. Chope (1830-1928)

Ps 103: 20-22; 145: 10; 148

Worthy is the Lamb, who was
*   slain,*
to receive power and wealth and
*   wisdom and strength*
and honour and glory and praise!

REVELATION 5:12

628.

Ye servants of God

(First tune)

Capo 3 (G)
LAUDATE DOMINUM (PARRY)

Charles Hubert Hastings Parry (1848-1918)

Alternative tune: LAUDATE DOMINUM (GAUNTLETT) (421)

2. God ruleth on high,
   Almighty to save;
   And still He is nigh,
   His presence we have;
   The great congregation
   His triumph shall sing,
   Ascribing salvation
   To Jesus our King.

3. Salvation to God,
   Who sits on the throne!
   Let all cry aloud,
   And honour the Son;
   The praises of Jesus
   The angels proclaim,
   Fall down on their faces,
   And worship the Lamb.

4. Then let us adore,
   And give Him His right,
   All glory and power,
   All wisdom and might,
   All honour and blessing,
   With angels above,
   And thanks never ceasing,
   And infinite love.

   Charles Wesley (1707-88)

   Rev 7: 9-12

Ye servants of God
(Second tune)

PADERBORN

Paderborn Gesangbuch (1765)

1. Ye servants of God, your ___ Master proclaim, and publish abroad His ___ wonderful name; the ___ name all-victorious of Jesus extol; His kingdom is ___ glorious, and ___ rules over all.

2. God ruleth on high,
   Almighty to save;
   And still He is nigh,
   His presence we have;
   The great congregation
   His triumph shall sing,
   Ascribing salvation
   To Jesus our King.

3. Salvation to God,
   Who sits on the throne!
   Let all cry aloud,
   And honour the Son;
   The praises of Jesus
   The angels proclaim,
   Fall down on their faces,
   And worship the Lamb.

4. Then let us adore,
   And give Him His right,
   All glory and power,
   All wisdom and might,
   All honour and blessing,
   With angels above,
   And thanks never ceasing,
   And infinite love.

Charles Wesley (1707-88)

Rev 7: 9-12

629.

You are my hiding place

Michael Ledner

Ps 32:7

Round — Slowly with feeling

You are my hid - ing place, _____ You al - ways fill my heart with

songs of de - liv - er - ance when - ev - er I am a - fraid. I will trust in

You, _____ I will trust in You; _____ let the weak say

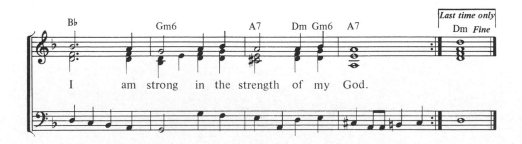

I am strong in the strength of my God.

Last time only — Dm *Fine*

630.
You are the King of Glory
(Hosanna to the Son of David)

Mavis Ford
Ps 24:10; Jn 12:13

With majesty

You are the King of Glo-ry, You are the Prince of Peace, You are the Lord of heav'n and earth, You're the Son of righteousness. An-gels bow down be - fore_You, Wor-ship and a - dore, for You have the words of e - ter-nal life,_You are Je-sus Christ the Lord.____ Ho-san-na to the Son of Da-vid!____ Ho-san-na to the King of__ kings! Glo - ry in the high-est hea - ven, for Je - sus the Mes-si - ah reigns.

631. You are the King who reigns

Capo 4(C)

David Boyd

Ps 146: 10; Hab 2: 14;
1 Thess 4: 14

1. You are the King who reigns in hea-ven and on earth. You are the King who reigns, the Au-thor of new birth.

Chorus

Lord, we sing Your praise, we ex-alt Your name. Your glo-ry fills this place, Your

2. You are the God who lives,
   Who died and rose again.
   You are the God who lives,
   Who covers all our sin.

3. You are the King who reigns
   In heaven and on earth.
   You are the King who reigns
   The Author of new birth.

632.
You are the Mighty King

Capo 3(C)

Stately

Eddie Espinosa

Is 9: 6; Mt 1: 23; Rev 19: 13

1. You are the Might-y King, the liv-ing Word; Mas-ter of ev-'ry-thing, You are the Lord. And I praise Your name, and I praise Your name.

2. You are Almighty God,
Saviour and Lord;
Wonderful Counsellor,
You are the Lord.

And I praise Your name,
And I praise Your name.

3. You are the Prince of Peace,
Emmanuel;
Everlasting Father,
You are the Lord.

And I love Your name,
And I love Your name.

4. *Repeat verse 1.*

---□ □ □---

Great and marvellous are your
  deeds,
  Lord God Almighty.
Just and true are your ways,
  King of the ages.
Who will not fear you, O Lord,
  and bring glory to your name?
For you alone are holy.
All nations will come
  and worship before you
for your righteous acts have been
  revealed.

REVELATION 15:3–4

---□ □ □---

633.
You are the Vine

Capo 2(C)

Danny Daniels
Jn 13:34-35; 15:1-11

You are the Vine, we are the

branch - es, keep us a - bid - ing in

You. bid - ing in

You. Then we'll

634.
You are worthy

John Daniel Lawtum

You are wor-thy, _____ Lord, You're wor-thy, _____ so I lift my heart, I lift my voice and cry 'Ho - ly'. _____ You have sav'd _____ me, _____ and I _____ love _____ You, _____ Je - sus ev - er-more I live to praise Your _____ name. _____

635.

You give me life

Phil Potter

Slowly with feeling

You give me life, new life You bring, since You gave
me Your life my spi-rit sings. You bring me love, new love You
bring, since You gave me Your love my spi-rit sings.
You give me joy, — new joy You bring, since You gave
me Your joy, my spi-rit sings. my spi-rit sings.

1st time
Last time only

636.
You give us beauty

Capo 3 (C)

Bill Tizzard

Is 61:3

Lightly

You give us beau - ty, beauty for ash - es, Lord in Is-ra - el.

You give us laugh - ter in-stead of mourn-ing, Lord You treat us well.

In-stead of heav - iness You give us praise, You make our hearts to sing. __ No

shame or dis-honour, just riches and honour You've given Your peo-ple to pos-sess. _

You give us beau - ty, beauty for ash - es, Lord how Your peo-ple are blessed.

637. # You have won my heart

Martin & Ruth Alley

With warmth and simplicity

1. You have won my heart,_____ You have won my heart, You have sat - is - fied my soul,_____ You have won my heart. You're my heart's de - sire.

last time (verse 3)

2. You shall have my love,
   You shall have my love,
   You have satisfied my soul,
   You shall have my love.

3. You're my heart's desire,
   You're my heart's desire,
   You have satisfied my soul,
   You're my heart's desire.

638.
You laid aside Your majesty
(I really want to worship You, my Lord)

Noel Richards

Is 53: 4-6; Phil 2: 6-11

Majestically

You laid a - side Your maj - es - ty, gave up ev - 'ry - thing for me, suf - fer'd at the hands_ of those You had cre - a - ted. You took all my guilt and shame, when You died_ and rose a - gain;_ now to - day_ You reign,_ in heav'n and earth ex - alt - ed.

639.
Your love for me is a mystery
(Lord, don't ever let me go)

Capo 3 (G)

Rod Boreham/Dave Bryant

Jn 4:14

Slowly with feeling

1. Your love for me ___ is a
mys-ter-y, and I don't un-der-stand how You ___
___ can ___ keep on loving me ___ ex-act-ly as I
am. Though I may not un-der-stand You,___
one thing I know, ___ You are___ all my heart de-
sires,___ Lord, don't ev-er let me go.

2. You're precious, always near to me
   And I am feeling sure
   That You will never ever let me down,
   I know that I'm secure.
   Though I may not understand You,
   One thing I know,
   You are all my heart desires,
   Lord, don't ever let me go.

3. And Your forgiveness floods my being,
   A river deep and wide,
   A stream of living water
   Flows from deep inside.
   And I still don't understand You,
   But this I know,
   You'll always be my heart's desire,
   I can't ever let You go,
   Lord, don't ever let me go.

640. Your loving kindness simply amazes me

Slowly with feeling
Chorus

Tony Gemmell
Ps 8:3-4

Your ___ loving kindness _____ simply a - mazes me, ___

simply a - mazes me.

2nd time Verse

1. When I ___ look at heaven ___ and the

works of Your hands, ___ how ___ is it,

Father, ___ You are mind - ful of man? ___

2. When I look at Jesus and the marks on His hands,
   How is it, Father, You are mindful of man?

————————— □ ▢ □ —————————

Hallelujah!
  For our Lord God Almighty
    reigns.
Let us rejoice and be glad
and give him glory!

REVELATION 19:6–7

————————— □ ▢ □ —————————

641.

You shall go out with joy
(The trees of the field)

Stuart Dauermann

Is 55:12

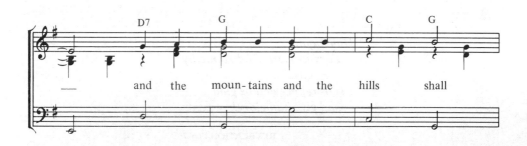

You shall go out with joy ___ and be led forth with peace, _

_ and the moun-tains and the hills shall break forth be - fore you. There'll be shouts of joy _

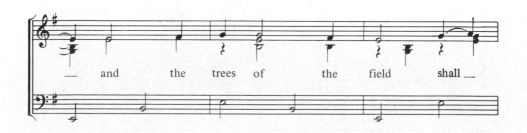

_ and the trees of the field shall _

642.

Yours Lord

Dave Bryant
Rom 12: 1-2; Col 3: 15

Yours Lord, wan-na be whol-ly Yours, want ev-'ry part of me to be rest-in' in You.

Help me Lord, al-ways to seek Your face, want You to be

643.   Yours, Lord, is the greatness

Helen Thomas
1 Chron 29: 10-13

Yours, Lord, is the great-ness, the pow-er, the glo-ry. Yours, Lord, is the great-ness, the vic-tor-y, the maj-es-ty. maj-es-ty. 1. For ev-'ry-thing in hea-ven and earth is Yours, You are the King, su-preme ov-er all.

2. All riches and honour come from You;
   You are our God, You make us strong.

3. And now, our God, we give You thanks,
   We praise Your glorious name.

644.

Your will, Your way

Peter & Diane Roe
Mt 6: 10; 1 Cor 2: 16

Your will, Your way, Your word, Your heart;____ Your mind, Your thoughts, Your king - dom and gov - ern - ment are all I need to____ come to____ birth in my life and in the earth.____

645.   You've joined our hearts

Author unknown
Arr. Margaret Evans
Jn 17:21

Capo 2(Am)   **Stately**

Index of Titles and First Lines

In order to assist churches where some musicians might be playing from individual music editions, the number to the *left* of the song refers to the number in this book, whilst the letters and numbers on the *right* indicate where the music can be located in the individual music editions; i.e. S2/201 shows that the music is number 201 in Songs of Fellowship Book 2. Prefix H refers to Hymns of Fellowship.

Author's titles, where different from first lines, are shown in *italics*.

1078

Scripture Index

1084

Thematic Index

(Arranged under the four main headings of *God the Father, Jesus, The Holy Spirit,* and *The Church*—the last section suggesting uses for songs within meetings.)

GOD THE FATHER

The Nativity

The Cross

1096

Adoration

Index of Tunes

(Pieces referred to are from Hymns of Fellowship. Numbers in *italics* refer to hymns for which the tune is suitable but not set)

Song no.

ABERYSTWYTH	286
ADORATION (ST JOHN)	16
AMAZING GRACE	10
ANGEL VOICES	15i
APPLEFORD	342
AIR HYD Y NOS	558ii
ARMAGEDDON	610
AURELIA	88, 505
AUSTRIA	123
BATTLE HYMN	368
BENSON	134
BLAENWERN	353i, *598*
BLESSED ASSURANCE	41
BULLINGER	183
CAMBERWELL	26
CARLISLE	487i, *465*
CASWALL	125, *291*
CHRIST AROSE!	356
CHURCH TRIUMPHANT	519ii, *590*
CONVERSE	598
CRIMOND	526
CRUGER	146
CWM RHONDA	144, *334*
DARWALL'S 148TH	627, *16, 301*
DAY OF REST	400i
DIADEM	7ii
DIADEMATA	75
DOMINUS REGIT ME	513i
DUKE STREET	103
EASTER HYMN	269
EIN' FESTE BURG	17
EVELYNS	26ii
EVENTIDE	2
FESTUS	31i
FINLANDIA	588
FROM STRENGTH TO STRENGTH	483ii
FULDA	590i
GERONTIUS	450
GETHSEMANE	361
GOPSAL	463, *301*
HALLELUJAH	151
HANOVER	428
HELMSLEY	332

Song no.

HEREFORD	424i
HORSLEY	532
HOW GREAT THOU ART	407
HYFRYDOL	266, *145, 151, 353*
I KNOW WHOM I HAVE BELIEVÈD	200
JERUSALEM	31ii
JUST AS I AM	304i
KINGSFOLD	196ii
LASST UNS ERFREUNEN	118
LATHBURY	46
LAUDATE DOMINUM (GAUNTLETT)	421, *628*
LAUDATE DOMINUM (PARRY)	628i, *421*
LAUDES DOMINI	603
LEONI	507
LIVING LORD	342
LOBE DEN HERREN	452
LONDONDERRY AIR	185
LONDON NEW	135
LOVE DIVINE	353ii
LOVE UNKNOWN	378
LUX EOI	145
LYDIA	294
LYNGHAM	394, *64, 17*
MACCABAEUS	545
MAIQUEZ	15ii
MANNHEIM	306
MARGARET	552
MARTYRDOM	392
MARYTON	296
MILES LANE	7i
MISERICORDIA	304ii
MONKLAND	324
MORNING LIGHT	489
MOSCOW	554
NATIVITY	64
NIAGARA	519i
NICEA	168i
NORTH COATES	291i
NOTTINGHAM	496
NUN DANKET	386
OLD 100TH	8
OTTAWA	362

Index of Composers, Arrangers and Sources of Tunes

(Pieces referred to are from Hymns of Fellowship)

Index of Authors,
Translators and Sources of Words

(Pieces referred to are from Hymns of Fellowship)

GUITAR CHORD CHART

The following chord diagrams show the fingering for the guitar chords in this songbook. They are divided into two parts—the first part covering all of the basic chords in each key, the second part (overleaf) explaining the more unusual derivations.

Key

o = *play open string*   2 = *index finger*   5 = *little finger*

x = *don't play string*   3 = *middle finger*   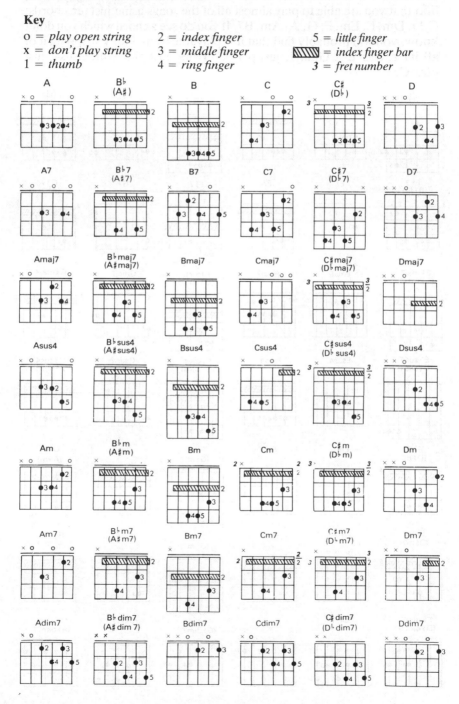 = *index finger bar*

1 = *thumb*   4 = *ring finger*   **3** = *fret number*

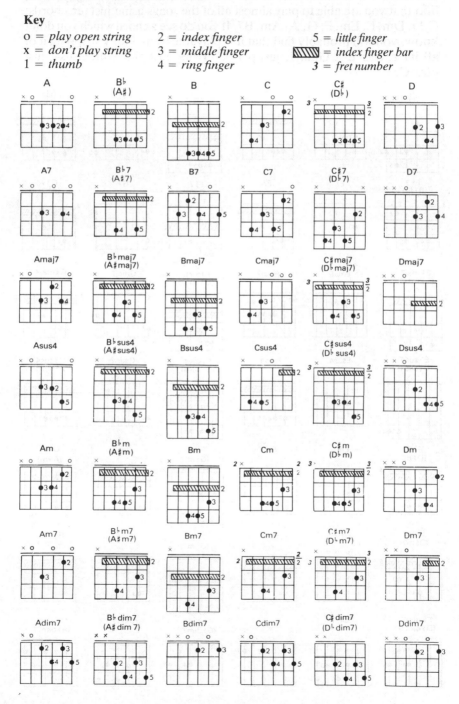

The chords which have been used throughout the book have been carefully chosen with the elementary guitarist in mind. Capo markings, in the left hand corner of many of the songs, allow simple chord shapes to be played with a capo in position. *Capo 3 (C)*, for example, means place the capo at the third fret and play the simple chords in brackets, which you will find are in C rather than E♭. If you use these capo markings you will find that you are able to play almost all of the songs using just ten chords: C, D, Dm, E, Em, F, G, A, Am, B7. If you do see a chord which you don't know, you will probably find that it is playable by mentally stripping it of all its 'extras' e.g. Gmaj7, just play G; Dm9, just play Dm; Csus4, just play C.

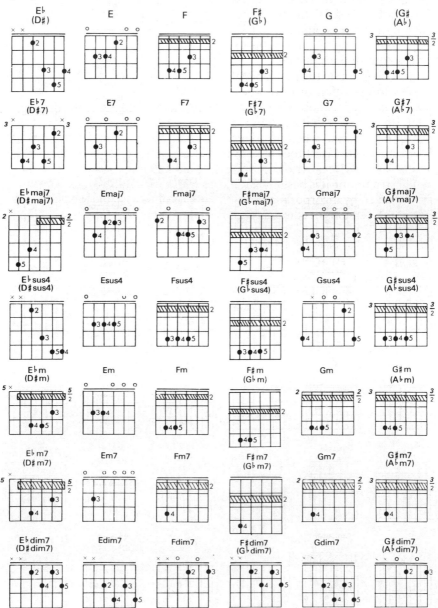

More unusual chords

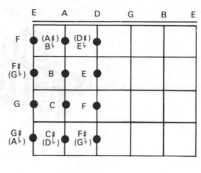

In this songbook you will come across some more unusual chords—mainly chords with different bass notes. If you see D/A, for example, this means play the chord of D with the note A in the bass. For a guitarist who is strumming, this bass note isn't too important and he can just play an ordinary chord of D, but the A bass note is useful for bass and keyboard players, and for guitarists who are picking and want to add colour to their playing.

D/A

The diagram on the right above shows the position of bass notes on the guitar for those who want to learn them. Looking at the diagram you can work out that a D/A is simple (see second diagram).

As already stated, when *strumming*, the bass note (as long as it is a note from the chord) isn't too important as it doesn't sound above the other guitar strings. Because one requires as loud and full a sound as possible when strumming it is best to play chords which use all six strings. This can be achieved by incorporating a different bass note. Use the following full sounding versions of common chords when strumming. For—

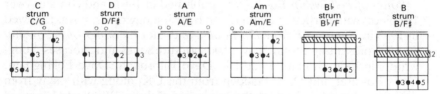

The following are the few more complex chords you will find in the songbook:

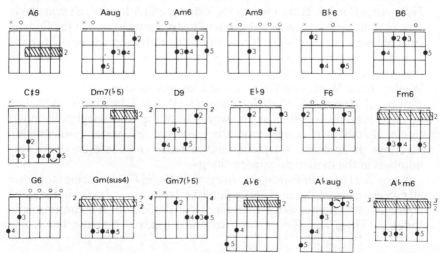

A DEVELOPING WORSHIP RESOURCE

Songs of Fellowship was born out of the growing number of new songs and Scripture choruses emerging from within the church. In the early days there was little printed music for these pieces and often variations of the same song developed as they were passed from one person to another. In order to make some of these new songs more widely available while reflecting the original inspiration of the writers, the first Songs of Fellowship music book of just 53 songs was published in 1979. The response showed there was a real need for such a compilation and this was also reflected in the popularity of two music albums containing some of these songs and released at about the same time.

Songs of Fellowship Book 1 was published in 1981, and contains over 150 pieces with particular emphasis on British songwriters. It was followed in 1983 by *Songs of Fellowship Book 2* and later by *Songs of Fellowship Book 3,* presenting a total of over 500 scripture songs and choruses. Songwriters include Graham Kendrick, Dave Bilbrough, Dave Fellingham, Chris Bowater and Dave Hadden from the UK, along with many from overseas particularly out of the ministries of John Wimber's Vineyard Fellowship and Scripture in Song.

Hymns of Fellowship was published at the same time as *Songs of Fellowship Book 3.* It contains 114 selected popular hymns, all sensitively re-scored for guitar as well as keyboard instruments to match the flowing style of Songs of Fellowship. It was conceived with the purpose of bringing to today's church a selection of the greatest hymns of praise and worship that transcend the passage of time. Included are hymns by Charles Wesley, Isaac Watts and Fanny Crosby, as well as many others.

Songs & Hymns of Fellowship Integrated Words Edition, first published in 1985, brought together all the words from the four songbooks into a single alphabetical compilation for easy use in praise and worship meetings. It contains 645 pieces and includes cross-references to song numbers in the individual music editions.

Songs & Hymns of Fellowship Integrated Music Edition brings together all 645 pieces from the previously published four music books in the same alphabetical sequence as the Integrated Words Edition. It incorporates an Index of Titles and First Lines, Scripture Index, Thematic Index and others—together with guitar chord charts. Scripture references are included against each song and hymn where appropriate. A special feature of the book is that all two-page songs and hymns appear on facing pages to avoid turning over, while maintaining the strict alphabetical order.

But Songs of Fellowship is much more than a songbook . . .

MUCH MORE THAN A SONGBOOK

Recorded Music

The Songs of Fellowship worship concept also includes a wide range of recorded music to accompany the songbooks. This range covers a great number of the songs in the Integrated Music edition, as well as an 'International' series of some of the best praise and worship material from around the world.

The Songs of Fellowship 'Live Worship' collection of albums reflects the wide influence of the songbooks at Bible Weeks and similar events around the country. These 'Live Worship' recordings capture something of the spontaneous joy and excitement of praise and worship at such events.

A breakthrough in teaching and learning new songs was achieved with the introduction of the *Sing Songs of Fellowship* recordings which cover all the songs from Books 2 and 3.

Worship Aids

A unique part of the Songs of Fellowship concept is the development of worship aids such as *Teach Yourself Praise Guitar, Simply Worship* and *Leading Worship*. These fully illustrated self-help books give practical assistance to guitarists and worship leaders who wish to develop their skills. Each book is accompanied by a cassette which is an integral part of the course. Further worship aids are under development.

Orchestral & Vocal Arrangements and Backing Tracks
(for Europe only)

Many churches have extended their musical range beyond the piano, organ and guitar to include brass, woodwind and strings. Songs of Fellowship now offers a service to provide arrangements for such instruments and for vocals as part of the Songs of Fellowship concept. Details are available from: The Songs of Fellowship Arrangement Service, P.O. Box 4, Sheffield, South Yorkshire S1 1DU. Please send a stamped addressed envelope size A4 (100 grammes postage) for song list and prices, stating what vocal or instrumental arrangement you are interested in.

Backing tracks are also available for a number of songs from the Songs of Fellowship range. These are recorded to professional studio standard, and are ideally suited for public performance or congregational accompaniment. Please write for current available selection to: Songs of Fellowship Trax, Gap Music, 15 Trueman Place, Aldbrook, Milton Keynes MK6 2HE.

Worship Seminars

Since the beginning of the 1980s, Songs of Fellowship has been instrumental in the educational aspects of creative worship and worship leading, through an annual series of residential worship conferences sponsored by Kingsway Trust, now The Servant Trust. These seminars are continuing under the auspices of the Christian Music Association with the full backing of The Servant Trust.

New Songs

New songs are continually written which are soon in demand by many churches. To meet this demand a new Songs of Fellowship Worship Resource has been developed—*New Songs*. This is an annual collection of about forty songs, carefully selected from British churches and abroad.

It includes songs by top British and American songwriters and from leading publishers such as Thankyou Music, Scripture in Song, Vineyard (Mercy), Hosanna! Music and Word Music. Careful research is also undertaken at local church level to bring unknown songs and writers to the attention of the wider chruch.

All songs are fully scored for piano, with guitar chords, and arranged in sequence to minimise turning over pages. Each year music cassettes of all the songs are produced to accompany the book.

Songs of Fellowship is much more than a songbook. It is a developing praise and worship resource, leading the way in serving the church in the United Kingdom and abroad.